Current Topics in Microbiology and Immunology

Volume 349

Current Topics in Microbiology and Immunology

Previously published volumes

Further volumes can be found at springer.com

Vol. 322: **Romeo, Tony (Ed.)**:
Bacterial Biofilms. 2008.
ISBN 978-3-540-75417-6

Vol. 323: **Tracy, Steven; Oberste, M. Steven; Drescher, Kristen M. (Eds.)**:
Group B Coxsackieviruses. 2008.
ISBN 978-3-540-75545-6

Vol. 324: **Nomura, Tatsuji; Watanabe, Takeshi; Habu, Sonoko (Eds.)**
Humanized Mice. 2008
ISBN 978-3-540-75646-0

Vol. 325: **Shenk, Thomas E.; Stinski, Mark F. (Eds.)**:
Human Cytomegalovirus. 2008.
ISBN 978-3-540-77348-1

Vol. 326: **Reddy, Anireddy S.N; Golovkin, Maxim (Eds.)**:
Nuclear pre-mRNA processing in plants. 2008
ISBN 978-3-540-76775-6

Vol. 327: **Manchester, Marianne; Steinmetz Nicole F. (Eds.)**:
Viruses and Nanotechnology. 2008.
ISBN 978-3-540-69376-5

Vol. 328: **van Etten, (Ed.)**:
Lesser Known Large dsDNA Viruses. 2008.
ISBN 978-3-540-68617-0

Vol. 329: **Griffin, Diane E.; Oldstone, Michael B.A. (Eds.)**: Measles. 2009
ISBN 978-3-540-70522-2

Vol. 330: **Griffin, Diane E.; Oldstone, Michael B.A. (Eds.)**:
Measles. 2009.
ISBN 978-3-540-70616-8

Vol. 331: **Villiers, E. M. de (Ed.)**:
TT Viruses. 2009. ISBN 978-3-540-70917-8

Vol. 332: **Karasev A. (Ed.)**:
Plant produced Microbial Vaccines. 2009.
ISBN 978-3-540-70857-5

Vol. 333: **Compans, Richard W.; Orenstein, Walter A. (Eds.)**:
Vaccines for Pandemic Influenza. 2009.
ISBN 978-3-540-92164-6

Vol. 334: **McGavern, Dorian; Dustin, Micheal (Eds.)**:
Visualizing Immunity. 2009.
ISBN 978-3-540-93862-0

Vol. 335: **Levine, Beth; Yoshimori, Tamotsu; Deretic, Vojo (Eds.)**:
Autophagy in Infection and Immunity. 2009.
ISBN 978-3-642-00301-1

Vol. 336: **Kielian, Tammy (Ed.)**:
Toll-like Receptors: Roles in Infection and Neuropathology. 2009.
ISBN 978-3-642-00548-0

Vol. 337: **Sasakawa, Chihiro (Ed.)**:
Molecular Mechanisms of Bacterial Infection via the Gut. 2009.
ISBN 978-3-642-01845-9

Vol. 338: **Rothman, Alan L. (Ed.)**:
Dengue Virus. 2009.
ISBN 978-3-642-02214-2

Vol. 339: **Spearman, Paul; Freed, Eric O. (Eds.)**:
HIV Interactions with Host Cell Proteins. 2009.
ISBN 978-3-642-02174-9

Vol. 340: **Saito, Takashi; Batista, Facundo D. (Eds.)**:
Immunological Synapse. 2010.
ISBN 978-3-642-03857-0

Vol. 341: **Bruserud, Øystein (Ed.)**:
The Chemokine System in Clinical and Experimental Hematology. 2010.
ISBN 978-3-642-12638-3

Vol. 342: **Arvin, Ann M. (Ed.)**:
Varicella-zoster Virus. 2010.
ISBN 978-3-642-12727-4

Vol. 343: **Johnson, John E. (Ed.)**:
Cell Entry by Non-Enveloped Viruses. 2010.
ISBN 978-3-642-13331-2

Vol. 345: **Simon, M. Celeste (Ed.)**:
Diverse Effects of Hypoxia on Tumor Progression. 2010.
ISBN 978-3-642-13328-2

Vol. 346: **Christian Rommel; Bart Vanhaesebroeck; Peter K. Vogt (Ed.)**:
Phosphoinositide 3-kinase in Health and Disease. 2010.
ISBN 978-3-642-13662-7

Vol. 347: **Christian Rommel; Bart Vanhaesebroeck; Peter K. Vogt (Ed.)**:
Phosphoinositide 3-kinasein Health and Disease. 2010.
ISBN 978-3-642-14815-6

Vol. 348: **Lyubomir Vassilev; David Fry (Eds.)**:
Small-Molecule Inhibitors of Protein-Protein Interactions. 2011.
ISBN 978-3-642-17082-9

Michael Karin
Editor

NF-κB in Health and Disease

Springer

Editor
Dr. Michael Karin
Department of Pharmacology
School of Medicine
University of California San Diego
9500 Gilman Drive
La Jolla, CA 92093-0723
USA
e-mail: karinoffice@ucsd.edu

ISSN 0070-217X

ISBN 978-3-642-16016-5 e-ISBN 978-3-642-16017-2

DOI 10.1007/978-3-642-16017-2

Springer Heidelberg Dordrecht London New York

Cover design: Deblik, Berlin

Printed on acid-free paper

Springer is part of Springer Science+Business Media (www.springer.com)

Contents

Contributors

K. Aggarwal, Division of Infectious Diseases, Department of Medicine, University of Massachusetts Medical School, Worcester, MA, 01605, USA

M. C. Arkan, 2nd Department of Medicine, Klinikum rechts der Isar, Technical University Munich, Ismaningerstr. 22, 81675, Munich, Germany

V. Baud, Institut Cochin, Université Paris Descartes, CNRS (UMR 8104), Paris, France, e-mail: veronique.baud@inserm.fr, Inserm, U1016, Paris, France

E. Cesarman, Department of Pathology and Laboratory Medicine, Weill Cornell Medical College, 1300 York Ave, New York, NY, 10065, USA

G. Cheng, Department of Microbiology, Immunology and Molecular Genetics, University of California Los Angeles, 615 Charles Young Dr S., 210A BSRB, Los Angeles, CA, 90095, USA

G. Courtois, INSERM U781, Hôpital Necker-Enfants Malades, Paris, France

E. Derudder, Program in Cellular and Molecular Medicine, Immune Disease Institute, Children's Hospital, Harvard Medical School, Boston, MA, 02115, USA

A. Dev, Department of Microbiology, Immunology and Molecular Genetics, University of California Los Angeles, 615 Charles Young Dr S., 210A BSRB, Los Angeles, CA, 90095, USA

L. Eckmann, Department of Medicine, University of California, 9500 Gilman Drive, La Jolla, San Diego, CA, 92093-0063, USA

S. Finkin, Department of Immunology and Cancer Research and Department of Pathology, IMRIC, Hadassah Medical School, Hebrew University, Ein Kerem, 91120, Jerusalem, Israel

S. Ganesan, Division of Infectious Diseases, Department of Medicine, University of Massachusetts Medical School, Worcester, MA, 01605, USA

M. R. Garbati, Biology Department, Boston University, 5 Cummington Street, Boston, MA, 02215, USA

G. Ghosh, Department of Chemistry and Biochemistry, University of California, San Diego, 9500 Gilman Drive, La Jolla, CA, 92093-0357, USA

T. D. Gilmore, Biology Department, Boston University, 5 Cummington Street, Boston, MA, 02215, USA

F. R. Greten, 2nd Department of Medicine, Klinikum rechts der Isar, Ismaningerstr. 22, 81675, Munich, Germany

A. Hoffmann, Department of Chemistry and Biochemistry, University of California, San Diego, 9500 Gilman Drive, La Jolla, CA, 92093-0357, USA

T. Huxford, Department of Chemistry and Biochemistry, San Diego State University, 5500 Campanile Drive, San Diego, CA, 92182-1030, USA

A. Israël, Unite de Signalisation Moleculaire et Activation Cellulaire, URA 2582 CNRS, Institut Pasteur, 25 rue du Dr Roux, Paris Cedex 15, 75724, France

S. Iyer, Department of Microbiology, Immunology and Molecular Genetics, University of California Los Angeles, 615 Charles Young Dr S., 210A BSRB, Los Angeles, CA, 90095, USA

T. Lawrence, Inflammation Biology Group, Centre d'Immunologie Marseille-Luminy, Parc Scientifique de Luminy, Case 906, 13288, Marseille, France

G. Natoli, Department of Experimental Oncology, European Institute of Oncology (IEO), IFOM-IEO Campus, Via Adamello 16, 20139, Milan, Italy

A. S. Neish, Department of Pathology and Laboratory Medicine, Emory University, 615 Michaels St, Atlanta, GA, 30322, USA

N. Paquette, Program of Developmental Immunology, Department of Pediatrics, Massachusetts General Hospital/Harvard Medical School, Boston, MA, 02114, USA

E. Pikarsky, Department of Immunology and Cancer Research and Department of Pathology, IMRIC, Hadassah Medical School, Hebrew University, Ein Kerem, 91120, Jerusalem, Israel

B. Razani, Department of Microbiology, Immunology and Molecular Genetics, University of California Los Angeles, 615 Charles Young Dr S., 210A BSRB, Los Angeles, CA, 90095, USA

N. Silverman, Division of Infectious Diseases, Department of Medicine, University of Massachusetts Medical School, Worcester, MA, 01605, USA, e-mail: neal.silverman@umassmed.edu

S.-C. Sun, Department of Immunology, The University of Texas MD Anderson Cancer Center and The University of Texas Graduate School of Biomedical Sciences, Houston, TX, 77030, USA, e-mail: ssun@mdanderson.org

Understanding the Logic of IκB:NF-κB Regulation in Structural Terms

Tom Huxford, Alexander Hoffmann and Gourisankar Ghosh

Abstract NF-κB is an inducible transcription factor that controls expression of diverse stress response genes. The entire mammalian NF-κB family is generated from a small cadre of five gene products that assemble with one another in various combinations to form active homo- and heterodimers. The ability of NF-κB to alter target gene expression is regulated at many levels. Chief among these regulatory mechanisms is the noncovalent association in the cell cytoplasm of NF-κB dimers with IκB inhibitor proteins. Removal of IκB leads to accumulation of active NF-κB within the cell nucleus where it binds to specific DNA sequences contained within the promoter regions of target genes and initiates recruitment of general transcription factors and assembly of the basal transcription machinery. Here we provide a detailed description of these fundamental NF-κB regulatory events using as a basis macromolecular structures and experimental data derived from structure-based biochemistry.

Contents

T. Huxford
Department of Chemistry & Biochemistry, San Diego State University,
5500 Campanile Drive, San Diego, CA 92182-1030, USA

A. Hoffmann and G. Ghosh (✉)
Department of Chemistry & Biochemistry, University of California,
San Diego, 9500 Gilman Drive, La Jolla, CA 92093-0357, USA
e-mail: gghosh@ucsd.edu

Current Topics Microbiology (2011) 349: 1-24
DOI: 10.1007/82_2010_99

Published Online: 16 September 2010

1 Introduction

Nearly 25 years of intensive research have uncovered many diverse functions for the dimeric transcription factor known as NF-κB (nuclear factor-kappaB) (Hayden and Ghosh 2008). NF-κB affects most aspects of cellular physiology—from immunity and inflammation to apoptosis, cell survival, growth, and proliferation. Only five genes encode the entire family of mammalian NF-κB transcription factors: NFKB1, NFKB2, RELA, RELB, and REL (Ghosh et al. 1998). Their polypeptide products give rise to the mature NF-κB subunits p50, p52, RelA (p65), RelB, and c-Rel, respectively, which combine in pairs to produce 15 distinct functioning NF-κB dimers (Gilmore 2006). While most of the dimer combinations are abundant in diverse cell types, others are more rare. A few have not been detected directly, but it remains likely that every possible NF-κB dimer combination exists in some cells and that some as yet undetected NF-κB dimers might exist under limited but specific cellular conditions.

The activity of these NF-κB dimers is directly controlled by a small set of proteins known as IκB (inhibitor of NF-kappaB) through the formation of stable IκB:NF-κB complexes (Whiteside and Israël 1997). The non-covalent association of IκB to NF-κB shifts the steady-state subcellular localization of NF-κB dimers to the cytoplasm. A complicated and fascinating kinase complex known as IKK (inhibitor of NF-kappaB kinase) is responsible for phosphorylating the complex-associated IκB leading to its targeted ubiquitination by a specific SCF-type E3 ubiquitin-protein ligase and degradation by the 26S proteasome (Chen 2005; Karin and Ben-Neriah 2000). Free NF-κB then rapidly accumulates in the nucleus where it binds to a class of related DNA sequences, known as κB DNA sites, present

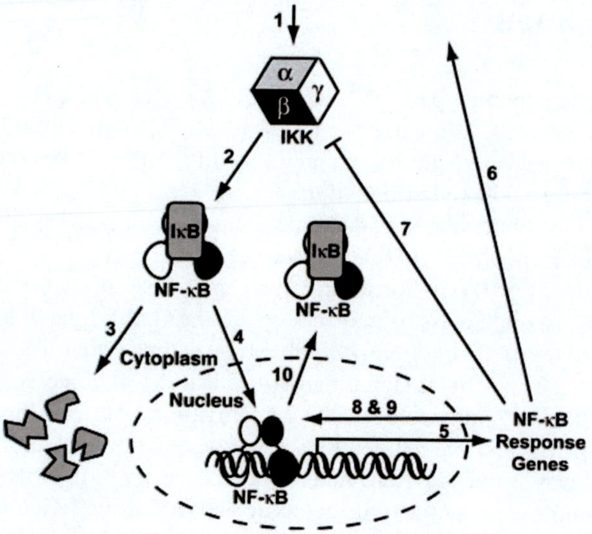

Fig. 1 Regulation of transcription factor NF-κB occurs at many levels. Several of these are numbered in this simplified representation of the canonical NF-κB activation pathway. These include: 1—receptor engagement, kinase cascades, and ubiquitin-mediated regulation of IKK activity; 2—phosphorylation of IκB in complex with inactive NF-κB; 3—Ubiquitin-dependent proteolysis of IκB by the 26 S proteasome; 4—nuclear accumulation of active NF-κB; 5—elevated expression of NF-κB target gene products; 6—the influence of NF-κB target gene products on cellular physiology; 7—expression of cytoplasmic factors that deactivate IKK; 8—the action of nuclear factors that influence NF-κB target gene expression; 9—nuclear accumulation of IκBα; 10—the export of inactive IκBα:NF-κB complexes from the nucleus and restoration of the pre-induction resting cell state

within the promoters and enhancers of hundreds of protein coding and non-coding genes and elevates their expression (Pahl 1999).

While this simple model for activation and inducible gene expression has not changed much since its outlines were first being sketched during the decade following the discovery of NF-κB, its connection by multiple investigations to diverse signal transduction pathways and signaling events have uncovered multiple layers of NF-κB regulation (Fig. 1). In this chapter, we will focus on regulation of transcription factor NF-κB at the levels of dimer formation, association with IκB inhibitors, and sequence-specific DNA binding by NF-κB. We will use as our guide the growing body of structural information together with biochemical investigations aimed at testing structure-based hypotheses. This analysis illustrates how functional specificity can be achieved within a family of functionally and structurally related factors through small sequence variations and modifications. Understanding how these subtle differences give rise to the specific events in NF-κB-mediated transcriptional regulation in response to distinct stimuli is key to our grasp of how NF-κB controls cell physiology.

2 NF-κB and IκB

Five polypeptide subunits, p50, p52, RelA (p65), c-Rel, and RelB, constitute the NF-κB family (Fig. 2). With the exception of RelA, transcription of the genes encoding the NF-κB polypeptides is upregulated by NF-κB, generating a positive feedback response upon cell stimulation.

Two of the family members, p50 and p52, are the processed products of NF-κB subunit precursors p105 and p100, respectively. Interestingly, the partial proteolytic processing of p105 is constitutive, whereas that of p100 is induced via specific signals. A small class of inducers, including BAFF ligand, lymphotoxin-β, and CD40, activates a distinct NF-κB activation pathway that leads to processing of p100 into p52. The cellular signaling that leads to p100 processing is referred to as the alternative or non-canonical NF-κB activation pathway (Senftleben et al. 2001). The primary NF-κB dimer that is activated through alternative NF-κB activation pathway is the p52:RelB heterodimer via activation of the IKKα subunit of the IKK complex. In contrast, the catalytic activity of the IKKβ subunit of IKK is activated in response to a separate class of inducers, which includes IL-1 (interleukin-1), TNF-α (tumor necrosis factor-α), and LPS (bacterial lipopolysaccharide), through signaling referred to as the canonical NF-κB activation pathway.

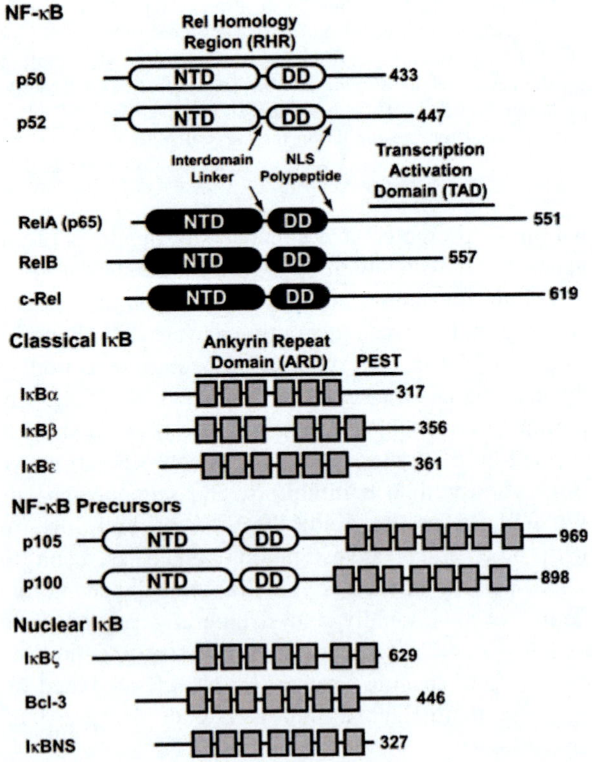

Fig. 2 Domain organization of NF-κB and IκB proteins. The five NF-κB polypeptides are depicted in schematic form with the arrangement of the elements and domains discussed in the text identified and human numbering indicated. The IκB proteins are divided into classical IκB, NF-κB precursors, and nuclear IκB

Induction of NF-κB activity through the canonical pathway ultimately activates NF-κB dimers that contain RelA and c-Rel subunits.

NF-κB subunit polypeptides share sequence homology throughout an N-terminal portion of roughly 300 amino acid residues in length referred to as the Rel homology region (RHR). The RHR is responsible for subunit association into active NF-κB dimers, NF-κB nuclear localization and DNA binding, and the association of NF-κB with IκB inhibitor proteins. The RHR can be divided into three structural regions: the NTD (N-terminal domain), DD (dimerization domain), and NLS polypeptide (Fig. 3a). Together the NTD and DD are responsible for DNA binding. The DD alone mediates association of NF-κB subunits to form active dimers. The NLS polypeptide is flexible in solution allowing it to adopt different conformations when bound to distinct partners such as IκB or importin-α proteins (Conti and Kuriyan 2000). The entire RHR of NF-κB is contacted by IκB upon binding to the inhibitor and a significant fraction of binding energy is contributed by the NLS polypeptide. C-terminal to the RHR of RelA, RelB, and c-Rel is a region that conveys transcriptional activation potential and, consequently, NF-κB dimers that possess at least one of these subunits function as activators of transcription. This TAD (transcriptional activation domain) region is not conserved between the NF-κB subunits at the amino acid sequence level and is, therefore, defined functionally. Both the NF-κB p50 and p52 subunits lack a C-terminal TAD and instead contain within this region the glycine-rich remnants

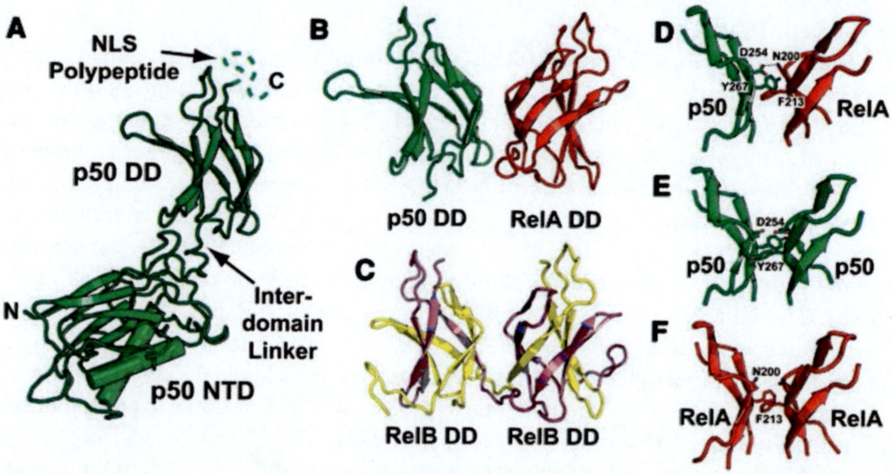

Fig. 3 Ribbon structure diagrams of NF-κB RHR and dimerization. **a** The NF-κB p50 subunit RHR is depicted in *green* ribbon diagram with elements and domains labeled according to the discussion in the text. The dashed C-terminal element represents the NLS polypeptide, which is unstructured in its unbound state. **b** The assembled dimerization domains of the p50 (*green*) and RelA (*red*) subunits viewed orthogonal to their vertical axis of 2-fold pseudosymmetry. **c** A similar view of the RelB DD homodimer reveals that the two subunits (*yellow* and *purple*) form an intertwined dimer. **d** Close-up view of the dimer interface with amino acid side chains from the text depicted and labeled. **e** NF-κB p50 homodimer DD interface. **f** RelA DD homodimer interface

of their incomplete proteolytic processing from p105 and p100 precursors. As a consequence of their lack of a C-terminal TAD, NF-κB dimers composed only of p50 and/or p52 subunits fail to activate transcription in vitro or in vivo.

Three polypetides, IκBα, IκBβ, and IκBε, mediate classical IκB activities as they relate to NF-κB binding in the nucleus and phosphorylation-dependent proteasome-mediated degradation in response to induction. IκBα, IκBβ, and IκBε preferentially bind to NF-κB dimers that contain at least one RelA or c-Rel subunit. These classical IκB proteins share a central ARD (ankyrin repeat domain) that contains six ankyrin repeats (Fig. 2). The ankyrin repeat is a roughly 33 amino acid tandem helical repeat motif that appears in multiple copies in numerous proteins (Bork 1993; Gaudet 2008). The ARD is flanked by sequences that are predicted to be unstructured. The N-terminal flexible regions in IκBα, IκBβ, and IκBε contain two serine residues within the consensus sequence DSGXXS that are sites for phosphorylation by the IKKβ subunit. Once phosphorylated, this N-terminal region serves as the recognition site for the E3 receptor subunit β-TrCP and, through the action of an SCF-type E3 ubiquitin-protein ligase and the 26S proteasome, leads directly to IκB proteolysis (Yaron et al. 1998). The importance of this N-terminal region for the inducible proteolysis of classical IκB proteins is illustrated by the fact that an IκBα molecule with its two IKK phosphorylation sites mutated to alanines functions as a "super-repressor" of NF-κB activation through the canonical NF-κB activation pathway (Muenchen et al. 2000). C-terminal to the ARD is a structurally flexible region rich in the amino acids proline, glutamic acid, serine, and threonine. This so-called PEST region is common to many proteins that exhibit rapid turnover in the cell (Rogers et al. 1986).

The unprocessed p105 and p100 also act as inhibitors of NF-κB (Hatada et al. 1993; Naumann et al. 1993). However, unlike the oligomerization exhibited by IκBα, IκBβ, and IκBε, where a monomeric IκB assembles with a single NF-κB dimer to form an inactive complex, p100 and p105 assemble into larger complexes wherein they integrate multiple inhibitor and NF-κB molecules (Savinova et al. 2009). We refer these larger complexes, which can be purified and biophysically analyzed, as "IκBsomes" and it has been shown computationally and experimentally that p100 and p105 function as legitimate IκB molecules (Basak et al. 2008). The complete degradation of p100 and p105 in IκBsomes could, in principle, release multiple NF-κB subunits, which then could initiate physiologic programs that are distinct from those regulated by the classical IκB inhibitors.

Three additional ARD-containing polypeptides have been shown to participate in NF-κB regulation. These are Bcl-3, IκBζ, and IκBNS (Fig. 2). Of these, Bcl-3 is the most well-studied because of its early discovery (Hatada et al. 1992; Ohno et al. 1990). Though they are grouped with other IκB proteins because of their structural similarity and abilities to bind NF-κB dimers, Bcl-3, IκBζ, and IκBNS exhibit significant differences from classical IκB proteins (Fiorini et al. 2002; Haruta et al. 2001; Kitamura et al. 2000; Yamazaki et al. 2001). First of all, they display binding specificity toward p50 and/or p52 subunits in NF-κB dimers. Furthermore, each of the three proteins migrates to the nucleus when over-expressed in cells, leading to their classification as "nuclear IκB proteins". In the nucleus, it appears that these proteins play regulatory roles that may include chromatin rearrangement, NF-κB dimer exchange, and co-activation of specific NF-κB target gene expression. IκBζ, for example, was shown in mice knockout studies to be necessary for the NF-κB-induced activation of the inflammatory cytokine IL-6 (interleukin-6) in response to LPS treatment of peritoneal macrophages (Yamamoto et al. 2004). The functional consequences of Bcl-3 are particularly complicated as it has been shown that both the phosphorylation status and partner selection dictate whether Bcl-3 might act as a co-activator, a co-repressor, or an inhibitor (Palmer and Chen 2008).

3 NF-κB Structure and Dimer Formation

The DD (dimerization domain) consists of approximately 100 amino acids toward C-terminal one-third of the RHR. Sequence identity and homology within the DD across the family are roughly 20 and 50%, respectively. The molecular structure of the DD has been determined at high resolution by X-ray crystallography for all five NF-κB subunits (Huang et al. 1997, 2005). The NF-κB DD folds into an immunoglobulin-like (Ig-like) fold where two anti-parallel β-sheets form a sandwich (Fig. 3b). One of these sheets forms the dimer interface by interacting symmetrically with neighboring DD. Fourteen amino acid residues are involved in dimer formation. However, as revealed by alanine scanning mutagenesis in the p50 subunit and subsequent assessment of dimer formation, few of these amino acids make energetic contributions to dimer stability (Sengchanthalangsy et al. 1999).

The NF-κB DD X-ray crystal structures provide clues as to why some of the dimers form preferentially to others. For instance, the NF-κB p50:RelA heterodimer is more stable than the homodimer of p50, while the RelA homodimer is the weakest of the three. Furthermore, heterodimers such as p50:RelA and p52:RelB are, in general, stable dimers. The RelB homodimer has not been detected in vivo, whereas p50 and p52 heterodimers are abundant. Therefore, it is surprising that the RelB homodimer can be formed in vitro. The X-ray crystal structure of a RelB homodimer DD revealed that it adopts a distinct domain-swapped structure (Fig. 3c).

A close inspection of these structures reveals that differential selectivity and stability of NF-κB dimers are controlled in two different ways: the first is variation in the amino acid residues that directly contact the other subunit across the dimer interface; the second is variation in surface or core amino acid residues that influence folding stability of the DD. While the first seems obvious, this second class of residues that affects dimerization through an indirect manner is at least as important.

The p50 DD homodimer X-ray crystal structure, which was the first solved, indicated a relatively weak dimer interface in which water is barely excluded. The interface is alarmingly loose with inter-atomic contact distances that are consistently longer than optimum. A binding constant for dimer-monomer dissociation (K_{Dim}) was determined by analytical ultracentrifugation at approximately 1.0 μM. This suggested that free NF-κB p50 subunit in solution at cellular concentrations ($\sim$0.1 μM) should exist both in monomeric and dimeric states.

3.1 Regulation of NF-κB Dimerization at the Interface

Although the inter-subunit distances in p50 and RelA homodimers are similar, suggesting overall similarity in their respective mechanisms of dimer formation, fewer hydrogen bonds at the RelA homodimer interface suggested that it would be weaker than the p50 homodimer. Three differences in the amino acids at the dimer interfaces of p50 and RelA homodimer suggest how the resulting dimerization of p50:p50, RelA:RelA, and p50:RelA dimers might be affected. Residues at positions 254 and 267 are an aspartic acid and a tyrosine, respectively, in p50. The equivalent positions in RelA are occupied by an asparagine and a phenylalanine. This results in the juxtaposition of an Asp-Asn pair in the p50:RelA heterodimer, which can form a hydrogen bond of nearly perfect length and geometry and stabilize dimerization (Fig. 3d). The analogous placement of Asp-Asp and Asn-Asn pairs decrease the stability of the p50 homodimer and RelA homodimer, respectively (Fig. 3e, f). The Tyr to Phe change accounts for the remaining difference in the number of hydrogen bonds at the dimer interface of p50 and RelA homodimers. The lack of a hydroxyl group on Phe makes RelA homodimer less stable than p50 homodimer, wherein the hydroxyl group of Tyr mediates several hydrogen bonds across the subunit interface.

Another example of a difference at the dimer interface that influences NF-κB dimer selectivity is the change from a Phe at position 307 in p50 to Val at the corresponding position at the dimer interface of RelA. The small valine side chains position themselves uncomfortably close as they approach one another at the p65 dimer interface. The aromatic phenylalanine ring in p50 orients itself differently optimizing Van der Waals interactions and avoiding a steric clash at the dimer interface of p50 homodimer.

The remaining amino acid residues at the NF-κB dimer interface are identical across the family. Therefore, the differences in affinity observed between different combinatorial dimers could be explained by the amino acid identity at these three positions only. However, this is not the case. Several inconsistencies, culminating with our observation of an unusual domain-swapped architecture of the RelB homodimer, indicated that non-interfacial amino acid residues also play a vital role in controlling assembly of active NF-κB dimers (Huang et al. 2005). In RelB, the three interfacial residues in question are Asn, Tyr, and Ile. Of these only Ile is distinct as equivalent Asn residues are present in RelA and c-Rel and an equivalent Tyr is present in p50 and p52. Mutation of Ile to either Val or Tyr, the residues present in p65 or p50, respectively, does not convert RelB into a regular side-by-side NF-κB homodimer. This suggests that subtle changes elsewhere in the domain are critical for the domain-swapping in the RelB DD homodimer structure.

3.2 Regulation of NF-κB Dimerization at a Distance

Understanding the role of surface and buried amino acid residues outside of the dimer interface that indirectly influence dimer selectivity and stability is more difficult to imagine. Furthermore, X-ray crystal structures do little to provide a clear explanation. The influence on dimerization of amino acid residues far from the subunit interface is more directly assessed by mutational analysis and measurement of dimerization affinity. In RelA, a cysteine at position 216 occupies a position in the core of the DD that is projected opposite to the dimer interface. When this cysteine is mutated to an alanine, p65 homodimer stability is significantly reduced. The simplest explanation for this reduced dimer stability is that removal of the sulfhydryl group destabilizes the DD core structure, which in turn affects the stability of interactions at the dimer interface.

Several amino acid residues located on the surface of RelB opposite to the dimer interface are hydrophobic. These surface-exposed hydrophobic amino acids are unique to RelB among the mammalian NF-κB family. Equivalent residues in other NF-κB subunit structures are polar and are involved in surface hydrogen bond formation to stabilize the DD structure. Mutation of these residues to polar residues decreases the affinity of RelB for dimerization with p52. It is likely that the mutant RelB forms a more stable homodimer, thereby decreasing its availability to heterodimer formation with p52. The importance of domain folding stability for NF-κB dimer assembly and subunit dimerization selectivity is further supported by the mutation of serine at position 319 of RelB. When this surface residue is mutated to Ala, RelB protein stability is dramatically reduced.

Stability of the NF-κB p50:RelA heterodimer is relatively high as judged by the fact that the heterodimer forms preferentially when p50 and RelA homodimers are mixed together. However, under similar conditions, p50:c-Rel heterodimer formation is not as efficient. This observation suggests that c-Rel homodimer might be more stable than RelA homodimer. This is particularly intriguing as RelA and c-Rel share greater than 70% sequence identity within their dimerization domains and inter-subunit contacting residues are identical in both proteins. We conclude that small variations in sequence can impact dimerization of two closely related proteins such as RelA and c-Rel. Finally, it is worth noting that despite its high degree of sequence and structural homology to the p50 subunit the NF-κB p52 homodimer is rarely observed in vivo. Although there exist many explanations for this negative result, it is possible that instability in the p52:p52 homodimer allows for its more stable assembly into functionally important NF-κB members such as the p52:RelA and p52:RelB heterodimers.

3.3 Conditional NF-κB Dimerization

Some of the NF-κB dimers are rarely observed in vivo such as RelA:RelB and c-Rel:RelB. It has been reported that phosphorylation of serine at position 276 of RelA allows the modified protein to form a heterodimer with RelB. It is clear from structural studies that phosphorylation of RelA at Ser276 cannot directly affect dimerization as the amino acid is positioned opposite to the dimer interface. What this observation suggests is that phosphorylation alters domain stability in a manner such that RelB is able to associate with RelA. Unpublished results from our laboratory suggest that RelB is largely unfolded in solution at physiological concentrations and that it becomes folded upon dimerization with p50 or p52. We also have found that the introduction of a glutamic acid or aspartic acid mutation at position 276 to mimic phosphorylation significantly decreases the folding stability of RelA. It is possible that phosphorylation-dependent destabilization of RelA functions to catalyze formation of a stable RelA:RelB heterodimer.

4 IκB Structure and Regulation of NF-κB

IκB proteins control induction of NF-κB in a stimulus-specific manner. In particular, the rapid and transient activation of NF-κB that is required to mount immune and inflammatory responses is mediated by the degradation of classical IκB proteins, IκBα, IκBβ, and IκBε, and the subsequent transcriptional upregulation of response genes. On the other hand, the non-classical IκB proteins, p105 and p100 induce a more prolonged gene activation program as these IκB proteins are co-opted for slow degradation processes.

4.1 IκBα Binding to the NF-κB p50:RelA Heterodimer

The primary functions of IκBα are to inhibit the DNA binding activity of NF-κB, to bias the steady-state localization of IκB:NF-κB complexes toward the cytoplasm, and to maintain an inhibited pool of NF-κB that is posed for rapid activation via fast IκBα degradation. The X-ray crystal structures of IκBα bound to the NF-κB p50:RelA heterodimer have provided insight into how IκBα inhibits NF-κB activity (Huxford et al. 1998; Jacobs and Harrison 1998). The binding surface is modular and can be divided into three distinct segments. First is the rigid body interaction between the ARD of IκBα and the p50:RelA dimer platform (Fig. 4). This interaction interface, which is mediated primarily by close-packed Van der Waals interactions, accounts for the greatest amount of buried surface area in the complex. The second mode of interaction is mediated by C-terminal NLS polypeptide region beyond the DD of RelA and the first two ankyrin repeats of the IκBα ARD. The C-terminal extended portion, which is flexible in its unbound state, binds to IκBα by forming two helices that mediate specific ion-pair and hydrophobic interactions between conserved amino acid side chains from both proteins. Indeed, the complementary interactions at this site are responsible for the majority of the binding energy of the complex. The third mode of interaction involves the C-terminal PEST region of IκBα, which binds the NTD of the RelA subunit through dynamic long-range electrostatic interactions. This interaction converts the RelA subunit NTD into a conformation relative to the DD that is distinct from that observed when RelA binds DNA (discussed in the next section).

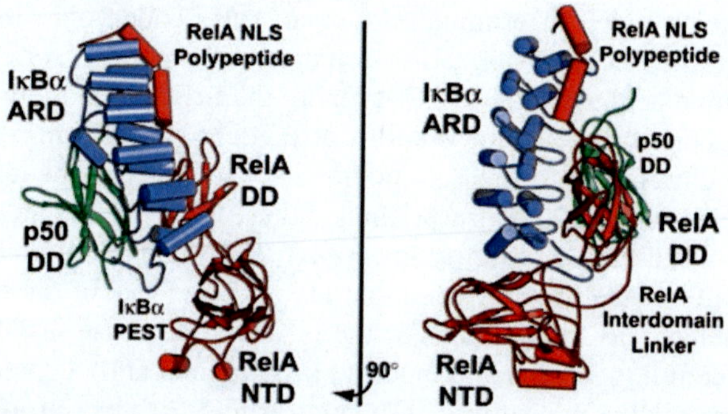

Fig. 4 Ribbon structure diagram of the IκBα inhibitor in complex with the NF-κB p50:RelA heterodimer. The helical ARD (ankyrin repeat domain) of IκBα is depicted in *light blue*. NF-κB p50 and p65 subunits are *green* and *red*, respectively. The complex is viewed similarly as in Fig. 3b (*left*) and then rotated 90° about the vertical axis (*right*)

The structures explain why binding of NF-κB to IκBα inhibits its ability to bind DNA. In addition, they suggest that IκBα conceals the NLS (nuclear localization signal) of RelA explaining the shift toward cytoplasmic localization of the IκBα:p50:RelA complex.

The IκBα:NF-κB complex crystal structure hints that IκB proteins might influence NF-κB dimer formation. IκBα sits atop the p50:p65 heterodimer interface forming a ternary interface suggesting that IκBα could function to further stabilize the NF-κB dimer. Since IκBα binding affinity is much higher than dimerization affinity (<1 nM compared to >0.1 μM), IκBα must bring together two NF-κB subunits at concentrations much lower than the K_{Dim}. One possible functional advantage of this IκB-mediated NF-κB dimer stabilization is that different IκB proteins could catalyze the assembly of otherwise rare NF-κB dimers. For example, and as mentioned previously, the free NF-κB p52 homodimer has not been observed in vivo. However, the p52 homodimer bound to the nuclear IκB protein Bcl-3 has been detected. This suggests that, although p52 preferably forms heterodimers, interaction with a specific IκB molecule can induce formation the homodimer.

4.2 Regulation of IκBα:NF-κB Complex Formation

Biophysical analysis on free IκBα in solution revealed that only the first four ankyrin repeats adopt a stable folded structure while the two remaining C-terminal repeats and the contiguous PEST sequence remain mostly unfolded (Croy et al. 2004). This is rare for ARD-containing proteins, most of which display high folding stability in solution (Kohl et al. 2003). Upon binding to NF-κB, however, the six ankyrin repeats of IκBα stack as a continuous folded domain (Bergqvist et al. 2006). These observations suggest that as the disordered NLS polypeptide region of RelA adopts an ordered structure upon binding to the more stable portion of the ARD, the unfolded C-terminal portions of IκBα undergo a similar transition upon binding to the folded dimerization domains of the p50:RelA heterodimer. By introducing amino acid substitutions that render the IκBα ARD more similar to the ankyrin repeat consensus, mutant versions of IκBα have been engineered in order that their two C-terminal repeats adopt the ankyrin fold independent of NF-κB binding (Ferreiro et al. 2007). Surprisingly, these pre-folded mutants showed a measurably reduced binding affinity for the NF-κB p50:p65 heterodimer (Truhlar et al. 2008). Kinetic analyses revealed that an increased rate of dissociation of the pre-folded mutants was responsible for the observed decrease in NF-κB binding. Therefore, by coupling folding and binding, IκBα significantly decreases its rate of dissociation from NF-κB resulting in a high affinity protein–protein interaction (K_D in the high pM range). These observations, based on structural studies and biophysical characterization, serve to explain why IκBα must be actively removed via 26 S proteasome-mediated proteolysis in order to supply free NF-κB for inducible gene expression. They also suggest that deviations from the consensus ankyrin repeat sequence endow IκBα with its signature NF-κB binding and regulatory properties.

4.3 The IκBβ:RelA Homodimer Complex

The X-ray crystal structure of the IκBβ:RelA homodimer complex revealed similar modes of interaction between IκB and NF-κB proteins (Malek et al. 2003). However, there are clear differences that are noteworthy. First, interactions between the ARD and an NLS are nearly identical. Interestingly, the NLS of the second RelA subunit also appears to interact weakly. Although IκBβ alone was shown to partially protect this second RelA subunit NLS polypeptide from proteolysis with limiting amounts of protease in vitro, it appears as if the IκBβ requires some other component to stabilize its complex with RelA homodimer. Second, the sixth and final ankyrin repeat of IκBβ appeared to be less intimately involved in the NF-kB binding as compared with the similar region of IκBα in the IκBκ:NF-κB complex structure. This may explain the why the C-terminal PEST sequence in IκBβ is not critical for interaction with the N-terminal domain of RelA as it appears to be positioned away from the protein–protein interface. Third, IκBβ contains a unique insertion of 42 amino acids in length located between ankyrin repeats 3 and 4. This insert, the majority of which is disordered in the X-ray structure, is projected into solution far from the protein–protein interface. It is likely that the insert is used for other purposes such as in binding to other factors.

The IκBβ:RelA complex also provides intriguing insights into how IκBβ might bind and regulate activity of the NF-κB c-Rel homodimer. It was previously reported that IκBβ interacts with c-Rel in a phosphorylation-dependent manner, whereby two serines in the IκBβ PEST sequence (amino acids 313 and 315 in murine IκBβ numbering) must be phosphorylated (Thompson et al. 1995). This suggests the intriguing possibility of two distinct modes of NF-κB inhibition by

IκBβ: one that relies primarily on interactions between the IκBβ ARD and RelA DD and NLS polypeptide and another that involves the phosphorylated IκBβ PEST and c-Rel. The requirement of PEST phosphorylation for IκBβ:c-Rel homodimer complex formation further suggests that the c-Rel NTD may play a role in IκBβ complex formation in a manner analogous to interactions between the analogous NTD of Rel and IκBα in the IκBα:NF-κB complex structure. Alternative binding modes by IκBβ could explain why IκBβ is not a good inhibitor of DNA binding by the RelA homodimer as the unphosphorylated IκBβ PEST does not engage the RelA NTD. In contrast, a PEST-phosphorylated IκBβ might be able to inhibit DNA binding by the c-Rel homodimer. In contrast to IκBα, which can readily dissociate RelA homodimer or p50:RelA heterodimer from their complexes with target DNA, IκBβ appears to be unable to carry out this function. Future experiments will determine whether IκBβ is capable of stripping c-Rel from κB DNA.

Finally, it has been observed that deletion of the insert between ankyrin repeats 3 and 4 of IκBβ reduces its affinity for c-Rel homodimer. κB-Ras, a small GTPase, was shown to be involved in IκBβ-mediated inhibition of NF-κB and might interact with IκBβ:NF-κB complexes through this inter-repeat loop (Chen et al. 2004; Fenwick et al. 2000).

4.4 NF-κB Regulation by IκBε

IκBε was originally reported to inhibit homodimers of RelA and c-Rel (Li and Nabel 1997; Simeonidis et al. 1997; Whiteside et al. 1997). However, a recent study also suggested that IκBε negative feedback regulates RelA:p50 to dampen IκBα-mediated oscillations (Kearns et al. 2006). Significant differences in domain architecture between IκBε and other classical IκB proteins include the relative absence of acidic amino acid residues within the C-terminal PEST region and an extended N-terminus. These differences may allow IκBε to use these peripheral regions to specifically recognize features unique to RelA or c-Rel homodimers. More structural and in vitro biochemical studies are required in order to gain mechanistic insight into how IκBε regulates NF-κB activity.

4.5 The Non-Classical IκB Proteins p105 and p100

The paradigm of NF-κB regulation in the cytoplasm for the better part of the past 20 years has hinged upon stimulus-dependent rapid degradation of IκBα followed by nuclear translocation of the NF-κB p50:RelA heterodimer. Recently, it has become increasingly clear that the NF-κB precursors p105 and p100 also function as IκB inhibitors. The ability of p105 to function as an IκB molecule was demonstrated previously (Mercurio et al. 1992; Rice et al. 1992). Furthermore, the biological significance of the inhibitory activities of both p105 and p100 have been evident for many years since mouse studies revealed that chromosomal deletion of their C-terminal ARD leads to severe misregulation of NF-κB (Ishikawa et al. 1997, 1998). However, as p105 and p100 also function as the immature precursors of the NF-κB subunits p50 and p52, respectively, dissecting the specific consequences on NF-κB regulation due to modification or disruption of these proteins has been a challenge. The p105 protein binds and inhibits all NF-κB subunits including p50, its own processed product. This is in contrast to the NF-κB inhibitory activity demonstrated by classical IκB proteins, which is directed toward specific NF-κB subunits. Recent experiments have established that multiple copies of p100 and p105 can assemble to form large complexes wherein diverse NF-κB subunits are bound (Savinova et al. 2009). We have referred to these large NF-κB signaling complexes as "IκBsomes". The observed differences in structural arrangement and binding specificity exhibited by non-classical inhibitors suggest that they might display distinct kinetic profiles of NF-κB activation and post-induction repression as compared to the classical inhibitors. Recent evidence suggests that over half of cellular RelA and c-Rel and all of RelB are bound to p100 and p105 in the steady state of most cells (Basak et al. 2007; Tergaonkar et al. 2005). Although their ability to function as IκB proteins is now firmly established, the unique physiological consequences of NF-κB regulation by p105 and p100 are just beginning to be determined (Chang et al. 2009; Srisk-antharajah et al. 2009).

4.6 Post-Induction Repression of NF-κB by IκB

Most NF-κB activating signals, such as TNF-α and IL-1, lead to the elevated expression of the NF-κB-inducible IκB proteins IκBα, IκBε, p105, and p100. The newly synthesized inhibitors can then function to repress NF-κB activity. Most notably, free IκBα can enter the nucleus where it is capable of binding and disrupting NF-κB:DNA complexes (Bergqvist et al. 2009) before returning the inactive NF-κB to the cytoplasm. However, the differences in kinetics of IκB protein expression coupled with their varied rates of constitutive and signal-induced degradation results in the periodic mobilization of NF-κB in waves of activity (Hoffmann et al. 2002; Kearns and Hoffmann 2009). Computational modeling of IκB:NF-κB regulation using a systems biology approach has correctly predicted the temporal control of NF-κB in response to several stimuli. Signaling through the cytokine-responsive IKKβ subunit liberates NF-κB dimers that were associated with classical IκB proteins whereas p100, which responds specifically to signaling from IKKα:NIK complexes, remains intact. However, newly synthesized p100 (produced by the RelA-target gene nfkb2) can multimerize to form a novel "IκBδ" activity within IkBsomes, and thus trap RelA:p50 NF-κB during the later stages of induction to provide negative feedback inhibition (Shih et al. 2009). This newly inhibited IκBδ complex can subsequently become the target for non-canonical signaling. Therefore, NF-κB signaling pathways are intricately intertwined and susceptible to alteration as cells respond continuously to their environment (Basak et al. 2008).

4.7 *Kinetics of IκB Degradation*

NF-κB activation kinetics correlate with the rates with which the proteasome degrades IκB proteins. This, in turn, depends upon the ability of the IKK complex to recognize and phosphorylate IκB proteins at specific sites. It is clear that the phosphorylation sites of classical IκB proteins are accessible to IKK when they are bound to NF-κB. Active IKK also phosphorylates unbound IκB proteins (Mathes et al. 2008). Phosphorylation of free IκBβ by IKK occurs at a slower rate compared to that of IκBα although the rate of IκBβ phosphorylation remains on the time scale of minutes. Small variations in the amino acid sequences at their respective phosphorylation sites account for the observed differences in the rates of IκBβ and IκBα phosphorylation by IKKβ (Wu and Ghosh 2003). Structural and biochemical studies indicate that phosphorylation sites of IκBβ remain accessible to IKK in the IκBβ:NF-κB complex and it is reasonable to assume that the same is true for IκBε (Malek et al. 2003). However, ubiquitin acceptors in IκBβ and -ε remain to be determined, as well as the molecular basis for distinct stimulus-induced degradation kinetics. The state of the IKK phosphorylation sites in p100 and p105 are unknown when the inhibitor proteins are multimerized within IκBsomes. Masking of these regions could serve as a mechanism for regulating the kinetics of phosphorylation of p100 and p105. Differences in the degradation kinetics of IκB may also arise from changes in the levels of ubiquitination, recognition by the proteasome, and unfolding of the IκB proteins prior to degradation. Detailed in vitro and cellular experiments to test these hypotheses are required in improve our understanding of NF-κB regulation arising from kinetic control of IκB degradation.

5 Recognition of DNA by NF-κB

NF-κB recognizes a double-stranded DNA element that is 9 to 11 bp (base pairs) long. Early comparisons of the first DNA sequences demonstrated to bind specifically to NF-κB dimers led to the following consensus sequence: 5′-GGGRNWYY CC-3′, where R = A or G; N = A, C, G, or T; W = A or T; and Y = C or T. The critical feature of this consensus is the presence of a series of G nucleotide bases the 5′ ends while the central portion of the sequence displays greater variation. DNA from gene enhancer regions that meet this consensus and can be shown to drive NF-κB-dependent reporter gene expression are termed "κB DNA" or "κB sites". Hundreds of such sequences have been confirmed experimentally and the total number of unconfirmed κB sites detected by computational methods is in the thousands. Many of these newer sites reveal significantly greater variation than allowed by the original consensus κB DNA sequence.

5.1 NF-κB:DNA Complex Structures

The three-dimensional structures of several NF-κB RHR dimers in complex with diverse κB DNA have provided important insights into the DNA recognition mechanism of NF-κB (Berkowitz et al. 2002; Chen et al. 1998a, b, 2000; Chen-Park et al. 2002; Cramer et al. 1997; Escalante et al. 2002; Fusco et al. 2009; Ghosh et al. 1995; Huang et al. 2001; Moorthy et al. 2007; Müller et al. 1995; Panne et al. 2007). In general, the κB DNA is pseudo-symmetric and each NF-κB monomer binds to one DNA half site (Fig. 5). In its DNA-bound conformation, the NF-κB subunit NTD is positioned such that a conserved basic surface interacts with the acidic DNA. This represents a nearly 180° rotation for the NTD relative to its conformation in the RelA subunit of the IκBα:NF-κB complex crystal structures. Translation and rotation of the NTD relative to the DD is afforded by the short stretch of 10 amino acids that link the two domains.

Amino acid side chains from the immunoglobulin-like NTD of each NF-κB RHR mediate all of the direct contacts to DNA bases. The NF-κB dimer interface is maintained upon κB DNA binding and multiple additional non-specific DNA backbone interactions are made by the NTD and DD. The structure of NF-κB was unique at the time of its determination by virtue of the fact that all of the contacts with DNA were mediated by amino acids on loops that connect beta-strand elements of secondary structure. The arrangement of the NF-κB dimer about the major groove of one entire turn of DNA gives rise to a global structure that is reminiscent of a butterfly with a DNA "body" and a pair RHR "wings". The

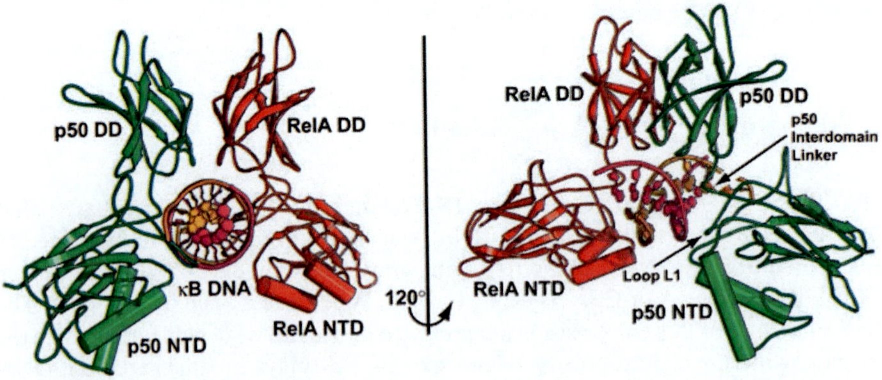

Fig. 5 Ribbon structure diagram of the NF-κB p50:RelA heterodimer in complex with κB DNA. Coloring as in Figs. 3 and 4 with DNA strands in *magenta* and *orange*. The view is as in Fig. 3b (*left*) and rotated 120° about the vertical axis (*right*) to show the interaction of loop L1 and the interdomain linker with DNA bases through the major groove

C-terminal NLS polypeptide is disordered when it is included in the NF-κB RHR constructs used for X-ray crystal structure determination.

5.2 NF-κB Recognition of κB DNA at the 5′-end

A grouping of conserved amino acid residues that emanate from a large loop, referred to as the loop L1, directly contact bases within κB DNA. In p50 (murine numbering) these residues are Arg54, Arg56, Tyr57, Glu60, His64, and Lys241 (Fig. 6). The two Arg, the Tyr, and the Glu are invariant in all NF-κB subunits. His64 directly contacts the 5′ G. This residue is conserved in the NF-κB p52 subunit. However, substitution with Ala at this position in c-Rel, RelA, and RelB gives rise to differences in the half site length preferred by these two classes of NF-κB subunits as the Ala cannot compensate for the loss of this base-specific contact. As a consequence, the NF-κB p50 and p52 subunits prefer a 5′ half site that begins 5′-GGG and is five bp in length while the other subunits (RelA, RelB, or c-Rel) bind preferentially to 4 bp half sites that begin 5′-GG. A central bp, which is always A:T, is not contacted by either subunit suggesting that homodimers of p50 or p52 would bind optimally to an 11 bp κB DNA (two 5 bp half sites and a central A:T bp) while RelA, RelB, and c-Rel prefer 9 bp κB DNA. This also perfectly explains the original observation of NF-κB p50:RelA heterodimer bound to the 10 bp κB DNA from the enhancer of the immunoglobin kappa light chain gene (Sen and Baltimore 1986).

The central A:T bp serves as a convenient point of reference in studying base-specific interactions by NF-κB subunits and κB DNA. The 5′ G that is contacted by His64 of the p50 subunit occupies the position ±5 bp from this origin. The G:C bp at positions ±4 and ±3 are contacted similarly by each of the NF-κB subunits. The two invariant arginines (Arg56 and Arg54 in murine p50) make direct contact with these two G bases and the invariant glutamate contacts the paired C at the ±3 position. Recognition of both nucleotide bases at this position suggests a more important role of the G:C bp at position ±3 than either the G:C bp at the ±5 and ±4 positions.

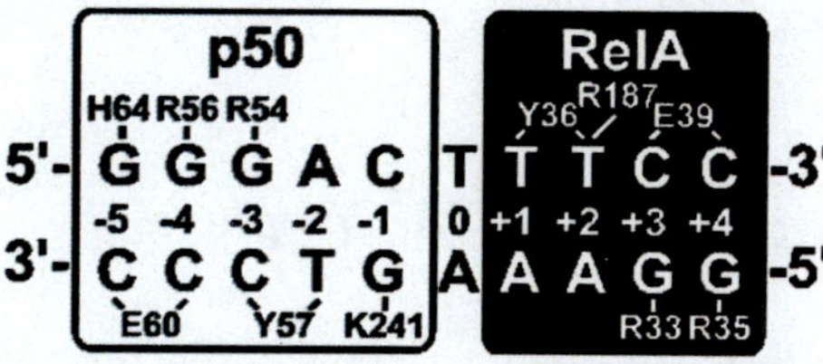

Fig. 6 Schematic representation of base-specific contacts mediated by NF-κB p50 and RelA subunits and κB DNA. In this case, the κB DNA is that from the original immunoglobin kappa light chain gene and the contacts are those observed in its X-ray crystal structure with the NF-κB p50:RelA heterodimer. Bases are numbered as discussed in the text. Amino acid numbering comes from the murine sequences

5.3 NF-κB Binding to the Inner Bases of κB DNA

Base pairs at positions ±2 and ±1 in κB DNA exhibit more variability in sequence than the peripheral bases. In the crystal structure of the NF-κB p50:RelA heterodimer in complex with κB DNA from the immunoglobin kappa light chain gene, an Arg residue contained within the linker region that joins the NTD and DD in the RelA subunits crosses over and contacts the T of an A:T bp at position +2. An identical Arg is present in c-Rel. An analogous Lys residue at the corresponding position in p50 and p52 can interact with both T in an A:T bp or G from a G:C bp at the same position. Base pairs at position ±1 in κB DNA do not participate in any contacts with either RelA and c-Rel. However, the Lys residue within the interdomain linker of p50 and p52 can mediate contacts at this position dependent on the DNA sequence. The corresponding residue in RelB is also a lysine (Lys274 in murine RelB). However, rather than contact DNA this Lys projects inward to make an ion pair with Asp272. This suggests that RelB subunits might tolerate more sequence diversity at the inner positions of its κB DNA targets.

An invariant Tyr of loop L1 (Tyr57 in murine p50 and Tyr36 in murine RelA) participates in stacking interactions with bases at both ±1 and ±2 of the same strand. This stacking is favored by the presence of two successive T bases, as their exocyclic 5-methyl groups favor the interaction. Although a Phe at the same position could substitute for Tyr in maintain these stacking interactions, Tyr also participates in hydrogen bonds through its hydroxyl group making tyrosine an absolutely required residue for DNA recognition and binding. Either two C bases or any combination of T and C can also be accommodated at these positions, but an A or G at either position is unfavorable. The critical role played by this invariant Tyr is illustrated by the overrepresentation of the sequence AAATT or AATTT at the central 5 positions of the κB sequences recognized by RelA and c-Rel homodimers. It is likely that these Tyr base stacking interactions toward the center of the 9 bp κB sites preferred by RelA and c-Rel compensate for the fact that these NF-κB subunits contact fewer flanking GC bp.

It is not clear from structural analyses alone why A:T is by far the preferred central bp (position 0). It is likely that the presence of this base pair is necessary to convey DNA bending and/or dynamic characteristics necessary for optimum NF-κB:DNA complex formation.

5.4 Stabilization of NF-κB:DNA Complexes

The interaction of proteins can significantly alter binding affinity of NF-κB:DNA complexes. This can be true even if the protein binding is distal from the NF-κB:DNA interface. Both protein:DNA and protein:protein interactions are interdependent. This means that assembly of NF-κB into larger enhanceosome complexes and can be affected by subtle changes in DNA conformation.

This point is illustrated by two loops, one from the DD and the other from the NTD, which play particularly important roles. The βf-βg loop of the NF-κB DD projects toward κB DNA but does not directly contact it. Two conserved acidic residues (Asp267 and Glu269 in chicken c-Rel) are located within this loop and reside near the DNA in the complex between c-Rel homodimer and the IL2-CDRE κB DNA complex. These residues would be expected repel DNA and weaken binding (Huang et al. 2001). However, these negative charges are neutralized by an Arg in loop L1. Loop L1 is the same loop that contributes five of the six base contacting residues. Loop L1 can be divided into three parts: N-terminal front, N-terminal back, and C-terminal flexible part. The C-terminal portion of loop L1 is flexible and can contact the DNA backbone of nucleotides flanking the κB sequence. The N-terminal front and back end forms a rigid core structure that remain unchanged both in DNA bound and unbound forms. The surface residues projected from the front portion contribute the DNA base-contacting residues. An Arg on the back surface of the N-terminal portion contacts the acidic residues of the βf-βg loop. Interestingly, not all NF-κB:DNA complex crystallographic structures show this protein–protein interaction. We suggest that DNA conformation differences play a role in dictating RHR interdomain interactions. In the case of oncogenic v-Rel, a viral homologue of c-Rel, two core residues within the rigid part of Loop L1 are mutated. These two residues are at least partly responsible for altered DNA binding profiles by v-Rel as compared to c-Rel (Phelps and Ghosh 2004). Finally, these two loops also undergo modification, which also appears to regulate NF-κB DNA recognition as discussed below.

5.5 *Post-Translational Modification and NF-κB:DNA Complex Regulation*

A recent report has shown that monomethylation of RelA at Lys37 in response to induction by TNF-α and IL-1 is required for the expression of a subset of NF-κB target genes (Ea and Baltimore 2009). The methylated form of RelA displays extended gene activation as a result of prolonged DNA binding by RelA. Although a detailed mechanism to explain how modification of this residue might affect DNA binding is lacking, its position within of loop L1 suggests that the effect is likely indirect through altering the conformation the residues that directly contact DNA. It is important to mention here that some of the DNA contacting residues from loop L1 contact one another further stabilizing the loop L1 conformation and allowing them all to act as a unit. In p50, Glu60 bridges Arg54 and Arg56 as together they contact DNA as a structured module. The stability and utility of this folded polypeptide structure was illustrated when it was found to be exploited by RNA in selection binding experiments (Huang et al. 2003). In RelA and c-Rel, a similar Glu brings together one of the two Arg residues form the loop L1 and the Arg from the interdomain linker. These cooperative interactions between the amino acids side chains not only maintain a properly oriented conformation of the functional groups primed to contact DNA, but also contribute to differential base pair selectivity. Hence modification of lysine could affect orientation of these residues as well as residues that are involved in contact residues at loop βf-βg (discussed earlier).

Cells expressing a RelA Ser276Ala mutant show dramatically reduced transcriptional activity. This serine has been shown to undergo phosphorylation by two different kinases, MSK and cAMP-dependent protein kinase (PKA), and this post-translational modification is essential for RelA transcriptional activity (Dong et al. 2008; Reber et al. 2009; Vermeulen et al. 2003; Zhong et al. 1998). Although the RelA Ser276Ala appears to bind DNA, defects in DNA affinity cannot be completely ruled out in light of the importance of other residues in the same loop in the protein:DNA complex formation. Phosphorylation at position 276 has also been shown to be required for coactivator recruitment. Therefore, in addition to affinity modulation, phosphorylation may play a role in changing chromatin dynamics through acetylation activity of CBP/p300.

5.6 NF-κB Subunit Exchange in the Nucleus

One aspect of NF-κB regulation that has not yet been adequately addressed experimentally is the potential for exchange of subunits between active NF-κB dimers in the nucleus. The available structural and biochemical data suggest that this is likely to occur, especially in light of the relatively low dimerization affinity exhibited by many of the NF-κB dimer combinations and the preference of different κB DNA half sites toward specific NF-κB subunits. Functionally, it seems reasonable that such an exchange might coincide with the transition of a gene promoter from a repressed to an activated state. Homodimers of p50 and p52 are present in the nucleus of uninduced cells. Rapid mobilization of additional NF-κB subunits to the nucleus in response to IκB degradation could then lead to replacement of these repressive NF-κB with dimers that possess inherent transcription activation potential. It is not known whether the repressive p50 and p52 dimers are directly exchanged with p50:RelA or other activating homo- and heterodimers or, alternatively, if the individual p50 or p52 subunit monomers can exchange with a RelA monomer on κB DNA. Interestingly, analysis of the mice lacking the gene encoding IκBNS revealed a significant decrease in IL-2 (interleukin-2) production. ChIP assays on native cells revealed that IκBNS co-localizes with p50 homodimer at κB DNA and remains associated even after the p50 is dissociated (Touma et al. 2007). Therefore, it is possible that nuclear NF-κB subunit exchange on κB DNA falls under the purview of the nuclear IκB proteins.

Acknowledgments T.H. is the recipient of an American Cancer Society grant RSG-08-287-01-GMC.

References

Basak S, Kim H, Kearns JD, Tergaonkar V, O'Dea E, Werner SL, Benedict CA, Ware CF, Ghosh G, Verma IM, Hoffmann A (2007) A fourth IκB protein within the NF-κB signaling module. Cell 128:369–381

Basak S, Shih VF, Hoffmann A (2008) Generation and activation of multiple dimeric transcription factors within the NF-κB signaling system. Mol Cell Biol 28:3139–3150

Bergqvist S, Croy CH, Kjaergaard M, Huxford T, Ghosh G, Komives EA (2006) Thermodynamics reveal that helix four in the NLS of NF-κB p65 anchors IκBα, forming a very stable complex. J Mol Biol 360:421–434

Bergqvist S, Alverdi V, Mengel B, Hoffmann A, Ghosh G, Komives EA (2009) Kinetic enhancement of NF-κB:DNA dissociation by IκBα. Proc Natl Acad Sci USA 106:19328–19333

Berkowitz B, Huang DB, Chen-Park FE, Sigler PB, Ghosh G (2002) The X-ray crystal structure of the NF-κ B p50.p65 heterodimer bound to the interferon beta -κB site. J Biol Chem 277:24694–24700

Bork P (1993) Hundreds of ankyrin-like repeats in functionally diverse proteins: mobile modules that cross phyla horizontally? Proteins 17:363–374

Chang M, Lee AJ, Fitzpatrick L, Zhang M, Sun SC (2009) NF-κ B1 p105 regulates T cell homeostasis and prevents chronic inflammation. J Immunol 182:3131–3138

Chen ZJ (2005) Ubiquitin signalling in the NF-κB pathway. Nat Cell Biol 7:758–765

Chen FE, Huang DB, Chen YQ, Ghosh G (1998a) Crystal structure of p50/p65 heterodimer of transcription factor NF-κB bound to DNA. Nature 391:410–413

Chen YQ, Ghosh S, Ghosh G (1998b) A novel DNA recognition mode by the NF-κ B p65 homodimer. Nat Struct Biol 5:67–73

Chen YQ, Sengchanthalangsy LL, Hackett A, Ghosh G (2000) NF-κB p65 (RelA) homodimer uses distinct mechanisms to recognize DNA targets. Structure 8:419–428

Chen Y, Vallee S, Wu J, Vu D, Sondek J, Ghosh G (2004) Inhibition of NF-κB activity by IκBbeta in association with κB-Ras. Mol Cell Biol 24:3048–3056

Chen-Park FE, Huang DB, Noro B, Thanos D, Ghosh G (2002) The κB DNA sequence from the HIV long terminal repeat functions as an allosteric regulator of HIV transcription. J Biol Chem 277:24701–24708

Conti E, Kuriyan J (2000) Crystallographic analysis of the specific yet versatile recognition of distinct nuclear localization signals by karyopherin alpha. Structure 8:329–338

Cramer P, Larson CJ, Verdine GL, Müller CW (1997) Structure of the human NF-κB p52 homodimer-DNA complex at 2.1 Å resolution. EMBO J 16:7078–7090

Croy CH, Bergqvist S, Huxford T, Ghosh G, Komives EA (2004) Biophysical characterization of the free IκBα ankyrin repeat domain in solution. Protein Sci 13:1767–1777

Dong J, Jimi E, Zhong H, Hayden MS, Ghosh S (2008) Repression of gene expression by unphosphorylated NF-κB p65 through epigenetic mechanisms. Genes Dev 22:1159–1173

Ea CK, Baltimore D (2009) Regulation of NF-κB activity through lysine monomethylation of p65. Proc Natl Acad Sci USA 106:18972–18977

Escalante CR, Shen L, Thanos D, Aggarwal AK (2002) Structure of NF-κB p50/p65 heterodimer bound to the PRDII DNA element from the interferon-beta promoter. Structure 10:383–391

Fenwick C, Na SY, Voll RE, Zhong H, Im SY, Lee JW, Ghosh S (2000) A subclass of Ras proteins that regulate the degradation of IκB. Science 287:869–873

Ferreiro DU, Cervantes CF, Truhlar SM, Cho SS, Wolynes PG, Komives EA (2007) Stabilizing IκBalpha by "consensus" design. J Mol Biol 365:1201–1216

Fiorini E, Schmitz I, Marissen WE, Osborn SL, Touma M, Sasada T, Reche PA, Tibaldi EV, Hussey RE, Kruisbeek AM et al (2002) Peptide-induced negative selection of thymocytes activates transcription of an NF-κB inhibitor. Mol Cell 9:637–648

Fusco AJ, Huang DB, Miller D, Wang VY, Vu D, Ghosh G (2009) NF-κB p52:RelB heterodimer recognizes two classes of κB sites with two distinct modes. EMBO Rep 10:152–159

Gaudet R (2008) A primer on ankyrin repeat function in TRP channels and beyond. Mol Biosyst 4:372–379

Ghosh G, van Duyne G, Ghosh S, Sigler PB (1995) Structure of NF-κB p50 homodimer bound to a κB site. Nature 373:303–310

Ghosh S, May MJ, Kopp EB (1998) NF-κB and Rel proteins: evolutionarily conserved mediators of immune responses. Annu Rev Immunol 16:225–260

Gilmore TD (2006) Introduction to NF-κB: players, pathways, perspectives. Oncogene 25:6680–6684

Haruta H, Kato A, Todokoro K (2001) Isolation of a novel interleukin-1-inducible nuclear protein bearing ankyrin-repeat motifs. J Biol Chem 276:12485–12488

Hatada EN, Nieters A, Wulczyn FG, Naumann M, Meyer R, Nucifora G, McKeithan TW, Scheidereit C (1992) The ankyrin repeat domains of the NF-κB precursor p105 and the protooncogene bcl-3 act as specific inhibitors of NF-κB DNA binding. Proc Natl Acad Sci USA 89:2489–2493

Hatada EN, Naumann M, Scheidereit C (1993) Common structural constituents confer IκB activity to NF-κB p105 and IκB/MAD-3. EMBO J 12:2781–2788

Hayden MS, Ghosh S (2008) Shared principles in NF-κB signaling. Cell 132:344–362

Hoffmann A, Levchenko A, Scott ML, Baltimore D (2002) The IκB-NF-κB signaling module: temporal control and selective gene activation. Science 298:1241–1245

Huang DB, Huxford T, Chen YQ, Ghosh G (1997) The role of DNA in the mechanism of NF-κB dimer formation: crystal structures of the dimerization domains of the p50 and p65 subunits. Structure 5:1427–1436

Huang DB, Chen YQ, Ruetsche M, Phelps CB, Ghosh G (2001) X-ray crystal structure of proto-oncogene product c-Rel bound to the CD28 response element of IL-2. Structure 9:669–678

Huang DB, Vu D, Cassiday LA, Zimmerman JM, Maher LJ 3rd, Ghosh G (2003) Crystal structure of NF-κB $(p50)_2$ complexed to a high-affinity RNA aptamer. Proc Natl Acad Sci USA 100:9268–9273

Huang DB, Vu D, Ghosh G (2005) NF-κB RelB forms an intertwined homodimer. Structure 13:1365–1373

Huxford T, Huang DB, Malek S, Ghosh G (1998) The crystal structure of the IκBα/NF-κB complex reveals mechanisms of NF-κB inactivation. Cell 95:759–770

Ishikawa H, Carrasco D, Claudio E, Ryseck RP, Bravo R (1997) Gastric hyperplasia and increased proliferative responses of lymphocytes in mice lacking the COOH-terminal ankyrin domain of NF-κB2. J Exp Med 186:999–1014

Ishikawa H, Claudio E, Dambach D, Raventos-Suarez C, Ryan C, Bravo R (1998) Chronic inflammation and susceptibility to bacterial infections in mice lacking the polypeptide (p)105 precursor (NF-κB1) but expressing p50. J Exp Med 187:985–996

Jacobs MD, Harrison SC (1998) Structure of an IκBα/NF-κB complex. Cell 95:749–758

Karin M, Ben-Neriah Y (2000) Phosphorylation meets ubiquitination: the control of NF-κB activity. Annu Rev Immunol 18:621–663

Kearns JD, Hoffmann A (2009) Integrating computational and biochemical studies to explore mechanisms in NF-κB signaling. J Biol Chem 284:5439–5443

Kearns JD, Basak S, Werner SL, Huang CS, Hoffmann A (2006) IκBepsilon provides negative feedback to control NF-κB oscillations, signaling dynamics, and inflammatory gene expression. J Cell Biol 173:659–664

Kitamura H, Kanehira K, Okita K, Morimatsu M, Saito M (2000) MAIL, a novel nuclear IκB protein that potentiates LPS-induced IL-6 production. FEBS Lett 485:53–56

Kohl A, Binz HK, Forrer P, Stumpp MT, Plückthun A, Grutter MG (2003) Designed to be stable: crystal structure of a consensus ankyrin repeat protein. Proc Natl Acad Sci USA 100:1700–1705

Li Z, Nabel GJ (1997) A new member of the IκB protein family, IκBε, inhibits RelA (p65)-mediated NF-κB transcription. Mol Cell Biol 17:6184–6190

Malek S, Huang DB, Huxford T, Ghosh S, Ghosh G (2003) X-ray crystal structure of an IκBβ:NF-κB p65 homodimer complex. J Biol Chem 278:23094–23100

Mathes E, O'Dea EL, Hoffmann A, Ghosh G (2008) NF-κB dictates the degradation pathway of IκBα. EMBO J 27:1357–1367

Mercurio F, Didonato J, Rosette C, Karin M (1992) Molecular cloning and characterization of a novel Rel/NF-κB family member displaying structural and functional homology to NF-κB p50/p105. DNA Cell Biol 11:523–537

Moorthy AK, Huang DB, Wang VY, Vu D, Ghosh G (2007) X-ray structure of a NF-κB p50/RelB/DNA complex reveals assembly of multiple dimers on tandem κB sites. J Mol Biol 373:723–734

Muenchen HJ, Lin DL, Walsh MA, Keller ET, Pienta KJ (2000) Tumor necrosis factor-alpha-induced apoptosis in prostate cancer cells through inhibition of nuclear factor-κB by an IκBα "super-repressor". Clin Cancer Res 6:1969–1977

Müller CW, Rey FA, Sodeoka M, Verdine GL, Harrison SC (1995) Structure of the NF-κB p50 homodimer bound to DNA. Nature 373:311–317

Naumann M, Nieters A, Hatada EN, Scheidereit C (1993) NF-κ B precursor p100 inhibits nuclear translocation and DNA binding of NF-κB/rel-factors. Oncogene 8:2275–2281

Ohno H, Takimoto G, McKeithan TW (1990) The candidate proto-oncogene bcl-3 is related to genes implicated in cell lineage determination and cell cycle control. Cell 60:991–997

Pahl HL (1999) Activators and target genes of Rel/NF-κB transcription factors. Oncogene 18:6853–6866

Palmer S, Chen YH (2008) Bcl-3, a multifaceted modulator of NF-κB-mediated gene transcription. Immunol Res 42:210–218

Panne D, Maniatis T, Harrison SC (2007) An atomic model of the interferon-beta enhanceosome. Cell 129:1111–1123

Phelps CB, Ghosh G (2004) Discreet mutations from c-Rel to v-Rel alter κB DNA recognition, IκBα binding, and dimerization: implications for v-Rel oncogenicity. Oncogene 23:1229–1238

Reber L, Vermeulen L, Haegeman G, Frossard N (2009) Ser276 phosphorylation of NF-κB p65 by MSK1 controls SCF expression in inflammation. PLoS One 4:e4393

Rice NR, MacKichan ML, Israël A (1992) The precursor of NF-κB p50 has IκB-like functions. Cell 71:243–253

Rogers S, Wells R, Rechsteiner M (1986) Amino acid sequences common to rapidly degraded proteins: the PEST hypothesis. Science 234:364–368

Savinova OV, Hoffmann A, Ghosh G (2009) The Nfkb1 and Nfkb2 proteins p105 and p100 function as the core of high-molecular-weight heterogeneous complexes. Mol Cell 34:591–602

Sen R, Baltimore D (1986) Multiple nuclear factors interact with the immunoglobulin enhancer sequences. Cell 46:705–716

Senftleben U, Cao Y, Xiao G, Greten FR, Krahn G, Bonizzi G, Chen Y, Hu Y, Fong A, Sun SC, Karin M (2001) Activation by IKKα of a second, evolutionary conserved, NF-κB signaling pathway. Science 293:1495–1499

Sengchanthalangsy LL, Datta S, Huang DB, Anderson E, Braswell EH, Ghosh G (1999) Characterization of the dimer interface of transcription factor NF-κB p50 homodimer. J Mol Biol 289:1029–1040

Shih VF, Kearns JD, Basak S, Savinova OV, Ghosh G, Hoffmann A (2009) Kinetic control of negative feedback regulators of NF-κB/RelA determines their pathogen- and cytokine-receptor signaling specificity. Proc Natl Acad Sci USA 106:9619–9624

Simeonidis S, Liang S, Chen G, Thanos D (1997) Cloning and functional characterization of mouse IκBε. Proc Natl Acad Sci USA 94:14372–14377

Sriskantharajah S, Belich MP, Papoutsopoulou S, Janzen J, Tybulewicz V, Seddon B, Ley SC (2009) Proteolysis of NF-κB1 p105 is essential for T cell antigen receptor-induced proliferation. Nat Immunol 10:38–47

Tergaonkar V, Correa RG, Ikawa M, Verma IM (2005) Distinct roles of IκB proteins in regulating constitutive NF-κB activity. Nat Cell Biol 7:921–923

Thompson JE, Phillips RJ, Erdjument-Bromage H, Tempst P, Ghosh S (1995) IκBβ regulates the persistent response in a biphasic activation of NF-κB. Cell 80:573–582

Touma M, Antonini V, Kumar M, Osborn SL, Bobenchik AM, Keskin DB, Connolly JE, Grusby MJ, Reinherz EL, Clayton LK (2007) Functional role for IκBNS in T cell cytokine regulation as revealed by targeted gene disruption. J Immunol 179:1681–1692

Truhlar SM, Mathes E, Cervantes CF, Ghosh G, Komives EA (2008) Pre-folding IκBα alters control of NF-κB signaling. J Mol Biol 380:67–82

Vermeulen L, De Wilde G, Van Damme P, Vanden Berghe W, Haegeman G (2003) Transcriptional activation of the NF-κB p65 subunit by mitogen- and stress-activated protein kinase-1 (MSK1). EMBO J 22:1313–1324

Whiteside ST, Isräel A (1997) IκB proteins: structure, function and regulation. Semin Cancer Biol 8:75–82

Whiteside ST, Epinat JC, Rice NR, Isräel A (1997) IκBε, a novel member of the IκB family, controls RelA and cRel NF-κB activity. EMBO J 16:1413–1426

Wu C, Ghosh S (2003) Differential phosphorylation of the signal-responsive domain of IκBα and IκBβ by IκB kinases. J Biol Chem 278:31980–31987

Yamamoto M, Yamazaki S, Uematsu S, Sato S, Hemmi H, Hoshino K, Kaisho T, Kuwata H, Takeuchi O, Takeshige K et al (2004) Regulation of Toll/IL-1-receptor-mediated gene expression by the inducible nuclear protein IκBζ. Nature 430:218–222

Yamazaki S, Muta T, Takeshige K (2001) A novel IκB protein, IκBζ, induced by proinflammatory stimuli, negatively regulates nuclear factor-κB in the nuclei. J Biol Chem 276:27657–27662

Yaron A, Hatzubai A, Davis M, Lavon I, Amit S, Manning AM, Andersen JS, Mann M, Mercurio F, Ben-Neriah Y (1998) Identification of the receptor component of the IκBα-ubiquitin ligase. Nature 396:590–594

Zhong H, Voll RE, Ghosh S (1998) Phosphorylation of NF-κB p65 by PKA stimulates transcriptional activity by promoting a novel bivalent interaction with the coactivator CBP/p300. Mol Cell 1:661–671

NF-κB/Rel Proteins and the Humoral Immune Responses of *Drosophila melanogaster*

Sandhya Ganesan, Kamna Aggarwal, Nicholas Paquette and Neal Silverman

Abstract Nuclear Factor-κB (NF-κB)/Rel transcription factors form an integral part of innate immune defenses and are conserved throughout the animal kingdom. Studying the function, mechanism of activation and regulation of these factors is crucial for understanding host responses to microbial infections. The fruit fly *Drosophila melanogaster* has proved to be a valuable model system to study these evolutionarily conserved NF-κB mediated immune responses. *Drosophila* combats pathogens through humoral and cellular immune responses. These humoral responses are well characterized and are marked by the robust production of a battery of anti-microbial peptides. Two NF-κB signaling pathways, the Toll and the IMD pathways, are responsible for the induction of these antimicrobial peptides. Signal transduction in these pathways is strikingly similar to that in mammalian TLR pathways. In this chapter, we discuss in detail the molecular mechanisms of microbial recognition, signal transduction and NF-κB regulation, in both the Toll and the IMD pathways. Similarities and differences relative to their mammalian counterparts are discussed, and recent advances in our understanding of the intricate regulatory networks in these NF-κB signaling pathways are also highlighted.

S. Ganesan, K. Aggarwal and N. Silverman (✉)
Division of Infectious Diseases, Department of Medicine,
University of Massachusetts Medical School, Worcester MA, 01605, USA
e-mail: neal.silverman@umassmed.edu

N. Paquette
Program of Developmental Immunology,
Department of Pediatrics, Massachusetts General Hospital/Harvard
Medical School, Boston MA, 02114, USA

Current Topics Microbiology (2011) 349: 25-60
DOI: 10.1007/82_2010_107

Published Online: 18 September 2010

Contents

1 Introduction

Nuclear Factor-kappaB/Rel proteins are an evolutionarily conserved class of transcription factors that play crucial roles in regulating many animal physiological processes such as, cell survival, proliferation, and most importantly, immune responses. In general, NF-κB/Rel proteins are found inactive in the cytoplasm associated with their inhibitory proteins or domains (IκBs), and various challenges trigger the degradation or cleavage of these IκBs thereby allowing the NF-κB transcription factor to translocate into the nucleus. NF-κB transcription factors play a central role in the induction of many cytokines and immune effector genes that initiate robust pro-inflammatory responses. Owing to the conserved structure and function of NF-κB/Rel proteins across the animal kingdom, various model systems have been extensively used to probe the molecular mechanisms of NF-κB activation and its role in inflammation, infection and disease.

Over the past 20 years, *Drosophila melanogaster* has been a favored model system for the study of NF-κB regulation and function in developmental biology and in immunity. The NF-κB factor Dorsal, and the Toll pathway which activates it, were first discovered in *Drosophila* because of their central role in establishing the dorsoventral pattern in the developing embryo (Nusslein-Volhard et al. 1987; Steward 1987). Moreover, the three *Drosophila* NF-κB factors, Dorsal,

Dorsal-related immunity factor (DIF) and Relish, are the master regulators of the insect humoral immune response, which is characterized by the rapid and robust production of a battery of potent antimicrobial peptides (AMPs). These AMPs, along with other cellular defense strategies such as clotting, melanization, phagocytosis and encapsulation, effectively eliminate many microbes. The *Drosophila* NF-κB/Rel signaling modules display a striking degree of conservation with mammals, and this has made *Drosophila* a valuable experimental model for studying these critical NF-κB innate immune responses against both insect and human pathogens (Mansfield et al. 2003; Apidianakis et al. 2005; Scully and Bidochka 2006; Vonkavaara et al. 2008).

This review focuses on the role of NF-κB/Rel transcription factors in the immune defenses of *Drosophila*, highlighting both similarities and differences in the corresponding mammalian systems, and also, how studies in the *Drosophila* model system contribute to our understanding of these signaling networks in mammals.

2 Microbial Recognition and Humoral Responses

2.1 Anti-microbial Peptides

The *Drosophila* humoral immune system responds to microbial challenge by triggering the expression of anti-microbial peptide genes through NF-κB signaling pathways. In fact, NF-κB/Rel proteins control the transcription of almost one half of the immune responsive genes, including the collection of cationic AMPs (De Gregorio et al. 2001, 2002). As a result of infection-induced NF-κB activation, AMPs that are undetectable in the hemolymph (blood) of unchallenged flies are rapidly elevated to concentrations up to 100 μM (Hoffmann and Reichhart 2002). As best we know, the regulation of AMP production occurs at the level of gene expression. AMP genes are direct targets of NF-κB activation and their transcription is induced to very high levels rapidly after infection. Although the bulk of AMP production occurs in the insect fat body (similar to the mammalian liver), AMP genes are also expressed in circulating phagocytic hemocytes and local epithelial tissues, particularly, the gut and the trachea (Ferrandon et al. 1998; Tzou et al. 2000; Liehl et al. 2006). Two NF-κB signaling pathways control AMP gene expression—the Toll and the IMD pathways. These pathways are activated by microbial cell walls and/or other virulence determinants by circulating, cell surface, and/or cytosolic receptors. Each pathway responds to distinct microbial components and induces the expression of somewhat overlapping subsets of AMP and other immune responsive genes. For example, the antifungals *Drosomycin* and *Metchnikowin* are strongly induced by the systemic Toll pathway, while the IMD pathway induces antibacterial peptides such as *Diptericin* (Lemaitre et al. 1997; Tzou et al. 2002). On the other hand, some AMP genes such as *Cecropin* and *Attacin* are co-operatively regulated by both the pathways (Manfruelli et al. 1999). Details on these regulatory events are discussed in more detail below.

2.2 Peptidoglycan Recognition and Immune Activation

Similar to the mammalian innate immune responses, microbial cell walls are one of the most potent agonists of insect humoral immunity. Bacterial infections trigger either the Toll or the IMD pathway, depending on the structure of their peptidoglycan (PGN) cell wall. PGN is a polymeric glycopeptide that forms the cell wall of most bacteria. PGN contains long glycan chains usually composed of alternating residues of *N*-acetyl glucosamine (NAG) and *N*-acetylmuramic acid (NAM), with short stem-peptides of alternating L- and D-amino acids attached to the lactyl group of NAM. The third position in the stem peptide is highly variable with a *meso*-diaminopimelic acid (DAP) in most Gram-negatives and various *Bacilli spp.* and L-lysine (lys) in many other Gram-positive microbes (Schleifer and Kandler 1972). These stem peptides are often cross-linked to each other by short peptide bridges to create a rigid cell wall structure. The Toll signaling pathway is most robustly triggered by Lys-type peptidoglycan, while the IMD pathway is activated by DAP-type peptidoglycan (Leulier et al. 2003; Kaneko et al. 2004). The distinction is not completely black and white, and bacterial species with DAP-type PGN also activate Toll signaling, albeit more weakly (Leulier et al. 2003; Leone et al. 2008).

Activation of both Toll and IMD pathways by bacterial PGNs requires peptidoglycan recognition proteins (PGRPs). PGRP was initially identified in lepidopterans as a protein capable of binding PGN (Yoshida et al. 1996; Kang et al. 1998; Ochiai and Ashida 1999). This was followed by the discovery of 13 PGRP genes (encoding 17 distinct proteins) in *Drosophila*, classified as short proteins (SA, SB1, SB2, SC1A, SC1B, SC2 and SD) and long proteins (LA, LB, LC, LD, LE and LF) (Werner et al. 2000). While the short proteins include a signal sequence and are secreted soluble proteins, the long PGRPs lack a signal sequence. Some long-form PGRPs encode a transmembrane domain and are cell surface receptors, e.g. PGRP-LC, while others are cytoplasmic, e.g. PGRP-LE. The PGRP domain is highly conserved from insects to mammals, whereas the other regions show very little similarity (Werner et al. 2000). The PGRP domain is structurally related to a class of PGN-digesting enzymes known as type 2 amidases (e.g. T7 lysozyme), which hydrolyzes the bond between the lactyl group in NAM and L-alanine in the stem-peptide of PGN (Mellroth et al. 2003). In fact, approximately one-half of the *Drosophila* PGRPs are type 2 amidases that degrade PGN and reduce its ability to stimulate immune responses (detailed in Sect. 6.1), while the other PGRPs lack key catalytic residue(s) and function as PGN receptors. In particular, PGRP-SA and PGRP-SD are two soluble PGN receptors that function in the Toll pathway (Michel et al. 2001; Bischoff et al. 2004), while PGRP-LC and

PGRP-LE recognize DAP-type PGN and trigger the IMD pathway (Choe et al. 2002; Gottar et al. 2002; Takehana et al. 2004; Kaneko et al. 2006).

2.2.1 Activation of the Toll Pathway

In the Toll pathway, PGN recognition involves two circulating receptor proteins, PGRP-SA and PGRP-SD. Recognition of some Lys-type PGN (e.g. *M. luteus*) specifically requires PGRP-SA (Michel et al. 2001; Gottar et al. 2002), while other PGNs (e.g. *S. aureus*) may be detected by either PGRP-SA or PGRP-SD (Bischoff et al. 2004). PGRP-SA binds Lys-type PGN and the crystal structure of PGRP-SA complexed with a Lys-type muropeptide has been solved (Chang et al. 2004; Reiser et al. 2004). However, the precise biochemical mechanisms that underlie the differential recognition of various Lys-type PGNs by PGRP-SA and/or PGRP-SD are not completely understood. In particular, the exact function of PGRP-SD remains a mystery, as genetic studies link it to Lys-type PGN recognition, while structural studies indicate that it binds DAP-type PGN (Leone et al. 2008). In fact, PGRP-SD has been shown to be responsible for the weak Toll activation triggered by DAP-type PGN (Leone et al. 2008).

Lys-type PGN recognition also requires a third protein known as Gram-negative-binding protein (GNBP1). GNBP1 was originally identified in silkworms, as a protein that binds Gram-negative PGN/β-(1,3)-glucan (Yoshida et al. 1986). Conversely, later studies showed that GNBP1 is required for the recognition of Lys-type PGN and is dispensable for the activation of the IMD pathway by DAP-type PGN (Gobert et al. 2003; Pili-Floury et al. 2004). While GNBP1 and the above mentioned receptors, PGRP-SA and PGRP-SD, may form one large complex upon PGN recognition (Filipe et al. 2005; Wang et al. 2006a, b), the precise mechanistic function of GNBP1 is controversial. Some reports conclude that GNBP1 hydrolyzes Lys-type PGN into muropeptide dimers, for optimal recognition by PGRP-SA (Filipe et al. 2005; Wang et al. 2006a, b), while other groups report no such activity associated with GNBP1 (Park et al. 2007; Buchon et al. 2009). Instead, these groups conclude that GNBP1 may be critical for activating downstream signaling events (more details below). Thus, many Gram-positive bacteria are sensed by their Lys-type PGN cell wall by the proteins, PGRP-SA/PGRP-SD and GNBP1.

In addition to bacterial PGN, fungal cell walls are also potent activators of the Toll pathway (Gottar et al. 2006). A receptor known as GNBP3 recognizes β-(1,3)-glucans from the fungal cell wall, and robustly triggers the Toll pathway (Gottar et al. 2006). Moreover, *GNBP3* mutant flies (*hades*) exhibit greatly reduced *Drosomycin* expression and reduced survival following *Candida albicans* infection (Gottar et al. 2006). Intriguingly, some fungi (e.g. *Geotrichum candidum*) also seem to activate the IMD pathway, through unknown mechanisms (Hedengren-Olcott et al. 2004). β-glucan recognition by GNBP3 and PGN recognition by PGRP-SA/SD/GNBP1 both feed into the Toll pathway via the same protease, Modular Serine Protease (Buchon et al. 2009).

The Modular Serine Protease (ModSP) was first discovered in biochemical analyses of the Toll pathway in the mealworm beetle, *Tenebrio molitor* (Kim et al. 2008). In this system, ModSP binds the PGRP-SA/GNBP1 complex following PGN recognition and triggers a serine protease cascade upon association with these receptors (Park et al. 2007; Kim et al. 2008). Likewise, in the *Drosophila* system, genetic experiments with a *ModSP* mutant demonstrate its central role in the Toll pathway activation by Lys-type PGN and β-glucans. Genetic experiments suggest that *Drosophila* ModSP also functions immediately downstream of both PGRP-SA/GNBP1 and GNBP3 (Buchon et al. 2009). Recruitment of ModSP to the PGN-receptor complex has been proposed to activate its proteolytic activity. Subsequently, ModSP initiates a cascade that proceeds through the sequential activation of CLIP domain containing serine proteases Grass and Spätzle processing enzyme (SPE) (Kambris et al. 2006; El Chamy et al. 2008). A third CLIP domain serine protease, Spirit, as well as some non-catalytic serine protease homologs (SPHs)—spheroide and sphinx1/2—may also function in this pathway. However, the role of these genes in the Toll pathway was discovered by RNAi-based approaches, and has not yet been confirmed by biochemistry or conventional genetics (Kambris et al. 2006). In any case, this proteolytic cascade culminates in the activation of SPE which directly cleaves pro-Spätzle and releases the active Toll ligand, Spätzle (Jang et al. 2006). Pro-Spätzle is a disulfide-linked dimer and upon processing the C-terminal 106 residue fragment binds Toll, induces receptor homodimerization, and activates intracellular signaling (Mizuguchi et al. 1998; Weber et al. 2003; Hu et al. 2004).

In addition to microbial cell walls, the Toll pathway can also be triggered by virulence factors, such as proteases released by some bacteria or fungi (Gottar et al. 2006; El Chamy et al. 2008). Entomopathogenic microbes often produce proteases to digest the insect cuticle (St Leger et al. 1992), and flies have evolved a mechanism to 'guard' against this signature of virulent infection. For example, both the PR1 protease of entomopathogenic fungi *M. anisopliae* and the subtilisin protease from *B. subtilis* can trigger the Toll pathway independent of the PGRP and GNBP-mediated cell wall-recognition pathways (Gottar et al. 2006; El Chamy et al. 2008). Instead, these virulent proteases appear to cleave and activate a host-

Fig. 1 *Drosophila* Toll pathway. *Drosophila* Toll pathway is a cytokine receptor pathway that responds indirectly to microbial infection. Distinct circulating receptor proteins recognize different microbial structures or activities and activate a protease cascade, which culminates in the processing of Spätzle. Lys-type PGN, from bacterial cell walls, is recognized by PGRP-SA/PGRP-SD and GNBP1, while GNBP3 detects β-(1, 3)-glucan from fungal cell walls. These upstream recognition events trigger a proteolytic cascade which proceeds through the serine proteases ModSP and Grass to activate Spätzle Processing Enzyme (SPE) which in turn cleaves pro-Spätzle to release the mature Toll ligand, Spätzle. In addition, virulence-associated proteases, released by pathogens, cleave and activate another pathway that requires the protease Persephone and converges on the activation of SPE. The intracellular Toll signaling pathway is very homologous to the mammalian MyD88-dependent signaling pathway. It signals through an upstream complex containing the adaptor proteins dMyD88, Tube and the kinase Pelle (an IRAK homolog). Pelle triggers the phosphorylation, K48-ubiquitination and proteasomal degradation of the IκB protein, Cactus, thereby releasing the *Drosophila* NF-κB/Rel factors DIF/Dorsal to translocate into the nucleus and transcribe target AMP genes, such as *Drosomycin* ►

encoded serine protease known as Persephone (Gottar et al. 2006). Persephone, in turn, converges on the same SPE utilized in the PGRP/GNBP pathways. However, this virulence protease-Persephone pathway is independent of ModSP and Grass (El Chamy et al. 2008; Buchon et al. 2009) (Refer to Fig. 1 for a model of how these microbial recognition pathways converge on Toll activation).

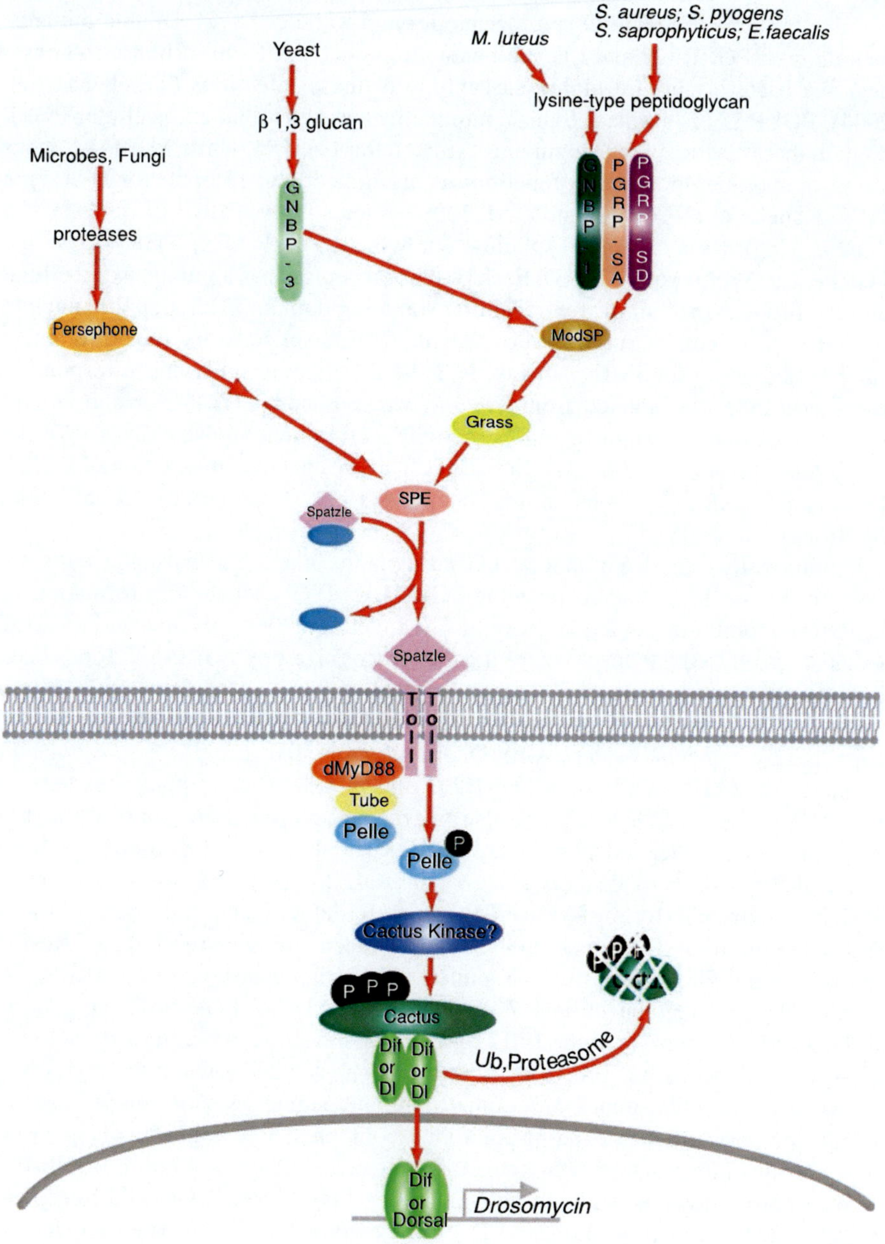

2.2.2 Activation of the IMD Pathway

Detection of DAP-type PGN by two long form PGRPs, PGRP-LC and PGRP-LE triggers the IMD pathway (Choe et al. 2002; Gottar et al. 2002; Ramet et al. 2002; Takehana et al. 2002, 2004; Leulier et al. 2003; Kaneko et al. 2006). DAP-type PGN forms the cell wall of most Gram-negative bacteria as well as some Gram positive bacteria (e.g. *Bacilli* spp.) (Schleifer and Kandler 1972). Double mutants, lacking both PGRP-LC and LE, are unable to induce AMPs in response to Gram-negative bacteria and are highly susceptible to these infections (Takehana et al. 2004). PGRP-LC is a type 2 transmembrane receptor, with an extracellular PGRP domain that is critical for recognizing extracellular bacteria, while PGRP-LE lacks a transmembrane domain and functions as an intracellular receptor for DAP-type PGN (Kaneko et al. 2006; Yano et al. 2008). Interestingly, PGRP-LC encodes for three receptors via alternate splicing, known as PGRP-LCx, PGRP-LCy and PGRP-LCa (Werner et al. 2003). Each of these receptors has a unique extracellular domain fused to the identical intracellular signaling domain. Although the function of PGRP-LCy remains unclear, the other PGRP-LC splice forms have prominent roles in activating the IMD pathway. PGRP-LCx alone is sufficient to respond to polymeric PGN (as isolated from *E. coli*), whereas both PGRP-LCx and PGRP-LCa are required to recognize a monomeric PGN fragment known as TCT (Werner et al. 2003; Kaneko et al. 2004). In fact, TCT causes heterodimerization of PGRP-LCx and PGRP-LCa (Whalen and Steward 1993; Chang et al. 2005, 2006; Mellroth et al. 2005).

Additionally, small monomeric PGN fragments like TCT that enter cells are recognized by the cytosolic receptor PGRP-LE. TCT induces the formation of head-to-tail homo-oligomers of PGRP-LE (Lim et al. 2006). It is unclear how TCT gains access into the cytosol where it can be recognized by PGRP-LE. It has been hypothesized that a transmembrane transporter may aid in the entry of TCT into the cytoplasm, however, no such protein has been identified. PGRP-LE is also triggered by cytosolic bacteria with DAP-type PGN, like *Listeria monocytogenes* (Yano et al. 2008). While both PGRP-LC and PGRP-LE are potent activators of the IMD pathway, PGRP-LE can also trigger an autophagic response through a Relish (NF-κB)-independent pathway that is critical to protect the animal against intracellular pathogens like *Listeria* (Yano et al. 2008). Interestingly, a cleaved, PGRP-domain only form of PGRP-LE can be found extracellularly, where it aids the recognition of DAP-type PGN by the transmembrane receptor PGRP-LC (Kaneko et al. 2006). However, it is unclear how this cleaved form of PGRP-LE reaches the extracellular milieu. With either PGRP-LC or PGRP-LE, recognition of DAP-type PGN triggers the IMD signaling pathway, which in turn leads to the activation of the NF-κB precursor protein Relish (detailed later in the review).

As in *Drosophila*, mammalian innate immune signaling pathways respond to many immune stimuli, including microbial components, endogenous danger signals and pro-inflammatory cytokines, and converge on the activation of NF-κB. The receptors involved include Toll-like receptors (TLRs), NOD-like Receptors (NLRs), RIG-I-like Receptors (RLRs), and cytokine receptors (i.e. TNFR and

IL-1R). These receptors are found in many different subcellular niches, including the cell surface, cytosol, or endosomal compartments. They recognize a variety of microbial signatures from bacterial, fungal, viral and parasitic pathogens and trigger overlapping signaling pathways that all lead to the activation of NF-κB and downstream responses.

The *Drosophila* NF-κB pathways display some striking similarities, as well as some notable differences, compared to these mammalian pathways. The paradigm for recognition of pathogens in the *Drosophila* Toll pathway is quite different from that exhibited by the mammalian TLRs. While mammalian TLRs are directly involved in detecting microbial derived products, such as LPS, lipopeptides, flagellin and nucleic acids, *Drosophila* Toll is a cytokine receptor that responds to microbial challenge indirectly. The key microbe detectors in the *Drosophila* Toll pathway are PGRP-SA, PGRP-SD and the GNBPs, which are not homologous to the TLRs. In case of the IMD pathway, PGRP-LC functions analogously to the TLRs as a cell surface receptor, and PGRP-LE is more similar to the cytosolic NOD receptor, although no molecular homology exists between TLRs or NLRs and the *Drosophila* PGRPs.

In the next section, we discuss in detail the more similar aspects of *Drosophila* NF-κB systems with that of mammals intracellular signal transduction and the mechanism of NF-κB activation in the Toll and the IMD pathways. These pathways show a remarkable degree of similarity to the MyD88-dependent and the MyD88-independent TLR pathways in mammals, respectively.

3 Intracellular Signaling in the Toll and IMD Pathways

Activation of the Toll or IMD pathways by any of the mechanisms outlined above leads to robust activation of *Drosophila* NF-κB/Rel family transcription factors. Recognition of DAP-type PGN through the IMD pathway triggers the activation of Relish. Activation of Toll, by Lys-type PGN, fungal cell walls or virulence-associated proteases, leads to the activation of either of the two p65-like factors—DIF or Dorsal. Each of these pathways uses distinct set of intracellular signaling components to drive NF-κB activation.

3.1 Toll Pathway

Activation *Drosophila* of Toll leads to the formation of a receptor proximal signaling complex containing the adaptor proteins MyD88, Tube and the kinase Pelle. Toll signals through its intracellular TIR domain, similar to the mammalian TLRs and IL-1R. Toll interacts with *Drosophila* MyD88 (homolog of mammalian MyD88) through a homotypic TIR interaction (Tauszig-Delamasure et al. 2002). MyD88 also has a death domain (DD) through which it assembles a heterotrimeric complex containing Tube and Pelle (homolog of the IRAK kinases in mammals) (Horng and Medzhitov 2001; Sun et al. 2002). Both Tube and Pelle also contain DDs. Tube associates with MyD88 through a homotypic DD interaction on one surface, while simultaneously recruiting Pelle, through another homotypic DD interaction, on the opposite surface (Schiffmann et al. 1999; Sun et al. 2002). Assembly of this signaling complex appears to be sufficient to activate the Toll pathway as over-expression of the MyD88 TIR domain triggers expression of the Toll pathway target gene *Drosomycin* (Tauszig-Delamasure et al. 2002). Recruitment of the kinase Pelle to this complex triggers its auto-phosphorylation and activation (Sun et al. 2004).

Activation of the kinase Pelle triggers the phosphorylation and degradation of Cactus. Cactus is the IκB-like protein which sequesters Dorsal and DIF in the cytoplasm. It is unclear whether Pelle directly phosphorylates Cactus or if other intermediate kinase(s) are involved. Although one study reported that Pelle phosphorylates Cactus in vitro (Grosshans et al. 1994), it remains unclear if Pelle phosphorylates the critical serine residues on Cactus which are known to be important for Toll signaling (see below for more detail) (Fernandez et al. 2001), or if Pelle-mediated phosphorylation of Cactus occurs in vivo. Experiments in which Pelle was forcibly anchored to the plasma membrane demonstrated that localization of this kinase to the membrane is sufficient to activate Toll signaling and this signaling requires kinase activity (Galindo et al. 1995). Thus, Pelle localization to the Toll receptor, via the MyD88 and Tube interaction network, is likely the critical event driving the activation of Pelle, the subsequent degradation of Cactus, and the nuclear translocation of DIF or Dorsal (Galindo et al. 1995; Reach et al. 1996; Edwards et al. 1997; Towb et al. 1998).

3.2 IMD Pathway

Intracellular signaling in the IMD pathway is also likely to involve a receptor–proximal multi-protein complex. In this pathway, PGRP-LC and PGRP-LE detect DAP-type PGN through their C-terminal PGN-binding PGRP domain and transduce signal through their extended N-terminal domains (Choe et al. 2005; Kaneko et al. 2006). Although PGRP-LC and LE are very similar in their PGRP domain, only a short stretch of about 20 amino acids is common to their N-terminal domains. In both receptors, deletion or mutation within this conserved domain abrogates signaling (Kaneko et al. 2006). This conserved domain has some weak similarity to the RHIM domain found in RIP1 and TRIF, signaling proteins that function in the mammalian TLR3 signaling pathway (Meylan et al. 2004). The molecular mechanism by which the RHIM-like domains in PGRP-LC and -LE regulate signaling is unclear. It may be involved in the dimerization of the entire N-terminal signaling domain, which has been reported to occur when PGRP-LC is over-expressed, and/or may interact with an unidentified factor (Choe et al. 2005). One factor that does bind both PGRP-LC and PGRP-LE is IMD, a death domain-containing protein (Georgel et al. 2001; Choe et al. 2005; Kaneko et al. 2006; Aggarwal et al. 2008). In the case of PGRP-LE, IMD binding requires the RHIM-like domain and this is a possible explanation for the function of the PGRP-LE RHIM-like motif. However, the association between IMD and PGRP-LC maps to another distinct region, which is not essential for signaling (Kaneko et al. 2006). Together, these data suggest that the RHIM-like domain of PGRP-LC has a function beyond IMD recruitment and that direct IMD recruitment to these receptors may not always be necessary for signaling. Regardless of the mechanism, IMD associates with these receptors and, in turn, is likely to recruit the *Drosophila* FADD homolog via a homotypic death domain interaction (Naitza et al. 2002). FADD, is then known to interact with the apical caspase DREDD (homolog of mammalian caspase-8) via a homotypic interaction between the death effector domain (DED) in these proteins (Hu and Yang 2000; Leulier et al. 2002). It will be interesting to learn whether recruitment of DREDD to the receptor–IMD–FADD complex is sufficient for its activation.

DREDD is critical for the initiation of downstream signaling events in the IMD pathway (Leulier et al. 2000; Stoven et al. 2003). In response to PGN stimulation, IMD is cleaved in a DREDD-dependent manner at a caspase cleavage site in the N-terminal region ($LEKD^{30}$) (Paquette et al. 2010). Immediately following this cleavage site is a consensus IAP-binding motif (IBM, $^{31}AAPV$). Both the caspase site and the IBM are highly conserved in multiple species of *Drosophila* as well as the *Anopheles gambiae* mosquito (Paquette et al. 2010). DREDD-mediated cleavage of IMD exposes the IBM, allowing IMD to associate with the *Drosophila* inhibitor of apoptosis 2 protein (DIAP2). The BIR1 and BIR2 domains of DIAP2 are responsible for interacting with the IBM of cleaved IMD, similar to the IBM–BIR interactions observed in the regulation of caspase-mediated programmed cell death (Shi 2002). Further in vivo evidence demonstrating the important role for the IBM-mediated association is provided by the imd^1 allele. This strong hypomorphic allele carries the relatively conserved substitution of Ala^{31} to Val, disrupting the IBM and markedly interfering with the association between cleaved-IMD and DIAP2 (Paquette et al. 2010).

DIAP2, similar to other IAP proteins, also includes a C-terminal RING domain, which is also critical for the IMD signaling pathway (Huh et al. 2007). In fact, DIAP2 lacking a functional RING domain fails to support IMD signaling and the RING domain is essential for the robust ubiquitination of IMD that is observed following its cleavage and association with DIAP2. IMD is conjugated with K63-polyubiquitin chains, similar to what is observed with the mammalian RIP1 and TRAF6 proteins in TNFR and IL-1R signaling, respectively (Ea et al. 2006; Lamothe et al. 2007). IMD ubiquitination involves two distinct E2 ubiquitin-ligase enzymes, which appear to act in a partially redundant manner (Zhou et al. 2005; Paquette et al. 2010). Uev1a, Bendless (Ubc13) form a well-established K63-chain generating enzyme complex (Hofmann and Pickart 1999; Windheim et al. 2008). Effete (Ubc5) has recently been shown to generate K63-chains, but can also generate other types of polyubiquitin (including K48 and linear ubiquitin chains) depending on the context (Kirkpatrick et al. 2006; Jin et al. 2008; Bianchi and

Fig. 2 *Drosophila* IMD pathway. Recognition of DAP-type PGN by the cell surface receptor ▶ PGRP-LC or the cytosolic receptor PGRP-LE triggers the IMD pathway. DAP-type PGN forms the cell wall of most Gram-negative bacteria and some Gram-positive bacteria, such as *Bacillus spp.* and *Listeria*. Extracellularly, detection of polymeric and monomeric PGN (TCT) occurs through homo or heterodimers of PGRP-LC splice forms, as depicted. PGRP-LE detects intracellular bacteria and stimulates the IMD pathway as well as an autophagic response. PGRP-LC and PGRP-LE signaling proceeds through IMD, FADD and the caspase DREDD, which are likely to form a complex on the activated receptor. DREDD-dependent cleavage of IMD exposes an IAP-binding motif in IMD, through which it binds DIAP2. This IMD-DIAP2 association leads to robust K63-ubiquitination of cleaved IMD by DIAP2, Uev1a, Bendless (Ubc13) and Effete (Ubc5). These K63-polyubiquitin chains are likely to serve as a scaffold for the recruitment and activation of the TAK1 kinase complex and the IKK complex. Once activated, TAK1 in turn activates both IKK and JNK kinase. Relish is phosphorylated by IKK and cleaved by DREDD to release the fully active N-terminal RHD for translocation into the nucleus and the transcriptional induction of AMP genes and other targets. The concurrent activation of JNKK leads to the phosphorylation and nuclear translocation of AP-1

Meier 2009). IMD fails to be ubiquitinated only when both Bendless/Uev1a and Effete ubiquitin conjugation enzymes are knocked down (Paquette et al. 2010). It is not yet clear what types of polyubiquitin chains Effete generates in the IMD signaling pathway. Polyubiquitinated IMD has been proposed to act as a scaffold for recruiting the downstream kinases TAK1 and IKK, via ubiquitin binding domains found in their partners TAB 2 and IKKγ, respectively, similar to mammalian NF-κB signaling (Kanayama et al. 2004; Zhuang et al. 2006; Bianchi and Meier 2009; Iwai and Tokunaga 2009). Once recruited and activated, TAK1 activates IKK, which in turn phosphorylates the NF-κB precursor protein Relish (Vidal et al. 2001; Silverman et al. 2003; Stoven et al. 2003; Erturk-Hasdemir et al. 2009). Relish is also cleaved, likely by the caspase DREDD, resulting in the uncoupling of the C-terminal IκB-like domain from the N-terminal NF-κB module, thereby allowing the N-terminal Rel Homology Domain (RHD) to translocate into the nucleus, while the C-terminal domain remains in the cytoplasm (Stoven et al. 2003). Although Relish phosphorylation is dispensable for its cleavage, it appears to enhance the activity of Relish as a transcription factor in the nucleus (Erturk-Hasdemir et al. 2009). In a separate arm of the pathway, TAK1 also activates the JNK kinase, which in turn triggers the phosphorylation and nuclear translocation of the AP-1 transcription factor (refer to Fig. 2 for IMD pathway model).

Toll and IMD signaling pathways culminate in the activation of the *Drosophila* NF-κB transcription factors Dorsal, DIF and Relish. Since the structure and function of these NF-κB members are very similar to mammals, a quick glance at the NF-κB factors in general, will enable us to appreciate the similarities in the regulation of NF-κB proteins in these systems.

4 NF-κB Proteins

The NF-κB/Rel family of transcription factors are master regulators of host immune responses in mammals as well as in *Drosophila*. In mammals, this family

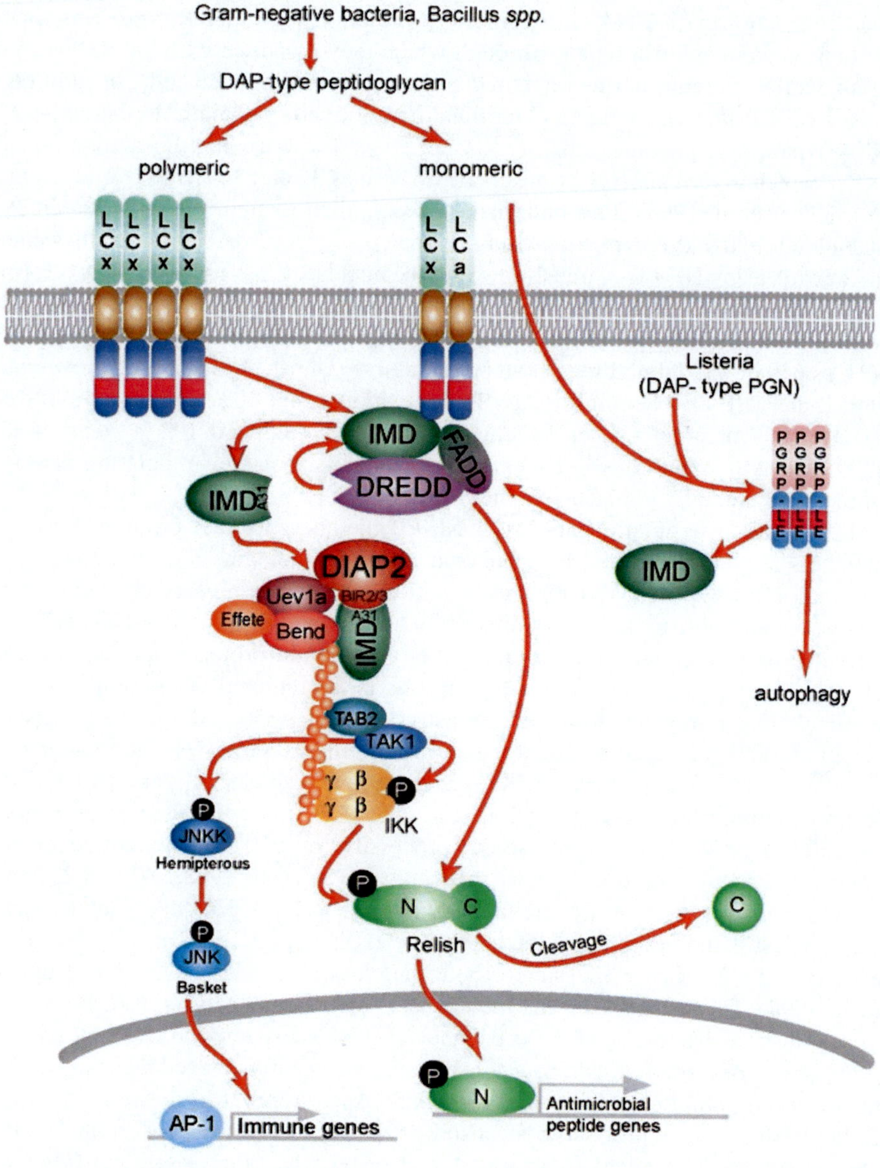

includes the Rel proteins (RelA (p65), RelB, c-Rel) and NF-κB precursor proteins (NF-κB1 (p105) and NF-κB2 (p100)). In *Drosophila,* the NF-κB/Rel family includes two p65-like factors—dorsal and DIF, and one NF-κB precursor protein, Relish. NF-κB proteins are subdivided into four classes based on their structure and evolutionary divergence (Huguet et al. 1997; Liang et al. 2004). Class I includes c-Rel, RelA (p65) and RelB. The class I proteins contain a conserved 300 residue N-terminal RHD which includes a nuclear localization signal (NLS) and mediates their interaction with DNA, IκB inhibitory proteins, and other Rel proteins. IκB proteins contain ankyrin repeats through which they associate with the RHDs and mask their NLS, sequestering them in the cytosol of unstimulated cells. In addition, class I NF-κB factors contain a C-terminal transactivating domain. In the classical NF-κB pathway, pro-inflammatory stimuli (*e.g.*: LPS) trigger the activation of IKKβ, which in turn phosphorylates IκBα on serines 32 and 36 (Brown et al. 1995; Traenckner et al. 1995). Phosphorylated IκBα is then recognized by the β-TrCP-SCF ubiquitin ligase complex, K48-ubiquitinated, and degraded by the proteasome, thereby releasing NF-κB to translocate into the nucleus. Class I NF-κB factors form homo- or heterodimers, with p65-p50 heterodimers being the most common and well studied. While many of these dimers are transcriptionally active, some dimers, such as p50 or p52 homodimers, can be repressive (Ghosh et al. 1998). *Drosophila* Dorsal and DIF also belong to class I, and exhibit about 40% identity within the RHD of the mammalian Rel proteins in this group (Steward 1987; Meng et al. 1999; Minakhina and Steward 2006). The mechanism of their regulation is very similar to mammals, as discussed above and below.

In contrast to regulation of class I NF-κB members by IκB proteins, class II members are auto-regulated by their own inhibitory domains. For example, NF-κB1 and NF-κB2 (p105, p100) harbor inhibitory ankyrin repeats in their C-terminus, in addition to the N-terminal RHD domain. NF-κB1 and NF-κB2 are activated by phosphorylation, ubiquitination and partial proteasomal degradation of the ankyrin repeats. This processing results in the removal of the inhibitory C-terminal ankyrin repeats, to reveal the active subunits, p50 and p52, respectively (Perkins 2007). It should be noted that activation of p100 follows a non-canonical pathway that is independent of IKKβ and instead involves activation of IKKα. IKKα in turn phosphorylates p100 and marks it for controlled degradation (Senftleben et al. 2001). Proteasomal processing of p105 is thought to occur constitutively, by a co translational mechanism (Lin et al. 1998). Although *Drosophila* Relish is structurally similar to NF-κB1 and NF-κB2, phylogenetic analysis suggest it should be placed in a separate class, class III, because it may have evolved from an earlier ancestor of both the class I and class II factors (Huguet et al. 1997). Consistent with this molecular evolutionary analysis, Relish regulation is distinct from that of NF-κB1 and NF-κB2. It is not activated by partial proteasomal degradation, but instead is endoproteolytically cleaved by a caspase to uncouple the inhibitory C-terminal IκB-like ankyrin repeats from the N-terminal RHD. Both cleavage products appear to be relatively stable; the N-terminal RHD translocates to the nucleus to activate target genes while the C-terminal IκB-like domain remains in the cytosol (Stoven et al. 2003; Erturk-Hasdemir et al. 2009).

Class IV, is occupied by the related NF-AT family of transcription factors. Although NF-AT proteins are structurally and phylogenetically related to the NF-κB RHD domain, and function in the immune response, the mechanism of activation is distinct and their most well studied functions are in the adaptive immune response (Huguet et al. 1997). Therefore, they will not be discussed further here, but more information can be found in these reviews (Rao et al. 1997; Serfling et al. 2004).

4.1 Dorsal and DIF

Drosophila Dorsal was the first identified NF-κB protein in *Drosophila*, due to its role in early embryonic patterning. In particular, *dorsal* was identified as one of the 12 maternal effect genes that drive the expression of zygotic genes required for the normal development of the dorso-ventral pattern in the developing embryo. Loss of function mutation in 11 of these genes, results in dorsalized embryos, while loss of function of the 12th gene, *cactus,* results in a ventralized embryo (Anderson and Nusslein-Volhard 1984; Roth et al. 1989; Schupbach and Wieschaus 1989). Together, these genes identified the Toll pathway. During embryogenesis, developmental cues activate Toll signaling on the ventral side, leading to Cactus degradation and creating a gradient of nuclear Dorsal (Roth et al. 1989; Steward 1989). Dorsal, in turn, drives the transcription of key genes, required for creating the body axis, like *twist* and *snail* (Jiang et al. 1991; Pan et al. 1991; Thisse et al. 1991; Ip et al. 1992). Although dorsal and the Toll pathway were initially identified for their role during development, the identification of κB-binding motifs in the promoter/enhancer regions of several AMP genes suggested that humoral response may also be regulated by NF-κB factors (Engstrom et al. 1993; Georgel et al. 1993; Kappler et al. 1993).

Subsequently, two other *Drosophila* NF-κB factors, DIF and Relish, were discovered (Ip et al. 1993; Dushay et al. 1996). Rapidly thereafter, Relish was linked to Gram-negative response through the IMD signaling pathway (Hedengren et al. 1999), while Toll-mediated humoral responses were shown to be DIF and/or Dorsal dependent (Ip et al. 1993; Manfruelli et al. 1999; Meng et al. 1999; Rutschmann et al. 2000a, b). In larvae, DIF and Dorsal function in a redundant fashion to control AMP gene expression (humoral immunity) and promote blood cell survival (cellular immunity) (Ip et al. 1993; Manfruelli et al. 1999; Matova and Anderson 2006, 2010). However, in adults, humoral responses are primarily controlled by DIF (Rutschmann et al. 2000a, b).

Like p50/p65 in mammals, Dorsal and DIF are regulated by the IκB protein Cactus (Geisler et al. 1992). Cactus is the only identified IκB protein in *Drosophila* and has six ankyrin repeats. In unstimulated cells, Dorsal exists in a complex with Cactus in the cytoplasm mediated by an interaction between the RHD of Dorsal and the ankyrin repeats of Cactus (Govind et al. 1992; Kidd 1992; Isoda and Nusslein-Volhard 1994; Tatei and Levine 1995). Toll activation results in the phosphorylation, K48-ubiquitination and degradation of Cactus, thereby releasing Dorsal which leads to its translocation into the nucleus (Belvin et al. 1995; Bergmann et al. 1996; Govind et al. 1996; Reach et al. 1996; Wu and Anderson 1998; Fernandez et al. 2001; Sun et al. 2004). The kinase that phosphorylates Cactus remains unclear. As mentioned earlier, Pelle may directly phosphorylate Cactus or other unidentified kinases may function here. Although *Drosophila* IKKβ has been shown to phosphorylate Cactus in vitro (Kim et al. 2000), neither IKKβ (*ird5*) nor IKKγ (*kenny*) are required for Toll signaling in vivo (Rutschmann et al. 2000a, b; Silverman et al. 2000; Lu et al. 2001). Studies to identify the regulatory region in

Cactus required for its signal-dependent degradation implicated serines at positions 74, 78 and 116 (Belvin et al. 1995; Bergmann et al. 1996; Reach et al. 1996; Fernandez et al. 2001). These residues are found in two motifs that are both similar to the phosphorylation sites at serine 32 and 36 of IκBα. However, regulation of Cactus degradation has been speculated to be much more complicated than IκBα, since mammalian IκBα has only three serines N-terminal of the ankyrin repeats while Cactus has 36 serines in this region. Moreover, these mechanisms should also allow for graded degradation of Cactus, as observed during dorsal–ventral patterning, while IκBα does not exhibit such a phenomenon (Fernandez et al. 2001). As mentioned above, β-TrCP, an F-box protein was originally found to be important for the K48-ubiquitination and degradation of phosphorylated IκBα in mammalian cells (Spencer et al. 1999; Winston et al. 1999). Similarly, *Drosophila* mutants deficient in *Slimb* (*Drosophila* homolog of β-TrCP), exhibit reduced expression of Dorsal target genes, *twist* and *snail,* suggesting that this is a shared mechanism of Cactus degradation in *Drosophila* and mammals (Spencer et al. 1999). One study indicated that Cactus degradation may not be sufficient to facilitate the robust nuclear translocation of Dorsal in embryos (Bergmann et al. 1996), and other studies suggest that Dorsal must also be phosphorylated for optimal nuclear localization (Whalen and Steward 1993; Gillespie and Wasserman 1994; Drier et al. 1999, 2000). Though both Dorsal and DIF are controlled by the Toll pathway, many of the above described specifics of signal-dependent activation of Dorsal have not been examined in detail for DIF. Once in the nucleus, DIF, and to a lesser degree Dorsal, activate a robust set of immune responsive genes (Lemaitre et al. 1996; De Gregorio et al. 2001; 2002; Irving et al. 2001).

4.2 Relish

Relish, a NF-κB precursor protein similar to p100 and p105, is activated by endoproteolytic cleavage at aspartate 545, within a caspase target site (LQHD) (Stoven et al. 2000; 2003; Cornwell and Kirkpatrick 2001). Relish is thought to be cleaved directly by the caspase DREDD for a number of reasons. DREDD directly interacts with Relish (Stoven et al. 2003), and Relish cleavage is completely abrogated in *DREDD* mutants (Stoven et al. 2003). Immunoprecipitated DREDD cleaves recombinant Relish in vitro (Erturk-Hasdemir et al. 2009). Moreover, RNAi knockdown of the other known *Drosophila* caspases have been reported to have no effect on Relish processing (Stoven et al. 2003; Erturk-Hasdemir et al. 2009). Following processing, the cleaved N-terminal portion of Relish which contains the DNA binding RHD domain translocates into the nucleus, while the C-terminal portion remains in the cytoplasm.

In addition to cleavage, Relish is also regulated by signal-induced phosphorylation. In particular, the Relish N-terminus is phosphorylated at two adjacent serines, 528 and 529, by the *Drosophila* IKK complex (Erturk-Hasdemir et al. 2009). This phosphorylation of Relish does not play a role in its cleavage, as evident from the normal cleavage observed in the non-phosphorylatable SS528/529AA Relish mutant. Instead, phosphorylation of Relish facilitates the recruitment of RNA polymerase II to the transcription start site of the AMP gene *Diptericin* (Erturk-Hasdemir et al. 2009).

Although IKK induced phosphorylation of Relish is not required for its cleavage, the IKK complex has a critical, non-catalytic role in Relish cleavage. Relish cleavage is abolished in *ird5* (IKKβ) or *kenny* (IKKγ) null mutants, but is rescued by expression of a kinase-dead IKKβ (Stoven et al. 2003; Erturk-Hasdemir et al. 2009). The mechanism by which the IKK complex functions non-catalytically to support Relish cleavage is unclear. One possible explanation may lie in the connection between IKKβ and the very C-terminal 107 amino acids of Relish. This domain is C-terminal to the IκB-like ankyrin repeats (Fig. 3), and is required for both phosphorylation and cleavage of Relish (Stoven et al. 2003). However, mutation of all serines and threonines in this region did not interfere with Relish phosphorylation and cleavage, indicating that this region is not a target for IKK catalytic activity (Erturk-Hasdemir et al. 2009). On the other hand, this C-terminal 107 amino acid region is responsible for the interaction between Relish and IKKβ, suggesting that a lack of association between these two proteins prevents both signaling and cleavage.

In addition to the caspase target site, the IKK phosphorylation sites and the IKK interaction site, other regions in Relish also modulate its activity. Relish contains a PEST domain near its C-terminus (Fig. 3), similar to mammalian p105. Although the p105 PEST domain contains IKK phosphorylation sites and is important for its proteasomal degradation, the Relish PEST domain is not involved in signal-induced cleavage or activation. On the other hand, PEST deleted Relish seems to exhibit enhanced nuclear localization and target gene expression (Stoven et al. 2003). A similar phenotype is also observed with deletion of a serine rich stretch in the Relish N-terminus (Fig. 3). Therefore, these two domains have been proposed to negatively regulate the nuclear translocation of Relish (Stoven et al. 2003). However, the specific mechanism involved in this regulation is not clear.

Cleavage of Relish results in a 68 kDa N-terminal fragment which includes the RHD domain and a 49 kDa C-terminal fragment containing the ankyrin repeat domain. Over expression of the N-terminal 69 kDa portion is sufficient to induce the expression of some AMP genes, but does not recapitulate the response seen with fully activated Relish, consistent with the notion that Relish must be phosphorylated for its full activity. However, the expression of the C-terminal ankyrin repeat domain separately, doesn't hinder the activation of Relish (Wiklund et al. 2009), unlike the inhibitory effect exerted on NF-κB activation when IκBα is overexpressed in mammalian cells.

4.3 Transcriptional Regulation of NF-κB Targets

Once inside the nucleus, Dorsal, DIF and Relish bind to their corresponding κB sites in the promoter/enhancer region of AMP and other target genes. Mammalian

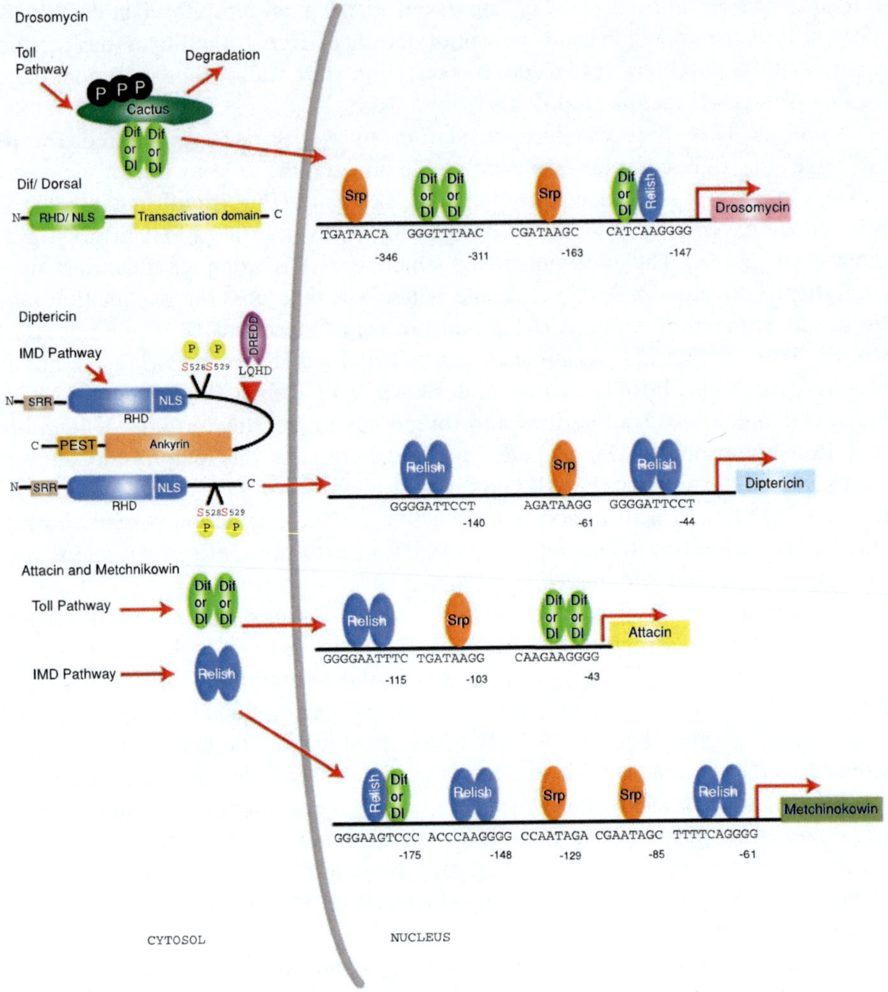

Fig. 3 κB site specificity of *Drosophila* NF-κB proteins: NF-κB factors, upon activation by the Toll and IMD pathways, translocate into the nucleus and bind to specific κB sites in the promoter/enhancer region of immune responsive AMP genes. DIF and Dorsal are activated by Toll signaling through degradation of the IκB inhibitor protein Cactus, while Relish activation is triggered by IMD signaling through DREDD-dependent endoproteolytic cleavage to remove the C-terminal IκB-like domain and the IKK-mediated phosphorylation of serines 528 and 529. In this figure, selected AMP genes *Drosomycin,Diptericin*, *AttacinA* and *Metchnikowin* with their proximal DIF, Dorsal or Relish binding κB sites and Serpent (Srp) binding GATA sites are represented (Senger et al. 2004; Busse et al. 2007; Tanji et al. 2007). Expression of *AttacinA* requires both DIF and Relish, and hence contains separate binding sites for each of them, while *Diptericin* requires only Relish and has two Relish specific sites. *Drosomycin* and *Metchnikowin* each contain a distinct DIF/Relish site, which is responsive to both DIF and Relish. It is not clear if this site binds a heterodimer (as suggested by this figure) or if it functions by binding either homodimer. In addition, the *Metchnikowin* enhancer includes separate Relish-specific sites, while *Drosomycin* has another DIF/Dorsal-specific site only. Refer to Sect. 4.3 in the text for details on the consensus κB and GATA sites and the complex regulation involved in the expression of AMPs

NF-κB/Rel factors bind a similar κB consensus motif [GGG(G/A)NN(T/C)(T/C)CC] (Baeuerle 1991). However, the exact composition of Rel protein dimers and associated co-activators bound to particular elements depends on the specific sequence of the κB site, as well as on other nearby transcription factors (Gross et al. 1996; Leung et al. 2004). One elegant study in the *Drosophila* immune response combined expression profiling of wild type, *relish,* or *spz, or relish, spz* animals and bioinformatic analysis of promoter sequences to identify Relish- and/or DIF-responsive κB sites (Busse et al. 2007). In particular, DIF prefers a sequence with three Gs followed by 4–5 AT-rich nucleotides [GGGAAA(A/T/G)(C/T)CC] while Relish prefers 4 Gs followed by a shorter AT-rich stretch [GGGGATT(T/C)(T/C)(T/C)]. Some sites were also found to bind both Relish and DIF, e.g. perfect palindromes [GGGAATTCCC] (Busse et al. 2007). The nature of the κB-sites found upstream of individual AMP genes (and other immune responsive genes) determines whether each gene will respond to Toll or IMD signaling (or both). For example, Tanji et al. 2007 reported that *Drosomycin* has two κB sites, one of which preferentially responds to Toll/DIF while the other also responds to IMD/Relish signaling. Optimal *Drosomycin* induction involves activation of both pathways and signaling through both κB sites. Similar complexity is found at other AMP genes, too; *Attacin-A* has two separate κB sites, one for DIF and one for Relish binding, and mutation of the DIF site renders it completely IMD pathway dependent (Busse et al. 2007). The enhancer region of *Metchnikowin* contains one κB site, which allows the binding of both DIF and Relish, in addition to two other Relish-specific sites (Levashina et al. 1998; Senger et al. 2004; Busse et al. 2007) (Fig. 3).

While DIF and Dorsal were believed to predominantly form homodimers, studies by Han and lp (1999) indicated that DIF, Dorsal and Relish may form heterodimers and cooperatively regulate the expression of certain AMPs (Gross et al. 1996; Han and Ip 1999). For example, expression of *Drosomycin*, a Toll-dependent gene is greatly enhanced by the co-expression of Relish and DIF. Moreover, Relish was found to interact with both DIF and Dorsal under over-expressed conditions (Han and Ip 1999). This idea is further supported by the recent evidence that synergistic activation of both Toll and IMD pathways is important for *Drosomycin* expression (Tanji et al. 2007). Consistent with this idea, a novel Dif/Relish heterodimer binding sequence, GGGA(A/T)TC(C/A)C, distinct from that of Dif or Relish homodimers was identified by Senger et al. 2004. Interestingly, the −147 κB site GGGGAACTAC in the enhancer region of *Drosomycin* closely resembles this DIF/Relish site (Senger et al. 2004). As in mammals, permutation of different homo/heterodimers of *Drosophila* Rel proteins may expand the regulatory potential of these proteins and further experimental data are needed to clarify these possibilities.

Optimal expression of AMP genes relies not only on the Rel-binding sites, but also depends on other regulatory regions in their promoter/enhancers (Uvell and Engstrom 2003; Senger et al. 2004). GATA sites (consensus: (no G) GATAA (no A) (no T)) have been found in close proximity to Rel binding sites and oriented in the same direction as the Rel sites in almost one-third of the immune responsive genes in *Drosophila* (Senger et al. 2004). Inversion of this orientation upstream of *Metchnikowin* or *CecropinA1* genes reduces their expression (Kadalayil et al. 1997; Senger et al. 2004). The authors propose that this peculiar orientation might provide a platform for the appropriate interaction between the GATA-binding transcription factor Serpent and the Rel proteins. Moreover, it may also allow the cooperative assembly of other factors required for transcription (Petersen et al. 1999; Senger et al. 2004).

Another distinct regulatory region found in many AMP genes is the 'R1 motif'. The R1 element was best studied in the *CecropinA* gene where it is found in addition to κB and GATA sites. κB and R1 sites independently regulate *CecA* expression through different transcription factors. Similar to κB, R1 binding activity is induced by immune challenge and R1 sites are essential for the proper expression of *CecA*, although, it is not clear how these R1 factors are regulated in response to immune challenge. R1 motif is also found in the upstream regions of other AMPs such as *Defensin*, *Drosomycin* and *Metchnikowin* (Uvell and Engstrom 2003). Many AMP genes also harbor binding sites for the JNK pathway transcription factor AP-1. Their functions remain controversial, but most likely they act as repressors of the NF-κB-mediated *Drosophila* humoral response, as discussed below (Kim et al. 2005; 2007).

5 Co-activators of *Drosophila* Rel Proteins

Rel transcription factors in *Drosophila* function in concert with co-activator proteins to drive the transcription of their target genes. DIF interacts with the co-activator dTRAP80, to induce transcription of target genes such as *Drosomycin*. dTRAP80 is a component of the multi-protein transcriptional Mediator co-activator complex (Park et al. 2003). In mammals, the co-activator protein called CREB-binding protein (CBP) assists NF-κB in the expression of certain immune effectors like IL-6 and IFNβ (Merika et al. 1998; Vanden Berghe et al. 1999; Qin et al. 2005). Similarly, maternally expressed *Drosophila* CBP (dCBP) is essential for the expression of the dorsal target gene, *twist,* during larval development. Dorsal interacts directly with dCBP through its RHD domain (Akimaru et al. 1997). The role of dCBP in the immune response has not been thoroughly examined. Another regulator of Dorsal and DIF dependent transcription is Deformed epidermal autoregulatory factor 1(DEAF1) (Reed et al. 2008; Kuttenkeuler et al. 2010). Many AMP genes such as *Drosomycin* and *Metchnikowin* have Deaf1-binding sites ("TTCGGNT") in their upstream regions and mutating these sites reduces their signal-dependent expression. Moreover, its strict nuclear localization and epistatic analysis have indicated that it might function together with DIF and Dorsal to drive AMP gene expression. Although it does not seem to influence Relish dependent transcription, Deaf1 regulation is not completely clear (Kuttenkeuler et al. 2010). Another possible co-activator family, involved in the immune response is the "POU" domain proteins Pdm1, Pdm2 and Dfr, which were identified as potential regulators of DIF-mediated *CecropinA* expression (Junell et al. 2007).

Akirins are a conserved class of proteins that modulate NF-κB activation in both *Drosophila* and mammalian innate immune pathways. Akirin has been proposed to be a co-activator of Relish, since knockdown of Akirin decreases *Diptericin* expression and epistatic analysis has placed it at the level of or downstream of Relish in the IMD pathway. Its strict nuclear localization further adds support to this hypothesis (Goto et al. 2008). Akirin does not contain any known DNA-binding domains and a direct interaction between Relish and Akirin was not detected. Mammals express two nuclear Akirin proteins. Although, the function of Akirin1 remains unclear, with no obvious phenotypes, the Akirin2 knockout is embryonic lethal. Fibroblasts from these knockout embryos showed defects in the production of an NF-κB-dependent cytokine, IL-6 in response to TNF, IL-1 and LPS, suggesting a function similar to *Drosophila* Akirin (Goto et al. 2008).

Another possible co-activator, known as Helicase89B, is critical for Rel protein-dependent transcription of both Toll and IMD target anti-microbial genes in *Drosophila* larvae. Curiously, *Helicase89B* does not appear to be critical for immune responses in the adult fly (Yagi and Ip 2005). Helicase89B is a SNF-like ATPase, most similar to yeast Mot1p. Like Mot1p, Hel89B was also reported to interact with TATA-binding protein (TBP) and thus, may function as an adaptor protein that links the Rel protein with the basal transcription complex. However, no direct interaction was observed between Hel89B and Rel proteins so its exact function requires further clarification (Yagi and Ip 2005).

6 Negative Regulators of the Toll and IMD Pathways

6.1 Catalytic PGRPs

While non-catalytic PGRPs such as PGRP-SA/SD, LC/LE function as PGN-binding receptors and activate the Toll and the IMD pathways, the catalytically active PGRPs negatively regulate the IMD pathway by degrading microbial PGN (Bischoff et al. 2006; Zaidman-Remy et al. 2006). As mentioned earlier, these PGRPs are type 2 amidases that cleave the amide bond separating the L-Ala in the stem peptide from the glycan backbone of PGN, greatly diminishing its immunostimulatory activity. In *Drosophila*, PGRP-LB, PGRP-SB1, PGRP-SC1a/b are known PGN processing amidases. Also, PGRP-SB2, and PGRP-SC2 are predicted to have amidase activity, based on the presence of a complete catalytic site (Werner et al. 2000; Kim et al. 2003; Mellroth et al. 2003; Bischoff et al. 2006; Mellroth and Steiner 2006; Zaidman-Remy et al. 2006). In addition, genetic studies using RNAi to knockdown either PGRP-LB or PGRP-SC1/2 in vivo firmly established that these amidases are important to down-modulate the IMD pathway, both systemically and in the gut (Bischoff et al. 2006; Zaidman-Remy et al. 2006).

Distinct from the type 2 amidase activity discussed above, PGRP-SA was shown to possess an L,D-carboxypeptidase activity, which enables it to specifically cleave DAP-type PGN. It was proposed that this activity functions as an 'editor' allowing PGRP-SA to signal Toll activation following binding of lysine-type PGN while binding to DAP-type PGN would instead, lead to the digestion of the PGN without signaling (Chang et al. 2004). However, this model is yet to be tested.

The four human PGRPs (also known as PGLYRPs) also function in host defense. PGLYRP-2 is a catalytic amidase and likely functions by down-modulating PGN-induced innate immune response in mammals, much like the catalytic *Drosophila* PGRPs (Royet and Dziarski 2007). On the other hand, the three non-catalytic mouse PGRPs, PGLYRP1, 3, and 4, do not appear to function as PGN receptors, as observed in the *Drosophila* system. Instead, these PGN-binding proteins appear to be directly bactericidal and, for example, contribute to microbial killing by DNA NETS released by activated neutrophils (Cho et al. 2005; Royet and Dziarski 2007).

6.2 Negative Regulators of Toll Signaling

Necrotic (nec) is a member of the SERine Protease INhibitor (serpin) family. *nec* mutants display constitutive activation of Toll and spontaneous *Drosomycin* expression and melanization (Levashina et al. 1999; Ligoxygakis et al. 2002). In fact, the previously mentioned protease-recognition system featuring Persephone (*psh*) was identified in a screen for suppressors of the *necrotic* (*nec*) phenotype (Ligoxygakis et al. 2002). Toll activation leads to the cleavage of Nec, removing its N-terminal polyglutamine extension. In vitro, cleaved Nec is still an active serpin, in some cases displaying increased activity. Thus, this feed back mechanism may regulate the protease pathways that control Spätzle processing (Pelte et al. 2006).

The *Drosophila* genome encodes for 29 serpins, including *nec,* some of which are also involved in regulating Toll activation and other aspects of the immune response. For example, Serpin-27A and Serpin-28D are major regulators of melanization (Ligoxygakis et al. 2002; Scherfer et al. 2008) while Serpin5 was recently linked to controlling Toll (Ahmad et al. 2009). Serpin-27A also controls the Spätzle processing protease Easter in the dorsal–ventral patterning pathway (Hashimoto et al. 2003; Ligoxygakis et al. 2003). Serpin 77Ba regulates the protease cascade that controls melanization, but seems to function specifically in the trachea. Interestingly, the up-regulation of tracheal melanization observed in the *Spn77Ba* mutant indirectly activates the Toll pathway and *Drosomycin* expression, through the Persephone serine protease cascade (Tang et al. 2008).

Cactus and Wnt inhibitor of Dorsal (WntD) are both feedback inhibitors of the intracellular Toll signaling pathway (Nicolas et al. 1998; Ganguly et al. 2005; Gordon et al. 2005). As described previously, Cactus sequesters Dorsal in the cytoplasm of unstimulated cells and prevents its nuclear localization. Cactus is also an early target of DIF/Dorsal transcriptional activation. Newly synthesized Cactus can then sequester DIF or Dorsal in the cytoplasm, down-modulating the response. Similarly, WntD also inhibits Dorsal activation, although the mechanism is not clearly understood. *wntD* mutants display elevated levels of nuclear Dorsal even in unstimulated conditions. Loss of WntD alters the transcriptional profile of embryonic genes, AMPs and other immune genes in response to infection (Ganguly et al. 2005; Gordon et al. 2005, 2008). For example, *Listeria* infection causes elevated expression of certain immune genes in *wntD* mutants, among which *edin* (elevated during infection) and *eiger*, in particular, have been shown to be necessary to fight the infection efficiently. At the same time, over-expression of these same proteins can also reduce the survival of flies (Dionne and Schneider 2008; Gordon et al. 2008), indicating that WntD acts a checkpoint to ensure controlled activation of immune responses against pathogens. It should be noted that *Drosophilaeiger* is a TNF family member. *eiger* has been shown to play a protective role particularly against extracellular pathogens, by activating cellular defenses such as phagocytosis. As mentioned above, when expressed at higher levels, *eiger* can also exacerbate the pathology of disease, probably through its ability to promote programmed cell death, similar to TNF (Schneider et al. 2007; Narasimamurthy 2009). However, *eiger* does not seem to be a component of the conventional Toll and IMD pathways, and a link to *Drosophila* Rel proteins, if any, is yet to be identified.

6.3 Negative Regulators of IMD Signaling

Rudra/PIMS/Pirk (hereafter Rudra) is a negative feedback regulator of IMD signaling that was identified as a PGRP-LC interacting protein in a yeast two-hybrid screen. Rudra interacts with both the PGN receptors of the IMD pathway, PGRP-LC and PGRP-LE, at least in part, through the conserved RHIM domain that is critical for signaling by both receptors (Aggarwal et al. 2008). Rudra is induced by PGN stimulation and associates with both the receptors as well as with the IMD protein, and disrupts the receptor proximal signaling complex (Aggarwal et al. 2008; Kleino et al. 2008). In addition, Rudra may also traffic PGRP-LC to the lysosome, for degradation (Lhocine et al. 2008). Rudra not only prevents the hyper-activation of the IMD pathway in response to pathogens, but also maintains intestinal homeostasis by preventing the induction of AMPs by commensal bacteria (Lhocine et al. 2008).

Caudal, a homeobox encoding transcription factor, is another negative regulator of AMP expression, e.g. *Dipterícin* and *Cecropin,* that functions in the gut to prevent IMD activation by commensal bacteria (Ryu et al. 2008). Gut-specific knock-down of caudal perturbs the balance of gut commensal populations, resulting in the dominance of certain microbes that are only minor members of the gut microbiota in wildtype animals. The dominance of these microbes causes an apoptotic pathology in the *Drosophila* midgut epithelium. This phenomenon is seen in conventionally reared flies, but not in germ free flies which are devoid of gut commensal flora (Ryu et al. 2008). Caudal also regulates constitutive, NF-κB-independent expression of *Drosomycin* and *Cecropin* in certain local epithelial tissues such as salivary glands, through Caudal binding sites in their promoter regions (Ryu et al. 2004).

Caspar is another negative regulator of the IMD pathway. Caspar is homologous to human Fas associated factor (FAF1) protein, which inhibits NF-κB activation by various inflammatory signals such as TNF, LPS, IL-1β. FAF1 is thought to function by interacting with p65/RelA and retaining p65 in cytoplasm (Park et al. 2004a, b). Caspar-deficient flies produce *Diptericin* in the absence of immune challenge and are more resistant to bacterial infections (Kim et al. 2006). Epistasis experiments with over-expressed Caspar and IMD signaling components suggested that Caspar functions by inhibiting DREDD (Kim et al. 2006). Further, Caspar contains a DED interaction domain, similar to FAF1, and this may mediate its interaction with the DED domain of *Drosophila* DREDD. Caspar also contains ubiquitin-associated (UAS) domains and ubiquitin-like domains, but whether any of these domains regulate IMD signaling awaits experimental data.

Several reports suggest that IMD pathway may also be regulated by the ubiquitin–proteasome pathway. RNAi knockdown of Defense repressor protein (DNR1), both in vitro and in vivo results in constitutive *Diptericin* expression even in non-immune challenged conditions (Foley and O'Farrell 2004; Guntermann et al. 2009). Although its exact role in the IMD pathway is not clear, DNR1 contains a conserved RING domain, characteristic of ubiquitin E3 ligases, suggesting that DNR1 may mediate ubiquitination of some IMD pathway component (Foley and O'Farrell 2004). In fact, a recent report showed that DNR1 RING domain could target DREDD for proteasomal degradation (Guntermann et al. 2009). Another finding that suggests a role for ubiquitin-/proteasome-mediated degradation in the down-modulation of the IMD pathway is that flies deficient in SCF ubiquitin-ligase components *Slimb* and *dcullin1* exhibit spontaneous Relish dependent *Diptericin* expression. This indicates that K48-ubiquitination and proteasomal degradation of certain signaling components may be involved in tuning down the signal (Khush et al. 2002). How, or if, DNR1 and the SCF function together is unknown.

Removal of K63-ubiquitin linkages associated with IMD is another mechanism by which the IMD pathway is regulated. As described above, following PGN stimulation, IMD is K63 ubiquitinated in a DREDD- and DIAP2-dependent manner. dUSP36, a de-ubiquitinase (DUB), targets this ubiquitination event to down-regulate *Diptericin* expression in response to PGN. USP36 removes K63-polyubiquitin chains from IMD and then appears to increase the addition of K48-ubiquitin chains and degradation of IMD (Thevenon et al. 2009). The E3 ligase for K48-ubiquitination of IMD is not yet identified, but DNR1 or Slimb are both candidates. This is reminiscent of RIP1 regulation by A20 in mammalian cells. A20 exhibits both similar K63 de-ubiquitinating and a separate K48 ubiquitin ligase activity, and is often referred to as an 'ubiquitin editor' (Wertz et al. 2004).

In mammals, in addition to A20, several other DUBs such as CYLD, DUBA, and Caezanne down-regulate NF-κB activation by removing K63 ubiquitin linkage in key signaling proteins such as RIP1, TRAF6 and IKKγ (Evans et al. 2001; Kayagaki et al. 2007; Enesa et al. 2008; Friedman et al. 2008). In this context, it would be interesting to know whether IKKγ also gets ubiquitinated in the IMD pathway. Interestingly, *Drosophila* also expresses a homolog of CYLD, with de-ubiquitinase activity, and among its other functions, *Drosophila* CYLD has also been implicated in anti-bacterial responses (Tsichritzis et al. 2007; Xue et al. 2007). These studies show a strong conservation of negative regulatory mechanisms in NF-κB pathways from flies to mammals.

The two branches of the IMD signaling cascade, leading to JNK and Relish activation, have been shown to down-regulate each other (Park et al. 2004a, b). Certain genes induced by Relish can target TAK1 for degradation and thus, reduce the activation of the JNK pathway (Park et al. 2004a, b). A specific example is Plenty of SH3s (POSH), which is up-regulated by Relish. POSH, in turn, regulates the duration of JNK and Relish activation, downstream of TAK1 in the IMD pathway. POSH is a RING finger containing E3 ligase. On one hand, it is important for the timely initiation of JNK and Relish dependent transcription, while on the other hand, it triggers the proteasomal degradation of TAK1 by the E3 ligase activity of its RING domain (Tsuda et al. 2005). Thus, POSH seems to play two contradictory roles in IMD signaling by regulating the amount of activated TAK1. JNK signaling also inhibits Relish-mediated transcription. In particular, the *Drosophila* AP-1 and STAT proteins (Jra and STAT92E), along with a HMG protein Dsp1 form a repressome complex on the *Attacin-A* promoter replacing Relish, thereby inhibiting Relish-dependent transcription. This repressome was reported to function by recruiting a histone deacetylase dHDAC1 and altering the chromatin structure of the Relish target promoter region (Kim et al. 2005, 2007). Although many Relish target genes contain AP-1 sites, this regulatory antagonism, between AP-1/STAT and Relish, has not yet been examined in detail at other AMP gene promoters. A similar negative regulatory mechanism has been observed with the CREB family transcription factor ATF3 in mammals. ATF3, induced by TLR4 signaling, inhibits LPS induced NF-κB transcription of certain cytokines such as IL-6 and IL-12 in a negative feedback loop. Similar to the *Drosophila* AP-1/STAT proteins, ATF3 also functions by associating with HDAC1 and altering the chromatin acetylation status (Gilchrist et al. 2006).

7 Beyond AMPs

7.1 Anti-viral Immunity

Drosophila mounts potent responses not only against bacterial and fungal pathogens, but also against viruses. However, it appears that these anti-viral effects may not be mediated by the AMPs that are induced by the Toll and the IMD pathways. Infection of flies with Cricket Paralysis virus (CrPV) and *Drosophila* C virus (DCV) does not induce AMP expression, and forced expression of single AMPs during the course of infection also does not protect the host (Sabatier et al. 2003; Dostert et al. 2005; Zambon et al. 2005; Tsai et al. 2008). However, mutants lacking various components of the IMD pathway are less efficient in clearing CrPV, indicating that other immune related functions of the IMD pathway, such as apoptosis may be playing a role (Costa et al. 2009). Similarly, in the case of *Drosophila* X virus, Toll pathway mutants were more sensitive (Zambon et al. 2005). The JAK-STAT pathway, a separate immune response pathway not involving NF-κB factors, is critical to control other viral infections, e.g. DCV infection (Dostert et al. 2005; Hedges and Johnson 2008). The RNAi pathway is also triggered by the genome and replication intermediates of viruses and has been shown to have important antiviral effects in insects (Li et al. 2002; Galiana-Arnoux et al. 2006; Wang et al. 2006a, b; Zambon et al. 2006).

7.2 Adaptive Immunity in Drosophila

Some studies have also indicated that *Drosophila* immune responses may not be limited to innate and non-specific mechanisms. Pham et al. (2007), demonstrated that flies, primed with a sublethal dose of the pathogen *S. pnuemoniae* are protected life-long, from subsequent infections by lethal doses of the same microbe, but not by other microbes (Pham et al. 2007). This indicates that *Drosophila* immunity also allows for pathogen-specific responses and the development of immunological ‘memory’. However, the mechanisms underlying this specificity and adaptation have not yet been characterized. Another finding that supports the existence of specific immune responses in flies (and mosquitoes) is the multiple splice isoforms of a gene known as Down’s syndrome cell adhesion molecule (Dscam). Dscam is an immunoglobulin superfamily protein which can generate up to 18,000 different isoforms in hemocytes (blood cells). Interestingly, these isoforms have been proposed to mediate pathogen-specific recognition and the expression of various isoforms is modulated by the presence of different infectious microbes (Watson et al. 2005; Dong et al. 2006).

8 Concluding Remarks

Innate immune NF-κB signaling in *Drosophila* shares a great deal of similarity with mammalian systems (Silverman and Maniatis 2001; Girardin et al. 2002). In the broadest sense, the signal relay culminating in NF-κB activation follows a similar pattern in both insects and mammals. Microbial recognition by innate immune receptors is followed by the formation of receptor proximal signaling complexes, generated primarily by homotypic interactions between conserved domains in adapter proteins. These receptor complexes induce regulatory ubiquitination events and activation of kinases, which trigger the degradation or processing of IκB like inhibitory proteins/domains leading to activation and nuclear translocation of NF-κB/Rel transcription factors. In fact, the signaling events in the Toll and IMD pathways share a striking amount of molecular similarity with the mammalian MyD88-dependent and MyD88-independent TLR pathways, respectively. Hence, studying these pathways in detail will likely provide further insights on the molecular mechanisms involved in the related mammalian signaling pathways.

However, on detailed inspection, some notable differences are evident. While the mammalian TLRs directly recognize their corresponding microbial ligands, *Drosophila* Toll is a cytokine receptor, with an endogenous ligand, Spätzle, that is processed from its precursor in response to infection. Another notable difference is that the NF-κB precursor Relish is activated by endoproteolytic caspase-dependent cleavage, which has not been observed with mammalian NF-κB precursors, p100 and p105. These differences, in combination with the overall similarities, make the *Drosophila* innate immune response, a fascinating model system for the study of innate immune NF-κB signaling.

References

Aggarwal K et al (2008) Rudra interrupts receptor signaling complexes to negatively regulate the IMD pathway. PLoS Pathog 4(8):e1000120

Ahmad ST et al (2009) Genetic screen identifies serpin5 as a regulator of the toll pathway and CHMP2B toxicity associated with frontotemporal dementia. Proc Natl Acad Sci USA 106(29):12168–12173

Akimaru H et al (1997) *Drosophila* CBP is required for dorsal-dependent twist gene expression. Nat Genet 17(2): 211–214

Anderson KV, Nusslein-Volhard C (1984) Information for the dorsal–ventral pattern of the *Drosophila* embryo is stored as maternal mRNA. Nature 311(5983):223–227

Apidianakis Y et al (2005) Profiling early infection responses: *Pseudomonas aeruginosa* eludes host defenses by suppressing antimicrobial peptide gene expression. Proc Natl Acad Sci USA 102(7):2573–2578

Baeuerle PA (1991) The inducible transcription activator NF-kappa B: regulation by distinct protein subunits. Biochim Biophys Acta 1072(1):63–80

Belvin MP et al (1995) Cactus protein degradation mediates *Drosophila* dorsal–ventral signaling. Genes Dev 9(7):783–793

Bergmann A et al (1996) A gradient of cytoplasmic cactus degradation establishes the nuclear localization gradient of the dorsal morphogen in *Drosophila*. Mech Dev 60(1):109–123

Bianchi K, Meier P (2009) A tangled web of ubiquitin chains: breaking news in TNF-R1 signaling. Mol Cell 36(5):736–742

Bischoff V et al (2004) Function of the drosophila pattern-recognition receptor PGRP-SD in the detection of Gram-positive bacteria. Nat Immunol 5(11):1175–1180

Bischoff V et al (2006) Downregulation of the *Drosophila* immune response by peptidoglycan-recognition proteins SC1 and SC2. PLoS Pathog 2(2):e14

Brown K et al (1995) Control of I kappa B-alpha proteolysis by site-specific, signal-induced phosphorylation. Science 267(5203):1485–1488

Buchon N et al (2009) A single modular serine protease integrates signals from pattern-recognition receptors upstream of the *Drosophila* Toll pathway. Proc Natl Acad Sci USA 106(30):12442–12447

Busse MS et al (2007) A kappaB sequence code for pathway-specific innate immune responses. Embo J 26(16):3826–3835

Chang CI et al (2004) A *Drosophila* pattern recognition receptor contains a peptidoglycan docking groove and unusual L, D-carboxypeptidase activity. PLoS Biol 2(9):E277

Chang CI et al (2005) Structure of the ectodomain of *Drosophila* peptidoglycan-recognition protein LCa suggests a molecular mechanism for pattern recognition. Proc Natl Acad Sci USA 102(29):10279–10284

Chang CI et al (2006) Structure of tracheal cytotoxin in complex with a heterodimeric pattern-recognition receptor. Science 311(5768):1761–1764

Cho JH et al (2005) Human peptidoglycan recognition protein S is an effector of neutrophil-mediated innate immunity. Blood 106(7):2551–2558

Choe KM et al (2002) Requirement for a peptidoglycan recognition protein (PGRP) in Relish activation and antibacterial immune responses in *Drosophila*. Science 296(5566):359–362

Choe KM et al (2005) *Drosophila* peptidoglycan recognition protein LC (PGRP-LC) acts as a signal-transducing innate immune receptor. Proc Natl Acad Sci USA 102(4):1122–1126

Cornwell WD, Kirkpatrick RB (2001) Cactus-independent nuclear translocation of *Drosophila* RELISH. J Cell Biochem 82(1):22–37

Costa A et al (2009) The Imd pathway is involved in antiviral immune responses in *Drosophila*. PLoS One 4(10):e7436

De Gregorio E et al (2001) Genome-wide analysis of the *Drosophila* immune response by using oligonucleotide microarrays. Proc Natl Acad Sci USA 98(22):12590–12595

De Gregorio E et al (2002) The Toll and Imd pathways are the major regulators of the immune response in *Drosophila*. Embo J 21(11):2568–2579

Dionne MS, Schneider DS (2008) Models of infectious diseases in the fruit fly *Drosophila melanogaster*. Dis Model Mech 1(1):43–49

Dong Y et al (2006) AgDscam, a hypervariable immunoglobulin domain-containing receptor of the Anopheles gambiae innate immune system. PLoS Biol 4(7):e229

Dostert C et al (2005) The Jak-STAT signaling pathway is required but not sufficient for the antiviral response of *Drosophila*. Nat Immunol 6(9):946–953

Drier EA et al (1999) Nuclear import of the *Drosophila* Rel protein Dorsal is regulated by phosphorylation. Genes Dev 13(5):556–568

Drier EA et al (2000) Cactus-independent regulation of dorsal nuclear import by the ventral signal. Curr Biol 10(1):23–26

Dushay MS et al (1996) Origins of immunity: Relish, a compound Rel-like gene in the antibacterial defense of *Drosophila*. Proc Natl Acad Sci USA 93(19):10343–10347

Ea CK et al (2006) Activation of IKK by TNFalpha requires site-specific ubiquitination of RIP1 and polyubiquitin binding by NEMO. Mol Cell 22(2):245–257

Edwards DN et al (1997) An activity-dependent network of interactions links the Rel protein Dorsal with its cytoplasmic regulators. Development 124(19):3855–3864

El Chamy L et al (2008) Sensing of 'danger signals' and pathogen-associated molecular patterns defines binary signaling pathways 'upstream' of Toll. Nat Immunol 9(10):1165–1170

Enesa K et al (2008) NF-kappaB suppression by the deubiquitinating enzyme Cezanne: a novel negative feedback loop in pro-inflammatory signaling. J Biol Chem 283(11):7036–7045

Engstrom Y et al (1993) kappa B-like motifs regulate the induction of immune genes in *Drosophila*. J Mol Biol 232(2):327–333

Erturk-Hasdemir D et al (2009) Two roles for the *Drosophila* IKK complex in the activation of Relish and the induction of antimicrobial peptide genes. Proc Natl Acad Sci USA 106(24):9779–9784

Evans PC et al (2001) Isolation and characterization of two novel A20-like proteins. Biochem J 357(Pt 3):617–623

Fernandez NQ et al (2001) Separable and redundant regulatory determinants in Cactus mediate its dorsal group dependent degradation. Development 128(15):2963–2974

Ferrandon D et al (1998) A drosomycin-GFP reporter transgene reveals a local immune response in *Drosophila* that is not dependent on the Toll pathway. Embo J 17(5):1217–1227

Filipe SR et al (2005) Requirements of peptidoglycan structure that allow detection by the *Drosophila* Toll pathway. EMBO Rep 6(4):327–333

Foley E, O'Farrell PH (2004) Functional dissection of an innate immune response by a genome-wide RNAi screen. PLoS Biol 2(8):E203

Friedman CS et al (2008) The tumour suppressor CYLD is a negative regulator of RIG-I-mediated antiviral response. EMBO Rep 9(9):930–936

Galiana-Arnoux D et al (2006) Essential function in vivo for Dicer-2 in host defense against RNA viruses in *Drosophila*. Nat Immunol 7(6):590–597

Galindo RL et al (1995) Interaction of the pelle kinase with the membrane-associated protein tube is required for transduction of the dorsoventral signal in *Drosophila* embryos. Development 121(7):2209–2218

Ganguly A et al (2005) *Drosophila* WntD is a target and an inhibitor of the Dorsal/Twist/Snail network in the gastrulating embryo. Development 132(15):3419–3429

Geisler R et al (1992) Cactus, a gene involved in dorsoventral pattern formation of *Drosophila*, is related to the I kappa B gene family of vertebrates. Cell 71(4):613–621

Georgel P et al (1993) Insect immunity: the diptericin promoter contains multiple functional regulatory sequences homologous to mammalian acute-phase response elements. Biochem Biophys Res Commun 197(2):508–517

Georgel P et al (2001) *Drosophila* immune deficiency (IMD) is a death domain protein that activates antibacterial defense and can promote apoptosis. Dev Cell 1(4):503–514

Ghosh S et al (1998) NF-kappa B and Rel proteins: evolutionarily conserved mediators of immune responses. Annu Rev Immunol 16:225–260

Gilchrist M et al (2006) Systems biology approaches identify ATF3 as a negative regulator of Toll-like receptor 4. Nature 441(7090):173–178

Gillespie SK, Wasserman SA (1994) Dorsal, a *Drosophila* Rel-like protein, is phosphorylated upon activation of the transmembrane protein Toll. Mol Cell Biol 14(6):3559–3568

Girardin SE et al (2002) Intracellular vs extracellular recognition of pathogens—common concepts in mammals and flies. Trends Microbiol 10(4):193–199

Gobert V et al (2003) Dual activation of the *Drosophila* toll pathway by two pattern recognition receptors. Science 302(5653):2126–2130

Gordon MD et al (2005) WntD is a feedback inhibitor of Dorsal/NF-kappaB in *Drosophila* development and immunity. Nature 437(7059):746–749

Gordon MD et al (2008) Pathogenesis of listeria-infected *Drosophila* wntD mutants is associated with elevated levels of the novel immunity gene edin. PLoS Pathog 4(7):e1000111

Goto A et al (2008) Akirins are highly conserved nuclear proteins required for NF-kappaB-dependent gene expression in *Drosophila* and mice. Nat Immunol 9(1):97–104

Gottar M et al (2002) The *Drosophila* immune response against Gram-negative bacteria is mediated by a peptidoglycan recognition protein. Nature 416(6881):640–644

Gottar M et al (2006) Dual detection of fungal infections in *Drosophila* via recognition of glucans and sensing of virulence factors. Cell 127(7):1425–1437

Govind S et al (1992) In vivo self-association of the *Drosophila* rel-protein dorsal. Proc Natl Acad Sci USA 89(17):7861–7865

Govind S et al (1996) Regulated nuclear import of the *Drosophila* rel protein dorsal: structure-function analysis. Mol Cell Biol 16(3):1103–1114

Gross I et al (1996) *Drosophila* immunity: a comparative analysis of the Rel proteins dorsal and Dif in the induction of the genes encoding diptericin and cecropin. Nucleic Acids Res 24(7):1238–1245

Grosshans J et al (1994) Activation of the kinase Pelle by Tube in the dorsoventral signal transduction pathway of *Drosophila* embryo. Nature 372(6506):563–566.

Guntermann S et al (2009) Dnr1-dependent regulation of the *Drosophila* immune deficiency signaling pathway. Dev Comp Immunol 33(1):127–134
Han ZS, Ip YT (1999) Interaction and specificity of Rel-related proteins in regulating *Drosophila* immunity gene expression. J Biol Chem 274(30):21355–21361
Hashimoto C et al (2003) Spatial regulation of developmental signaling by a serpin. Dev Cell 5(6):945–950
Hedengren M et al (1999) Relish, a central factor in the control of humoral but not cellular immunity in *Drosophila*. Mol Cell 4(5):827–837
Hedengren-Olcott M et al (2004) Differential activation of the NF-kappaB-like factors Relish and Dif in *Drosophila melanogaster* by fungi and Gram-positive bacteria. J Biol Chem 279(20):21121–21127
Hedges LM, Johnson KN (2008) Induction of host defence responses by *Drosophila* C virus. J Gen Virol 89(Pt 6):1497–1501
Hoffmann JA, Reichhart JM (2002) *Drosophila* innate immunity: an evolutionary perspective. Nat Immunol 3(2):121–126
Hofmann RM, Pickart CM (1999) Noncanonical MMS2-encoded ubiquitin-conjugating enzyme functions in assembly of novel polyubiquitin chains for DNA repair. Cell 96(5):645–653
Horng T, Medzhitov R (2001) *Drosophila* MyD88 is an adapter in the Toll signaling pathway. Proc Natl Acad Sci USA 98(22):12654–12658
Hu S, Yang X (2000) dFADD, a novel death domain-containing adapter protein for the *Drosophila* caspase DREDD. J Biol Chem 275(40):30761–30764
Hu X et al (2004) Multimerization and interaction of Toll and Spatzle in *Drosophila*. Proc Natl Acad Sci USA 101(25):9369–9374
Huguet C et al (1997) Rel/NF-kappa B transcription factors and I kappa B inhibitors: evolution from a unique common ancestor. Oncogene 15(24):2965–2974
Huh, J. R. et al (2007). "The Drosophila inhibitor of apoptosis (IAP) DIAP2 is dispensable for cell survival, required for the innate immune response to gram-negative bacterial infection, and can be negatively regulated by the reaper/hid/grim family of IAP-binding apoptosis inducers." J Biol Chem 282(3): 2056-68
Ip YT et al (1992) Dorsal-twist interactions establish snail expression in the presumptive mesoderm of the *Drosophila* embryo. Genes Dev 6(8):1518–1530
Ip YT et al (1993) Dif, a dorsal-related gene that mediates an immune response in *Drosophila*. Cell 75(4):753–763
Irving P et al (2001) A genome-wide analysis of immune responses in *Drosophila*. Proc Natl Acad Sci USA 98(26):15119–15124
Isoda K, Nusslein-Volhard C (1994) Disulfide cross-linking in crude embryonic lysates reveals three complexes of the *Drosophila* morphogen dorsal and its inhibitor cactus. Proc Natl Acad Sci USA 91(12):5350–5354
Iwai K, Tokunaga F (2009) Linear polyubiquitination: a new regulator of NF-kappaB activation. EMBO Rep 10(7):706–713
Jang IH et al (2006) A Spatzle-processing enzyme required for toll signaling activation in *Drosophila* innate immunity. Dev Cell 10(1):45–55
Jiang J et al (1991) The dorsal morphogen gradient regulates the mesoderm determinant twist in early *Drosophila* embryos. Genes Dev 5(10):1881–1891
Jin L et al (2008) Mechanism of ubiquitin-chain formation by the human anaphase-promoting complex. Cell 133(4):653–665
Junell A et al (2007) Isolation of regulators of *Drosophila* immune defense genes by a double interaction screen in yeast. Insect Biochem Mol Biol 37(3):202–212
Kadalayil L et al (1997) Adjacent GATA and kappa B-like motifs regulate the expression of a *Drosophila* immune gene. Nucleic Acids Res 25(6):1233–1239
Kambris Z et al (2006) *Drosophila* immunity: a large-scale in vivo RNAi screen identifies five serine proteases required for Toll activation. Curr Biol 16(8):808–813
Kanayama A et al (2004) TAB 2 and TAB 3 activate the NF-kappaB pathway through binding to polyubiquitin chains. Mol Cell 15(4):535–548

Kaneko T et al (2004) Monomeric and polymeric gram-negative peptidoglycan but not purified LPS stimulate the *Drosophila* IMD pathway. Immunity 20(5):637–649

Kaneko T et al (2006) PGRP-LC and PGRP-LE have essential yet distinct functions in the *Drosophila* immune response to monomeric DAP-type peptidoglycan. Nat Immunol 7(7):715–723

Kang D et al (1998) A peptidoglycan recognition protein in innate immunity conserved from insects to humans. Proc Natl Acad Sci USA 95(17):10078–10082

Kappler C et al (1993) Insect immunity. Two 17 bp repeats nesting a kappa B-related sequence confer inducibility to the diptericin gene and bind a polypeptide in bacteria-challenged *Drosophila*. Embo J 12(4):1561–1568

Kayagaki N et al (2007) DUBA: a deubiquitinase that regulates type I interferon production. Science 318(5856):1628–1632

Khush RS et al (2002) A ubiquitin-proteasome pathway represses the *rosophila* immune deficiency signaling cascade. Curr Biol 12(20):1728–1737

Kidd S (1992) Characterization of the *Drosophila* cactus locus and analysis of interactions between cactus and dorsal proteins. Cell 71(4) 623–635

Kim YS et al (2000) Lipopolysaccharide-activated kinase, an essential component for the induction of the antimicrobial peptide genes in *Drosophila melanogaster* cells. J Biol Chem 275(3):2071–2079

Kim MS et al (2003) Crystal structure of peptidoglycan recognition protein LB from *Drosophila melanogaster*. Nat Immunol 4(8):787–793

Kim T et al (2005) Downregulation of lipopolysaccharide response in *Drosophila* by negative crosstalk between the AP1 and NF-kappaB signaling modules. Nat Immunol 6(2):211–218

Kim M et al (2006) Caspar, a suppressor of antibacterial immunity in *Drosophila*. Proc Natl Acad Sci USA 103(44):16358–16363

Kim LK et al (2007) Down-regulation of NF-kappaB target genes by the AP-1 and STAT complex during the innate immune response in *Drosophila*. PLoS Biol 5(9):e238

Kim CH et al (2008) A three-step proteolytic cascade mediates the activation of the peptidoglycan-induced toll pathway in an insect. J Biol Chem 283(12):7599–7607

Kirkpatrick DS et al (2006) Quantitative analysis of in vitro ubiquitinated cyclin B1 reveals complex chain topology. Nat Cell Biol 8(7):700–710

Kleino A et al (2008) Pirk is a negative regulator of the *Drosophila* Imd pathway. J Immunol 180(8):5413–5422

Kuttenkeuler NP et al (2010) A large-scale RNAi screen identifies Deaf1 as a regulator of innate immune responses in *Drosophila*. J Innate Immun 2(2):181–194

Lamothe B et al (2007) Site-specific Lys-63-linked tumor necrosis factor receptor-associated factor 6 auto-ubiquitination is a critical determinant of I kappa B kinase activation. J Biol Chem 282(6):4102–4112

Lemaitre B et al (1996) The dorsoventral regulatory gene cassette spatzle/Toll/cactus controls the potent antifungal response in *Drosophila* adults. Cell 86(6):973–983

Lemaitre B et al (1997) *Drosophila* host defense: differential induction of antimicrobial peptide genes after infection by various classes of microorganisms. Proc Natl Acad Sci USA 94(26):14614–14619

Leone, P. et al (2008) Crystal structure of *Drosophila* PGRP-SD suggests binding to DAP-type but not lysine-type peptidoglycan. Mol Immunol 45(9):2521-30

Leulier F et al (2000) The *Drosophila* caspase Dredd is required to resist gram-negative bacterial infection. EMBO Rep 1(4):353–358

Leulier F et al (2002) Inducible expression of double-stranded RNA reveals a role for dFADD in the regulation of the antibacterial response in *Drosophila* adults. Curr Biol 12(12):996–1000

Leulier F et al (2003) The *Drosophila* immune system detects bacteria through specific peptidoglycan recognition. Nat Immunol 4(5):478–484

Leung TH et al (2004) One nucleotide in a kappaB site can determine cofactor specificity for NF-kappaB dimers. Cell 118(4):453–464

Levashina EA et al (1998) Two distinct pathways can control expression of the gene encoding the *Drosophila* antimicrobial peptide metchnikowin. J Mol Biol 278(3):515–527

Levashina EA et al (1999) Constitutive activation of toll-mediated antifungal defense in serpin-deficient *Drosophila*. Science 285(5435):1917–1919

Lhocine N et al (2008) PIMS modulates immune tolerance by negatively regulating *Drosophila* innate immune signaling. Cell Host Microbe 4(2):147–158

Li H et al (2002) Induction and suppression of RNA silencing by an animal virus. Science 296(5571):1319–1321

Liang Y et al (2004) NF-kappaB and its regulation on the immune system. Cell Mol Immunol 1(5):343–350

Liehl P et al (2006) Prevalence of local immune response against oral infection in a *Drosophila*/Pseudomonas infection model. PLoS Pathog 2(6):e56

Ligoxygakis P et al (2002) A serpin mutant links Toll activation to melanization in the host defence of *Drosophila*. Embo J 21(23):6330–6337

Ligoxygakis P et al (2003) A serpin regulates dorsal-ventral axis formation in the *Drosophila* embryo. Curr Biol 13(23):2097–2102

Lim JH et al (2006) Structural basis for preferential recognition of diaminopimelic acid-type peptidoglycan by a subset of peptidoglycan recognition proteins. J Biol Chem 281(12):286–295

Lin L et al (1998) Cotranslational biogenesis of NF-kappaB p50 by the 26S proteasome. Cell 92(6):819–828

Lu Y et al (2001) The antibacterial arm of the *Drosophila* innate immune response requires an IkappaB kinase. Genes Dev 15(1):104–110

Manfruelli P et al (1999) A mosaic analysis in *Drosophila* fat body cells of the control of antimicrobial peptide genes by the Rel proteins Dorsal and DIF. Embo J 18(12): 3380–3391

Mansfield BE et al (2003) Exploration of host-pathogen interactions using *Listeria monocytogenes* and *Drosophila melanogaster*. Cell Microbiol 5(12):901–911

Matova N, Anderson KV (2006) Rel/NF-kappaB double mutants reveal that cellular immunity is central to *Drosophila* host defense. Proc Natl Acad Sci USA 103(44):16424–16429

Matova N, Anderson KV (2010) *Drosophila* Rel proteins are central regulators of a robust, multi-organ immune network. J Cell Sci 123(Pt 4):627–633

Mellroth P, Steiner H (2006) PGRP-SB1: an *N*-acetylmuramoyl L-alanine amidase with antibacterial activity. Biochem Biophys Res Commun 350(4):994–999

Mellroth P et al (2003) A scavenger function for a *Drosophila* peptidoglycan recognition protein. J Biol Chem 278(9):7059–7064

Mellroth P et al (2005) Ligand-induced dimerization of *Drosophila* peptidoglycan recognition proteins in vitro. Proc Natl Acad Sci USA 102(18):6455–6460

Meng X et al (1999) Toll receptor-mediated *Drosophila* immune response requires Dif, an NF-kappaB factor. Genes Dev 13(7):792–797

Merika M et al (1998) Recruitment of CBP/p300 by the IFN beta enhanceosome is required for synergistic activation of transcription. Mol Cell 1(2):277–287

Meylan E et al (2004) RIP1 is an essential mediator of Toll-like receptor 3-induced NF-kappa B activation. Nat Immunol 5(5):503–507

Michel T et al (2001) *Drosophila* Toll is activated by Gram-positive bacteria through a circulating peptidoglycan recognition protein. Nature 414(6865):756–759

Minakhina S, Steward R (2006) Nuclear factor-kappa B pathways in *Drosophila*. Oncogene 25(51):6749–6757

Mizuguchi K et al (1998) Getting knotted: a model for the structure and activation of Spatzle. Trends Biochem Sci 23(7):239–242

Naitza S et al (2002) The *Drosophila* immune defense against gram-negative infection requires the death protein dFADD. Immunity 17(5):575–581

Narasimamurthy R (2009) Structure-function analysis of Eiger, the *Drosophila* TNF homolog. Cell Res 19:392–394

Nicolas E et al (1998) In vivo regulation of the IkappaB homologue cactus during the immune response of *Drosophila*. J Biol Chem 273(17):10463–10469
Nusslein-Volhard C et al (1987) Determination of anteroposterior polarity in *Drosophila*. Science 238(4834):1675–1681
Ochiai M, Ashida M (1999) A pattern recognition protein for peptidoglycan. Cloning the cDNA and the gene of the silkworm, *Bombyx mori*. J Biol Chem 274(17):11854–11858
Pan DJ et al (1991) Functional analysis of the *Drosophila* twist promoter reveals a dorsal-binding ventral activator region. Genes Dev 5(10):1892–1901
Paquette N et al (2010) Caspase-mediated cleavage, IAP binding, and ubiquitination: linking three mechanisms crucial for *Drosophila* NF-kappaB signaling. Mol Cell 37(2):172–182
Park JM et al (2003) Signal-induced transcriptional activation by Dif requires the dTRAP80 mediator module. Mol Cell Biol 23(4):1358–1367
Park JM et al (2004) Targeting of TAK1 by the NF-kappa B protein Relish regulates the JNK-mediated immune response in *Drosophila*. Genes Dev 18(5):584–594
Park MY et al (2004) Fas-associated factor-1 inhibits nuclear factor-kappaB (NF-kappaB) activity by interfering with nuclear translocation of the RelA (p65) subunit of NF-kappaB. J Biol Chem 279(4):2544–2549
Park JW et al (2007) Clustering of peptidoglycan recognition protein-SA is required for sensing lysine-type peptidoglycan in insects. Proc Natl Acad Sci USA 104(16):6602–6607
Pelte N et al (2006) Immune challenge induces N-terminal cleavage of the *Drosophila* serpin Necrotic. Insect Biochem Mol Biol 36(1):37–46
Perkins ND (2007) Integrating cell-signalling pathways with NF-kappaB and IKK function. Nat Rev Mol Cell Biol 8(1):49–62
Petersen UM et al (1999) Serpent regulates *Drosophila* immunity genes in the larval fat body through an essential GATA motif. Embo J 18(14):4013–4022
Pham LN et al (2007) A specific primed immune response in *Drosophila* is dependent on phagocytes. PLoS Pathog 3(3):e26
Pili-Floury S et al (2004) In vivo RNA interference analysis reveals an unexpected role for GNBP1 in the defense against Gram-positive bacterial infection in *Drosophila* adults. J Biol Chem 279(13):12848–12853
Qin BY et al (2005) Crystal structure of IRF-3 in complex with CBP. Structure 13(9):1269–1277
Ramet M et al (2002) Functional genomic analysis of phagocytosis and identification of a *Drosophila* receptor for *E. coli*. Nature 416(6881):644–648
Rao A et al (1997) Transcription factors of the NFAT family: regulation and function. Annu Rev Immunol 15:707–747
Reach M et al (1996) A gradient of cactus protein degradation establishes dorsoventral polarity in the *Drosophila* embryo. Dev Biol 180(1):353–364
Reed DE et al (2008) DEAF-1 regulates immunity gene expression in *Drosophila*. Proc Natl Acad Sci USA 105(24):8351–8356
Reiser JB et al (2004) Crystal structure of the *Drosophila* peptidoglycan recognition protein (PGRP)-SA at 1.56 A resolution. J Mol Biol 340(4):909–917
Roth S et al (1989) A gradient of nuclear localization of the dorsal protein determines dorsoventral pattern in the *Drosophila* embryo. Cell 59(6):1189–1202
Royet J, Dziarski R (2007) Peptidoglycan recognition proteins: pleiotropic sensors and effectors of antimicrobial defences. Nat Rev Microbiol 5(4):264–277
Rutschmann S et al (2000) The Rel protein DIF mediates the antifungal but not the antibacterial host defense in *Drosophila*. Immunity 12(5):569–580
Rutschmann S et al (2000) Role of *Drosophila* IKK gamma in a toll-independent antibacterial immune response. Nat Immunol 1(4):342–347
Ryu JH et al (2004) The homeobox gene Caudal regulates constitutive local expression of antimicrobial peptide genes in *Drosophila* epithelia. Mol Cell Biol 24(1):172–185
Ryu JH et al (2008) Innate immune homeostasis by the homeobox gene caudal and commensal-gut mutualism in *Drosophila*. Science 319(5864):777–782
Sabatier L et al (2003) Pherokine-2 and -3. Eur J Biochem 270(16):3398–3407

Scherfer C et al (2008) *Drosophila* Serpin-28D regulates hemolymph phenoloxidase activity and adult pigmentation. Dev Biol 323(2):189–196

Schiffmann DA et al (1999) Formation and biochemical characterization of tube/pelle death domain complexes: critical regulators of postreceptor signaling by the *Drosophila* toll receptor. Biochemistry 38(36):11722–11733

Schleifer KH, O Kandler (1972) Peptidoglycan types of bacterial cell walls and their taxonomic implications. Bacteriol Rev 36(4):407–477

Schneider DS et al (2007) *Drosophila eiger* mutants are sensitive to extracellular pathogens. PLoS Pathog 3(3):e41

Schupbach T, Wieschaus E (1989) Female sterile mutations on the second chromosome of *Drosophila melanogaster*. I. Maternal effect mutations. Genetics 121(1):101–117

Scully LR, Bidochka MJ (2006) Developing insect models for the study of current and emerging human pathogens. FEMS Microbiol Lett 263(1):1–9

Senftleben U et al (2001) Activation by IKKalpha of a second, evolutionary conserved, NF-kappa B signaling pathway. Science 293(5534):1495–1499

Senger K et al (2004) Immunity regulatory DNAs share common organizational features in *Drosophila*. Mol Cell 13(1):19–32

Serfling E et al (2004) NFAT and NF-kappaB factors-the distant relatives. Int J Biochem Cell Biol 36(7):1166–1170

Shi Y (2002) A conserved tetrapeptide motif: potentiating apoptosis through IAP-binding. Cell Death Differ 9(2):93–95

Silverman N, Maniatis T (2001) NF-kappaB signaling pathways in mammalian and insect innate immunity. Genes Dev 15(18): 2321–2342

Silverman N et al (2000) A *Drosophila* IkappaB kinase complex required for Relish cleavage and antibacterial immunity. Genes Dev 14(19):2461–2471

Silverman N et al (2003) Immune activation of NF-kappaB and JNK requires *Drosophila* TAK1. J Biol Chem 278(49):48928–48934

Spencer E et al (1999) Signal-induced ubiquitination of IkappaBalpha by the F-box protein Slimb/beta-TrCP. Genes Dev 13(3):284–294

St Leger RJ et al (1992) Molecular cloning and regulatory analysis of the cuticle-degrading-protease structural gene from the entomopathogenic fungus *Metarhizium anisopliae*. Eur J Biochem 204(3):991–1001

Steward R (1987) Dorsal, an embryonic polarity gene in *Drosophila*, is homologous to the vertebrate proto-oncogene, c-rel. Science 238(4827):692–694

Steward R (1989) Relocalization of the dorsal protein from the cytoplasm to the nucleus correlates with its function. Cell 59(6):1179–1188

Stoven S et al (2000) Activation of the *Drosophila* NF-kappaB factor Relish by rapid endoproteolytic cleavage. EMBO Rep 1(4):347–352

Stoven S et al (2003) Caspase-mediated processing of the *Drosophila* NF-kappaB factor Relish. Proc Natl Acad Sci USA 100(10):5991–5996

Sun H et al (2002) A heterotrimeric death domain complex in Toll signaling. Proc Natl Acad Sci USA 99(20):12871–12876

Sun H et al (2004) Regulated assembly of the Toll signaling complex drives *Drosophila* dorsoventral patterning. Embo J 23(1):100–110

Takehana A et al (2002) Overexpression of a pattern-recognition receptor, peptidoglycan-recognition protein-LE, activates imd/relish-mediated antibacterial defense and the prophenoloxidase cascade in *Drosophila* larvae. Proc Natl Acad Sci USA 99(21):13705–13710

Takehana A et al (2004) Peptidoglycan recognition protein (PGRP)-LE and PGRP-LC act synergistically in *Drosophila* immunity. Embo J 23(23):4690–4700

Tang H et al (2008) A serpin that regulates immune melanization in the respiratory system of *Drosophila*. Dev Cell 15(4):617–626

Tanji T et al (2007) Toll and IMD pathways synergistically activate an innate immune response in *Drosophila melanogaster*. Mol Cell Biol 27(12):4578–4588

Tatei K, Levine M (1995) Specificity of Rel-inhibitor interactions in *Drosophila* embryos. Mol Cell Biol 15(7):3627–3634

Tauszig-Delamasure S et al (2002) *Drosophila* MyD88 is required for the response to fungal and Gram-positive bacterial infections. Nat Immunol 3(1):91–97

Thevenon D et al (2009) The *Drosophila* ubiquitin-specific protease dUSP36/Scny targets IMD to prevent constitutive immune signaling. Cell Host Microbe 6(4):309–320

Thisse C et al (1991) Sequence-specific transactivation of the *Drosophila* twist gene by the dorsal gene product. Cell 65(7):1191–1201

Towb P et al (1998) Recruitment of Tube and Pelle to signaling sites at the surface of the *Drosophila* embryo. Development 125(13):2443–2450

Traenckner EB et al (1995) Phosphorylation of human I kappa B-alpha on serines 32 and 36 controls I kappa B-alpha proteolysis and NF-kappa B activation in response to diverse stimuli. Embo J 14(12):2876–2883

Tsai CW et al (2008) *Drosophila melanogaster* mounts a unique immune response to the Rhabdovirus sigma virus. Appl Environ Microbiol 74(10):3251–3256

Tsichritzis T et al (2007) A *Drosophila* ortholog of the human cylindromatosis tumor suppressor gene regulates triglyceride content and antibacterial defense. Development 134(14):2605–2614

Tsuda M et al (2005) The RING-finger scaffold protein Plenty of SH3 s targets TAK1 to control immunity signalling in *Drosophila*. EMBO Rep 6(11):1082–1087

Tzou P et al (2000) Tissue-specific inducible expression of antimicrobial peptide genes in *Drosophila* surface epithelia. Immunity 13(5):737–748

Tzou P et al (2002) Constitutive expression of a single antimicrobial peptide can restore wild-type resistance to infection in immunodeficient *Drosophila* mutants. Proc Natl Acad Sci USA 99(4):2152–2157

Uvell H, Engstrom Y (2003) Functional characterization of a novel promoter element required for an innate immune response in *Drosophila*. Mol Cell Biol 23(22):8272–8281

Vanden Berghe W et al (1999) The nuclear factor-kappaB engages CBP/p300 and histone acetyltransferase activity for transcriptional activation of the interleukin-6 gene promoter. J Biol Chem 274(45):32091–32098

Vidal S et al (2001) Mutations in the *Drosophila* dTAK1 gene reveal a conserved function for MAPKKKs in the control of rel/NF-kappaB-dependent innate immune responses. Genes Dev 15(15):1900–1912

Vonkavaara M et al (2008) *Drosophila melanogaster* as a model for elucidating the pathogenicity of *Francisella tularensis*. Cell Microbiol 10(6):1327–1338

Wang L et al (2006) Sensing of Gram-positive bacteria in *Drosophila*: GNBP1 is needed to process and present peptidoglycan to PGRP-SA. Embo J 25(20):5005–5014

Wang XH et al (2006) RNA interference directs innate immunity against viruses in adult *Drosophila*. Science 312(5772):452–454

Watson FL et al (2005) Extensive diversity of Ig-superfamily proteins in the immune system of insects. Science 309(5742):1874–1878

Weber AN et al (2003) Binding of the *Drosophila* cytokine Spatzle to Toll is direct and establishes signaling. Nat Immunol 4(8):794–800

Werner T et al (2000) A family of peptidoglycan recognition proteins in the fruit fly *Drosophila melanogaster*. Proc Natl Acad Sci USA 97(25):13772–13777

Werner T et al (2003) Functional diversity of the *Drosophila* PGRP-LC gene cluster in the response to lipopolysaccharide and peptidoglycan. J Biol Chem 278(29):26319–26322

Wertz IE et al (2004) De-ubiquitination and ubiquitin ligase domains of A20 downregulate NF-kappaB signalling. Nature 430(7000):694–699

Whalen AM, Steward R (1993) Dissociation of the dorsal-cactus complex and phosphorylation of the dorsal protein correlate with the nuclear localization of dorsal. J Cell Biol 123(3):523–534

Wiklund ML et al (2009) The N-terminal half of the *Drosophila* Rel/NF-kappaB factor Relish, REL-68, constitutively activates transcription of specific Relish target genes. Dev Comp Immunol 33(5):690–696

Windheim M et al (2008) Two different classes of E2 ubiquitin-conjugating enzymes are required for the mono-ubiquitination of proteins and elongation by polyubiquitin chains with a specific topology. Biochem J 409(3):723–729

Winston JT et al (1999) The SCFbeta-TRCP-ubiquitin ligase complex associates specifically with phosphorylated destruction motifs in IkappaBalpha and beta-catenin and stimulates IkappaBalpha ubiquitination in vitro. Genes Dev 13(3):270–283

Wu LP, Anderson KV (1998) Regulated nuclear import of Rel proteins in the *Drosophila* immune response. Nature 392(6671):93–97

Xue L et al (2007) Tumor suppressor CYLD regulates JNK-induced cell death in *Drosophila*. Dev Cell 13(3):446–454

Yagi Y, Ip YT (2005) Helicase89B is a Mot1p/BTAF1 homologue that mediates an antimicrobial response in *Drosophila*. EMBO Rep 6(11):1088–1094

Yano T et al (2008) Autophagic control of listeria through intracellular innate immune recognition in *Drosophila*. Nat Immunol 9(8):908–916

Yoshida H et al (1986) Beta-1,3-glucan receptor and peptidoglycan receptor are present as separate entities within insect prophenoloxidase activating system. Biochem Biophys Res Commun 141(3):1177–1184

Yoshida H et al (1996) Purification of a peptidoglycan recognition protein from hemolymph of the silkworm, *Bombyx mori*. J Biol Chem 271(23):3854–3860

Zaidman-Remy A et al (2006) The *Drosophila* amidase PGRP-LB modulates the immune response to bacterial infection. Immunity 24(4):463–473

Zambon RA et al (2005) The Toll pathway is important for an antiviral response in *Drosophila*. Proc Natl Acad Sci USA 102(20):7257–7262

Zambon RA et al (2006) RNAi is an antiviral immune response against a dsRNA virus in *Drosophila melanogaster*. Cell Microbiol 8(5):880–889

Zhou R et al (2005) The role of ubiquitination in *Drosophila* innate immunity. J Biol Chem 280(40):34048–34055

Zhuang ZH et al (2006) *Drosophila* TAB 2 is required for the immune activation of JNK and NF-kappaB. Cell Signal 18(7):964–970

Specialized Chromatin Patterns in the Control of Inflammatory Gene Expression

Gioacchino Natoli

Abstract Inflammatory responses to microbial and non-microbial stimuli involve coordinate changes in the expression of hundreds of genes. The inflammatory gene expression programs display two important features: first, alternative stimuli affect both a large set of common genes and a variable number of stimulus-specific genes. Second, different genes are activated with different kinetics over several hours after the initial stimulus. Mechanistically, these features reflect the interplay between two main groups of determinants: the combinatorial control of transcription by multiple transcription factors, with NF-κB and the IRFs playing a central and essential role in the induction of a large fraction of inflammatory genes; and the presence of well-defined, in part cell-type specific, patterns of chromatin organization at *cis*-regulatory regions of inflammatory genes. Recent advancements in this field are providing paradigms of general value explaining how inducible responses to environmental stimuli are controlled.

Contents

G. Natoli (✉)
Department of Experimental Oncology, European Institute of Oncology (IEO), IFOM-IEO Campus, Via Adamello 16, 20139 Milan, Italy
e-mail: gioacchino.natoli@ifom-ieo-campus.it

Current Topics Microbiology (2011) 349: 61-72

DOI: 10.1007/82_2010_106

Published Online: 21 September 2010

1 Specialization and Selectivity in the Inflammatory Gene Expression Programs

Every organism is continuously exposed to a wide array of environmental stimuli to which it constantly, and in most cases imperceptibly, reacts. In the specific case of microbes, the ability to sense them and mount suitable responses to their presence is without any doubt an essential property of multicellular life on earth (Janeway and Medzhitov 2002). It is also essential that any response to the environment be tailored onto the stimulus, in order to prevent over-reactions to harmless agents and under-reactions to stimuli that may threaten the integrity and the survival of the organism. The relevance of this "tuning" of the response for the survival of multicellular organisms is demonstrated by the evolutionary properties of those genes that encode proteins that participate in the response to external stimuli (*environmental* genes). While genes controlling developmental pathways and the organization of the body plan are extremely conserved across species, environmental genes display a high rate of duplications and losses during evolution (Ponting 2008). Typical examples are the cysteine-rich scavenger receptors, the Toll-like receptors (TLRs) and the chemokine genes (Ponting 2008). This remarkable propensity to innovation (and the ensuing specialization in the environmental gene repertoires) reflects the diversity of environments (and microbial stimuli) to which different species are exposed.

At the level of individual organisms, specialization in recognition of and reaction to, microbial stimuli is reflected in different gene expression programs activated by alternative, albeit related, stimuli (Nau et al. 2002). A paradigmatic case is represented by the selective activation of interferon-regulated (and IRF3-dependent) antiviral genes by TLR3 and TLR4, while activation of all other TLRs is without effects on these genes (Doyle et al. 2002; Toshchakov et al. 2002). Although combinatorial control of transcription by multiple synergistically acting TFs may be advocated to explain such specificity, an additional and essential regulatory layer is provided by specific patterns of chromatin organization at different groups of inflammatory genes.

2 Specialized Chromatin Organizations at Different Groups of Inflammatory Genes

The first indication that subsets of inflammatory genes have different chromatin states came from early studies analyzing NF-κB binding to inflammatory genes activated with different kinetics after LPS stimulation of macrophages (Saccani et al. 2001, 2002). Although entry of NF-κB in the nucleus after a stimulus like TNFα or LPS is fast and synchronous, kinetics of recruitment to target genes was found to be asynchronous and complex. While some genes were bound by NF-κB without any obvious delay after nuclear entry, others were bound and activated with slower kinetics, in some cases even hours after NF-κB nuclear translocation, in spite of the presence of high affinity DNA binding sites (Saccani et al. 2001). Although the molecular basis for this behavior was unclear at that time, differential recruitment was found to correlate with different levels of histone acetylation at the two groups of genes. While rapidly bound genes showed constitutively high histone H3 acetylation, genes recruiting NF-κB with slower kinetics were characterized by low to undetectable basal levels of H3 acetylation. Moreover, although acetylation at these genes increased after stimulus, it usually did not reach the same levels found at rapidly activated genes. Finally, pretreatment of macrophages with γIFN before LPS stimulation was found to increase acetylation of slow genes and to switch them into fast NF-κB recruiters. These correlative data suggested a role for nucleosome organization as a barrier to recruitment of NF-κB and gene activation. A cause–effect relationship between different chromatin states and gene activation came from a study by Ramirez-Carrozzi et al. that demonstrated a differential requirement for the Swi/Snf chromatin remodeling complexes in the activation of subsets of inflammatory genes in LPS-stimulated macrophages (Ramirez-Carrozzi et al. 2006). Mechanistically, Swi/Snf is believed to use the energy released from ATP hydrolysis (carried out by two alternative ATPases, Brg1, and Brm) to alter DNA–histone contacts and expose DNA originally occluded by the nucleosomal surface (Boeger et al. 2008). Genes requiring chromatin remodeling for activation included all secondary genes and a subgroup of primary response genes, in most cases activated with comparatively slow kinetics. Importantly, differential requirement for remodeling correlated with accessibility to nucleases and restriction enzymes: genes with a constitutive nuclease-accessible configuration in the promoter/transcription start site (TSS) region were in general activated in the absence of a functional Swi/Snf, while genes requiring Swi/Snf underwent a Brg1/Brm-dependent increase in accessibility to nucleases that preceded their activation. The basally repressed state was at least in part dependent on another chromatin remodeling complex, Mi2/Nurd, as indicated by increased activation of inflammatory genes when its helicase component (Mi2β/Chd4) was depleted.

3 The Genomic Determinants of Nucleosomal Organization at Inflammatory Genes

While these studies indicated the existence of at least two distinct groups of inflammatory genes, in terms of kinetics of activation, chromatin organization and requirement for nucleosome remodeling for expression, they did not solve an essential issue: how permissive versus repressive nucleosomal states are determined. What is becoming increasingly clear is that the underlying genomic sequence contributes to two main features of nucleosomal organization: the position of at least a fraction of nucleosomes and the degree (high versus low) of nucleosome occupancy of genomic regions (Jiang and Pugh 2009;

Kaplan et al. 2008; Segal et al. 2006). In determining both of these properties it is also clear that the final nucleosomal organization reflects the combination of nucleosome positioning and nucleosome anti-positioning (or nucleosome-excluding) sequences (Jiang and Pugh 2009). At some specific regions, mainly located at the 5′ and 3′ of genes, nucleosomes tend to be well-positioned because of the combination of adjacent positioning and exclusion sequences: in turn, positioned nucleosomes generate physical barriers that impose the positions of adjacent nucleosomes (Mavrich et al. 2008). Conversely, at several other genomic regions nucleosomes tend to have a fuzzy localization, reflecting the absence of clear sequence contexts dictating their positions. The obvious role exerted by the genomic sequence in the organization of the nucleosomal landscape represents the basis of computational model predicting with high efficiency both nucleosome positioning and occupancy at genomes of different organisms (Kaplan et al. 2008). While these data provide general principles on nucleosome organization, they do not clarify if and how a specific nucleosome organization can be exploited for regulatory purposes.

A major breakthrough was recently provided by Smale and colleagues in a study describing how a common and simple genomic organization is sufficient to create a nucleosomal state that is by itself highly permissive for gene expression (Ramirez-Carrozzi et al. 2009). Analysis of the genomic features of the promoters of Swi/Snf-independent primary response genes revealed a striking enrichment for CpG islands, while promoters with a lower CpG content were associated with either secondary genes or Swi/Snf-dependent primary genes. This simple classification was complicated only by the existence of a small group of genes lacking a CpG island but nevertheless independent of Swi/Snf for activation (Table 1). These data suggested the possibility that the sole presence of a CpG island may suffice to create a nucleosomal state permissive for rapid and unopposed gene activation in response to stimulation. This idea was supported by two main observations: first, the presence of a CpG island correlated with lower nucleosomal density in vivo; second, CpG island promoters were less efficient than non-CpG island promoters at assembling nucleosomes in competitive in vitro assays (Table 1). Moreover, it should be added that the computational models mentioned above for the prediction of nucleosome positions and occupancy indicate that while overall GC content correlates with nucleosome occupancy, CpG islands are in fact thermodynamically disfavored at assembling nucleosomes (Kaplan et al. 2008). Mechanistically, the inefficient organization of nucleosomes by CpG island promoters is dependent on the lack of AA/TT dinucleotides with a helical periodicity (10–11nt), which are required to bend DNA in a manner suitable to wrap the core histone octamer. Based on these considerations, it was suggested that the evolutionary pressure to retain CpG islands may relate to their ability to autonomously organize a chromatin state that is highly permissive for transcription. This may be of relevance both for constitutive activity of housekeeping genes and for rapid activation of inducible genes.

Table 1 A tentative simplified partitioning of inflammatory genes based on their association with a CpG island and their specific chromatin features according to Ramirez-Carrozzi et al. (2009) and Hargreaves et al. (2009)

	Swi/Snf dependence	Basal transcription (Pol II, H3K4me3)	Nucleosome occupancy in vivo (H3 ChIP)	Nucleosome assembly (in vitro competitive assays)	Induction by alternative stimuli
PRIMARY RESPONSE GENES					
with CpG island	No	Yes	Low	-	TLR 2,3,4: + TNF: + Ifnb: -
w/out CpG island	No	No or Low	High	+	TLR 2,3,4: + TNF: - Ifnb: -
	Yes*	No	High	++	TLR 2: +/- *** TLR 3, 4: + TNF: - Ifnb: +
SECONDARY RESPONSE GENES					
with CpG island**	No	No	High	Not tested	TLR 2: - TLR 3, 4: + TNF: - Ifnb: +
w/out CpG island	Yes	No	High	++	TLR 2,3,4: + TNF: - Ifnb: +

* This group includes an IRF3-dependent subset of genes

** Rare in the dataset by Ramirez-Carrozzi et al (2009)

*** TLR2 is unable to activate IRF3 and the genes it regulates

Thus, genes containing a CpG island in their promoters are generally activated in a manner that does not require chromatin remodeling by Swi/Snf.

The promoter/TSS region of such genes is almost invariantly associated with high levels of chromatin modifications characteristic of active chromatin, including acetylation of lysine 9 and 14 and trimethylation of lysine 4 in histone H3 (H3K4me3) (Table 1). These modifications are constitutive, namely present before any stimulation. Then, how are these modifications established? We can envision at least three different, not mutually exclusive mechanisms. One possibility, in keeping with the data described above, is that nucleosome instability generates features of open chromatin that are somehow recognized by histone acetyltransferases thus leading to their constitutive recruitment. However, H3K4 trimethylation is largely a cotranscriptional modification and its presence suggests the existence of basal levels of transcription (Shilatifard 2006). Data by Hargreaves et al. demonstrate that in fact primary response genes associated with CpG islands are constitutively associated with RNA polymerase II (Pol II) and transcribed (Hargreaves et al. 2009). This basal transcription has very peculiar features: first, Pol II bears a typical modification of early elongating complexes, phosphorylated Ser5 in the carboxy-terminal repeats of its large subunit; conversely, phosphorylation of Ser2, which is characteristic of actively elongating Pol II (Phatnani and Greenleaf 2006), is not present, and this is consistent with the resistance of basal Pol II-mediated transcription to DRB, an inhibitor of the protein kinase that targets Ser2 (Cdk9). A second peculiar feature of basal transcription is that it generates long, unspliced and unstable transcripts, in a manner at least in part dependent on the Sp1 transcription factor (which binds GC-rich sequences). It is likely that it is the process of basal transcription itself (rather than its products) that conveys functionality by recruiting methyltransferases and acetyltransferases to these genes, thus maintaining their poised state. Finally, a third possibility is that specialized domains in components of the H3K4 methyltransferase and histone acetyltransferase complexes bind unmethylated CpG DNA. For instance, the CXXC domain in the mixed lineage leukemia (MLL) protein specifically recognizes unmethylated CpGs (Ayton et al. 2004), thus providing a direct link between the existence of a CpG island and H3K4 trimethylation of the adjacent nucleosomes. Similarly, Cfp1 (CXXC finger protein 1) has a CXXC domain specific for unmethylated CpG DNA (Lee and Skalnik 2005). As Cfp1 is part of the Set1 methyltransferase complexes, which accounts for the bulk of H3K4me3 in mammalian cells (Lee and Skalnik 2008), it may provide a direct link between CpG island and constitutive histone modifications.

Finally, it should not be overlooked that some Swi/Snf independent primary response genes are not associated with a CpG island (Ramirez-Carrozzi et al. 2009) (Table 1). It is possible that activation of these genes require different chromatin remodeling complexes. Alternatively, they may display a nucleotide composition that, similarly to CpG islands, disfavors the assembly of stable nucleosomes.

4 A Role of the Nucleosome Barrier in Stimulus-selective Gene Induction

The data described above indicate the existence of identifiable patterns in the chromatin organization of inducible genes activated by inflammatory stimuli. These different organization schemes have an obvious impact on the enzymatic requirements for transcriptional induction of different classes of genes: while CpG island-containing genes are in a pre-activated state, the others must undergo a more complex series of biochemical modifications to recruit the transcriptional machinery. Such complex changes are signal-dependent and therefore lay the grounds for signal-selective activation of individual genes by different stimuli. At one extreme of the spectrum is a stimulus like TNFα, which is virtually unable to induce Swi/Snf-dependent remodeling and therefore exclusively activates genes with a CpG island and a poised chromatin configuration (Ramirez-Carrozzi et al. 2009) (Table 1). As TNFα is a strong inducer of NF-κB and AP-1, it looks clear that these TFs may be unable to drive Swi/Snf-dependent chromatin remodeling themselves. At the opposite extreme is IFNβ, which activates IRF and STAT family TFs but not NF-κB or AP-1: the genes activated by IFNβ are mainly in the group of those requiring Swi/Snf-dependent chromatin remodeling. Inability to activate NF-κB and AP-1 results in poor or no induction of the majority of Swi/Snf-independent, CpG island-associated genes. The possibility that IRF proteins may be specifically able to activate Swi/Snf-dependent remodeling is strongly suggested by additional evidence. In particular, all IRF3-dependent primary response genes required Swi/Snf for activation (and in nearly all cases these genes were devoid of a CpG island). Therefore, the ability of individual stimuli to activate IRF3 is essential for the induction of a specific subset of primary genes with a repressed chromatin configuration (low acetylation and H3K4me3) in unstimulated macrophages. At these genes it may be envisioned that the role of IRF3 is specifically to recruit Swi/Snf and relieve inhibition by well-positioned and stable nucleosomes. In a sense, this may represent a sort of division of labor between TFs acting to recruit the transcriptional machinery (like NF-κB) and TFs acting to generate a permissive chromatin state (like IRFs). Finally, stimuli acting on TLRs other than TLR3 and TLR4, which are the only TLRs triggering IRF3, are able to induce both Swi/Snf-independent genes and the group of Swi/Snf-dependent genes that do not require IRF3 (Ramirez-Carrozzi et al. 2009). Therefore, the repertoire of genes they induce is somehow intermediate between narrow-spectrum inducers like IFNβ and TNFα, and broad-spectrum inducers like TLR3/4 agonists.

Another important aspect to consider is that while nucleosome positions are to some extent encoded in the underlying sequence (Kaplan et al. 2008), some chromatin remodeling complexes act to constrain nucleosome positions in a manner that maximizes their barrier function. Evidence that this concept holds true in the specific system discussed here is the observation that depletion of the helicase component of the Mi2/NuRD chromatin remodeling complex (Chd4) increases activation of several inflammatory genes (Ramirez-Carrozzi et al. 2006).

5 Chromatin Remodeling and Kinetics of NF-κB Activation: A Complex Interplay

Although kinetics of activation of inflammatory genes are extremely complex (and tend to show inter-experimental variability), it is clear that genes requiring Swi/Snf-dependent chromatin remodeling are, as a group, characterized by slower activation kinetics than those with a poised chromatin configuration (like those containing a CpG island). It is intuitively obvious that these differences reflect the time required by chromatin remodellers to modify nucleosomes and make the underlying DNA accessible. The time lag between the initial stimulus and the completion of remodeling explains why stimuli that induce a short pulse of NF-κB are unable to activate subsets of NF-κB target genes (Hoffmann et al. 2002). Hoffmann et al. found that induction of some NF-κB-dependent genes in TNFα-stimulated fibroblasts required the presence of NF-κB in the nucleus for a relatively long time (more than 2 h), while many other genes were induced even in response to a single and short cycle of NF-κB activity. In mouse fibroblasts a short pulse of TNFα treatment generates a transient NF-κB response that is terminated in about 1 h by newly synthesized IkBα. Pulsed TNFα treatment was unable to induce a subset of NF-κB targets in wild type cells, while it was able to induce these genes in cells lacking IkBα, in which NF-κB activation in response to the same treatment is sustained. As it is unlikely that the absence of IkBα impacts on the response in any other manner than altering its duration, these data demonstrate that alternative kinetics of NF-κB activation directly impact on the transcriptional response, and specifically on the identity of the activated genes. Although data on chromatin configuration of inflammatory genes in fibroblasts are not available, it is likely that the reason why some genes require a long-lasting presence of NF-κB in the nucleus to be activated reflects differences in accessibility to NF-κB, and that such differences are due to alternative nucleosomal patterns or stability. Assuming that similar mechanisms are at play in fibroblasts and macrophages, a short NF-κB pulse will not induce those genes requiring chromatin remodeling to expose critical genomic elements.

Following up this work, two papers by Covert et al. and Werner et al. (Covert et al. 2005; Werner et al. 2005) showed that stimulus-specific differences in the temporal control of NF-κB activity is apparently sufficient to generate distinct biological responses. While NF-κB activity induced by a pulse of TNFα is rapidly attenuated by negative feedback mechanisms (and in particular IkBα resynthesis), NF-κB activity induced by a pulse of LPS in fibroblasts is sustained due to an autocrine loop dependent on TNFα induction and secretion. TNFα and possibly additional cytokines are responsible for the late phase of NF-κB activation and NF-κB-dependent gene induction. Therefore, a source of difference between TNFα- and LPS-induced gene expression programs in mouse fibroblasts is simply that TNFα induces NF-κB activity once, while LPS does it twice, using TNFα as the main inducer of the second wave of activation: the distinct NF-κB activation profiles generated this way resulted in different gene expression profiles, as late expression of several genes was selectively induced by LPS in a TNFα-dependent manner. It is also clear, however, that not all differences between the LPS and the TNFα-induced gene expression programs can be explained by alternative NF-κB activation kinetics. In the mouse fibroblasts studied by Werner et al., at least one-third of the genes induced at an early time point (1 h) were stimulus specific, indicating that the unique signaling properties of each receptor are responsible for selective induction of several genes (Werner et al. 2005).

The idea that the sustained presence of NF-κB in the nucleus is required for the activation of genes whose chromatin configuration is initially not permissive for activation is compatible with two scenarios. One possibility is that the κB sites are anyway constitutively accessible to NF-κB independently of how nucleosomes are distributed, with chromatin exerting an inhibitory effect on downstream events required for gene activation. The second scenario is simply that nucleosomal organization directly interferes with NF-κB binding. The first possibility is somehow suggested by the observation that when κB sites are incorporated in a nucleosome their interaction with NF-κB is not impaired at all (Angelov et al. 2004), a result somehow difficult to reconcile with the several crystal structures reported for NF-κB (which predict that NF-κB cannot contact a site embedded in a nucleosome) (Chen et al. 1998; Huxford et al. 1999; Natoli et al. 2005). The second scenario is supported by several pieces of experimental evidence: the asynchronous recruitment of NF-κB to genes bearing high affinity κB sites (Saccani et al. 2001); the substantial overlap between genes that bind NF-κB with slow kinetics and genes that require remodeling for activation (Ramirez-Carrozzi et al. 2006; Saccani et al. 2001); and finally the evidence that lack of remodeling at secondary genes is associated with loss of NF-κB recruitment (Kayama et al. 2008). Kayama et al. reported the surprising result that the absence of MyD88, a signal transducer involved in TLR signaling, resulted in defective activation of secondary genes regulated by LPS in spite of the absence of major defects in the activation of the main signaling pathways (Kayama et al. 2008). Defective secondary gene expression was associated with lack of remodeling, lack of increase in H3K4me3 and no recruitment of NF-κB to the promoter/TSS region of these genes. These data place recruitment of NF-κB downstream of nucleosome remodeling events and indirectly suggest that in vivo nucleosomes do exert an inhibitory activity on NF-κB binding. At the same time, the results by Kayama et al. demonstrate that signals emanating from the receptor and transduced via MyD88 directly control chromatin remodeling. A simple and reasonable inference is that the final targets of such signals are transcription factors attracting chromatin-remodeling complexes. If this were the case, the inhibitory nucleosome organization at a subgroup of inflammatory genes lays the grounds for synergistic interactions among transcription factors with distinct biochemical activities. While NF-κB is apparently unable to remodel chromatin but is a potent transcriptional activator, other TFs (like IRF3) may invade nucleosomal chromatin and allow subsequent exposure of additional binding sites.

6 Conclusions

The data reviewed here indicate that several features of the inflammatory response rely on the interplay between inflammatory transcription factors like NF-κB and the IRFs, and a defined chromatin organization that is in part "written" in the underlying genomic sequences and in part enforced or antagonized by specialized molecular machines, including chromatin remodeling complexes and the transcriptional machinery (that is ultimately responsible for the constitutive accessibility of several CpG island-containing genes). Nucleosomal organization seems to control the basal access of the promoter/TSS region to the basal transcriptional machinery and the access of NF-κB to its sites in chromatin (in a manner that has not been recapitulated in vitro yet). Nucleosomes may impact not only on the kinetics of activation of inflammatory genes but also on the specificity of activation in response to alternative stimuli. Constitutively accessible genes with a permissive nucleosomal configuration might in general be activated in response to a broad range of inputs since no additional signals are required to remove inhibitory nucleosomes. Conversely, overcoming an inhibitory nucleosomal configuration may require specific signals that not all stimuli are able to switch on.

These concepts provide a general framework, but still cannot describe the response in its complexity. For instance, a major challenge for the future is to understand how cell-type specific outputs in response to similar inputs (e.g. TNF or LPS) are determined. It is clear that differentiated cells of different tissues or organs substantially diverge in their ability to activate the inflammatory gene expression program, both in qualitative and quantitative terms, which likely implies the existence of a functional interface between cell-type specific factors and inflammatory transcription factors (whose expression and mode of action is otherwise rather uniform in different cell types). Whether such differences depend on alternative nucleosomal states remains to be clarified.

Acknowledgments Research in GN lab is supported by the EC FP6 programme (Marie Curie excellence grant Trans-Tar), the FP7 programme (integrated project Model-In) and the Italian Association for Research on Cancer (A.I.R.C.).

References

Angelov D, Lenouvel F, Hans F, Muller CW, Bouvet P, Bednar J, Moudrianakis EN, Cadet J, Dimitrov S (2004) The histone octamer is invisible when NF-kappaB binds to the nucleosome. J Biol Chem 279:42374–42382

Ayton PM, Chen EH, Cleary ML (2004) Binding to nonmethylated CpG DNA is essential for target recognition, transactivation, and myeloid transformation by an MLL oncoprotein. Mol Cell Biol 24:10470–10478

Boeger H, Griesenbeck J, Kornberg RD (2008) Nucleosome retention and the stochastic nature of promoter chromatin remodeling for transcription. Cell 133:716–726

Chen FE, Huang DB, Chen YQ, Ghosh G (1998) Crystal structure of p50/p65 heterodimer of transcription factor NF-kappaB bound to DNA. Nature 391:410–413
Covert MW, Leung TH, Gaston JE, Baltimore D (2005) Achieving stability of lipopolysaccharide-induced NF-kappaB activation. Science 309:1854–1857
Doyle S, Vaidya S, O'Connell R, Dadgostar H, Dempsey P, Wu T, Rao G, Sun R, Haberland M, Modlin R, Cheng G (2002) IRF3 mediates a TLR3/TLR4-specific antiviral gene program. Immunity 17:251–263
Hargreaves DC, Horng T, Medzhitov R (2009) Control of inducible gene expression by signal-dependent transcriptional elongation. Cell 138:129–145
Hoffmann A, Levchenko A, Scott ML, Baltimore D (2002) The IkappaB-NF-kappaB signaling module: temporal control and selective gene activation. Science 298:1241–1245
Huxford T, Malek S, Ghosh G (1999) Structure and mechanism in NF-kappa B/I kappa B signaling. Cold Spring Harb Symp Quant Biol 64:533–540
Janeway CA Jr, Medzhitov R (2002) Innate immune recognition. Annu Rev Immunol 20: 197–216
Jiang C, Pugh BF (2009) Nucleosome positioning and gene regulation: advances through genomics. Nat Rev Genet 10:161–172
Kaplan N, Moore IK, Fondufe-Mittendorf Y, Gossett AJ, Tillo D, Field Y, Leproust EM, Hughes TR, Lieb JD, Widom J, Segal E (2008) The DNA-encoded nucleosome organization of a eukaryotic genome. Nature 458:362–366.
Kayama H, Ramirez-Carrozzi VR, Yamamoto M, Mizutani T, Kuwata H, Iba H, Matsumoto M, Honda K, Smale ST, Takeda K (2008) Class-specific regulation of pro-inflammatory genes by MyD88 pathways and IkappaBzeta. J Biol Chem 283:12468–12477
Lee JH, Skalnik DG (2005) CpG-binding protein (CXXC finger protein 1) is a component of the mammalian Set1 histone H3-Lys4 methyltransferase complex, the analogue of the yeast Set1/COMPASS complex. J Biol Chem 280:41725–41731
Lee JH, Skalnik DG (2008) Wdr82 is a C-terminal domain-binding protein that recruits the Setd1A Histone H3-Lys4 methyltransferase complex to transcription start sites of transcribed human genes. Mol Cell Biol 28:609–618
Mavrich TN, Ioshikhes IP, Venters BJ, Jiang C, Tomsho LP, Qi J, Schuster SC, Albert I, Pugh BF (2008) A barrier nucleosome model for statistical positioning of nucleosomes throughout the yeast genome. Genome Res 18:1073–1083
Natoli G, Saccani S, Bosisio D, Marazzi I (2005) Interactions of NF-kappaB with chromatin: the art of being at the right place at the right time. Nat Immunol 6:439–445
Nau GJ, Richmond JF, Schlesinger A, Jennings EG, Lander ES, Young RA (2002) Human macrophage activation programs induced by bacterial pathogens. Proc Natl Acad Sci USA 99:1503–1508
Phatnani HP, Greenleaf AL (2006) Phosphorylation and functions of the RNA polymerase II CTD. Genes Dev 20:2922–2936
Ponting CP (2008) The functional repertoires of metazoan genomes. Nat Rev Genet 9:689–698
Ramirez-Carrozzi VR, Braas D, Bhatt DM, Cheng CS, Hong C, Doty KR, Black JC, Hoffmann A, Carey M, Smale ST (2009) A unifying model for the selective regulation of inducible transcription by CpG islands and nucleosome remodeling. Cell 138:114–128
Ramirez-Carrozzi VR, Nazarian AA, Li CC, Gore SL, Sridharan R, Imbalzano AN, Smale ST (2006) Selective and antagonistic functions of SWI/SNF and Mi-2beta nucleosome remodeling complexes during an inflammatory response. Genes Dev 20:282–296
Saccani S, Pantano S, Natoli G (2001) Two waves of nuclear factor kappaB recruitment to target promoters. J Exp Med 193:1351–1359
Saccani S, Pantano S, Natoli G (2002) p38-Dependent marking of inflammatory genes for increased NF-kappa B recruitment. Nat Immunol 3:69–75
Segal E, Fondufe-Mittendorf Y, Chen L, Thastrom A, Field Y, Moore IK, Wang JP, Widom J (2006) A genomic code for nucleosome positioning. Nature 442:772–778
Shilatifard A (2006) Chromatin modifications by methylation and ubiquitination: implications in the regulation of gene expression. Annu Rev Biochem 75:243–269

Toshchakov V, Jones BW, Perera PY, Thomas K, Cody MJ, Zhang S, Williams BR, Major J, Hamilton TA, Fenton MJ, Vogel SN (2002) TLR4, but not TLR2, mediates IFN-beta-induced STAT1alpha/beta-dependent gene expression in macrophages. Nat Immunol 3:392–398
Werner SL, Barken D, Hoffmann A (2005) Stimulus specificity of gene expression programs determined by temporal control of IKK activity. Science 309:1857–1861

IKK Regulation and Human Genetics

Gilles Courtois and Alain Israël

Abstract The IKK kinase complex is the core element of the NF-κB cascade. It is essentially made of two kinases (IKKα and IKKβ) and a regulatory subunit, NEMO/IKKγ. Additional components may exist, transiently or permanently, but their characterization is still uncertain. In this review, we will focus on the NEMO molecule, and describe the results which have been obtained, and the hypotheses which have been proposed, to explain how NEMO controls the activation of the IKK complex. NEMO is one of the very few non-redundant components of the NF-κB cascade, and the localization of the gene that encodes it on the X chromosome suggests it is likely to be the target of mutations leading to pathologies: this is indeed the case, and we will also present the current status of our knowledge regarding NEMO-associated pathologies.

Contents

G. Courtois
INSERM U781, Hôpital Necker-Enfants Malades, Paris France

A. Israël (✉)
Unite de Signalisation Moleculaire et Activation Cellulaire, URA 2582 CNRS, Institut Pasteur, 25 rue du Dr Roux, 75724, Paris Cedex 15, France
e-mail: aisrael@pasteur.fr

Current Topics Microbiology (2011) 349: 73-95
DOI: 10.1007/82_2010_98

Published Online: 16 September 2010

1 Introduction

NF-κB represents a family of transcription factors that are normally kept inactive in the cytoplasm through interaction with inhibitory molecules of the IκB family. In response to multiple stimuli, such as inflammatory cytokines, bacterial or viral products, or various types of stress, the IκB molecules become phosphorylated on two critical serine residues. This modification allows their polyubiquitination and destruction by the proteasome. As a consequence, free NF-κB enters the nucleus and activates transcription of a variety of genes participating in the immune and inflammatory response, cell adhesion, growth control and protection against apoptosis.

The kinase(s) responsible for the phosphorylation of the IκB inhibitors have remained elusive for many years, until the biochemical purification of a cytoplasmic high-molecular weight complex migrating around 700–900 kDa and containing two related catalytic subunits, IKKα and IKKβ (Chen et al. 1996; Didonato et al. 1997). An additional component of the so-called IKK complex, NEMO/IKKγ (thereafter referred to as NEMO), has subsequently been identified through genetic complementation of an NF-κB-defective cell line (Yamaoka et al. 1998) and sequencing of purified IKK-associated polypeptides (Mercurio et al. 1999; Rothwarf et al. 1998). Although NEMO does not have catalytic properties, cell lines defective for NEMO are unable to activate NF-κB in response to many stimuli, demonstrating the key role of this protein in the NF-κB pathway.

2 The Kinase Subunits

The two kinase subunits of the IKK complex, IKKα and IKKβ, have been purified and cloned on the basis of their ability to phosphorylate the IκB inhibitors, following biochemical purification of the complex (Didonato et al. 1997; Mercurio et al. 1997). IKKα and IKKβ exhibit a similar structure (50% sequence identity), and include a N-terminal kinase domain, a helix-loop-helix (HLH) which is involved in modulating IKK kinase activity, and a leucine zipper (LZ), whose role is to allow homo- or heterodimerization of the kinases (Fig. 1). In addition, IKKα exhibits a putative nuclear localization signal (Sil et al. 2004), possibly linked to its nuclear activity. IKKβ contains a ubiquitin-like domain whose function is

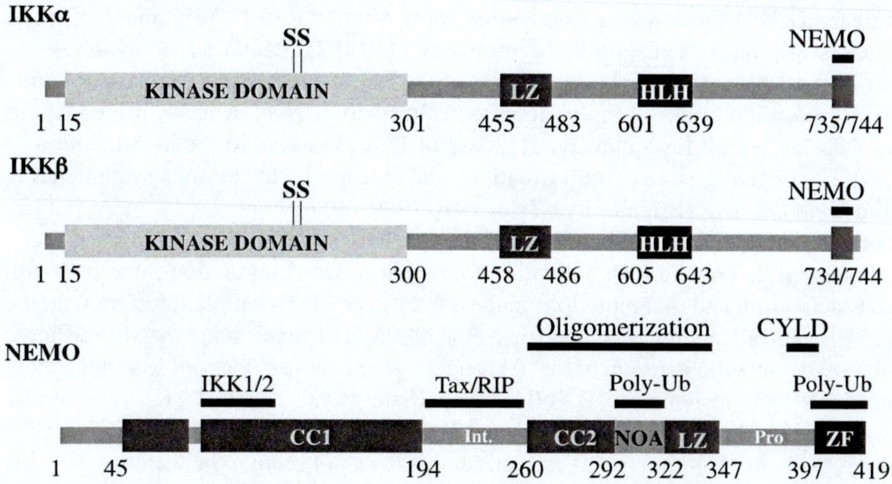

Fig. 1 Structure of the three components of the IKK complex. The IKKα and IKKβ kinase subunits: The domains of the two kinase subunits are indicated. The kinase domain is located at the N-terminus (the two Ser residues of the activation loop are shown: aminoacids 176–180 of IKKα and 177–181 of IKKβ). The function of the leucine zipper (LZ) domain is to allow homo- or heterodimerization of the kinases. The role of the helix loop helix (HLH) domain is less clear, but it seems to be involved in the modulation of the kinase activity. Finally, a $\sim$ 10 aminoacids region at the extreme C-terminus of the kinases is required for their interaction with NEMO. The NEMO molecule: Human NEMO is a 419 aminoacids dimeric molecule essentially structured under the form of a series of parallel intermolecular coiled coils, a probably unstructured region (indicated as Pro for Proline-rich) and a C-terminal Zinc Finger. *CC1* coiled-coil 1, *CC2* coiled-coil 2, *NOA* ubiquitin binding domain, *ZF* Zinc Finger (also an ubiquitin binding domain). The determination of the structure of the region between CC1 and CC2 (Int.) indicated that it is also structured as a dimeric intermolecular coiled coil. The structure of CC1 and Pro has not been determined yet. It must be stressed that the dimeric structure of NEMO is relatively unstable in the absence of interacting partners (kinases, polyubiquitin, etc.). The region of interaction with some of these partners has been indicated: the N-terminus is involved in the interaction with the two kinases. The Intermediate (Int.) region is involved in the interaction with viral transactivators such as HTLV1 Tax and KSHV v-FLIP, as well as with RIP1 (see Fig. 2). The entire C-terminal region is required for transmission of the signal, and the NOA and the ZF domains bind poly-ubiquitin chains

currently unknown, but which does not seem to be recognized by the ubiquitin binding domains which have been tested so far (May et al. 2004).

The interaction domain between the kinase subunits and NEMO lies at the C-terminus of IKKα and IKKβ. Interestingly, a cell-permeable 11 aminoacids peptide derived from the C-terminus of IKKβ (aa 735–745) behaves as a specific inhibitor of NF-κB by inhibiting the IKK–NEMO interaction, and has been proved to be effective in two distinct experimental mouse models of acute inflammation (May et al. 2000).

The exact mechanism by which the kinase subunits get activated remains obscure. However, it is clear that in order to become active they need to be phosphorylated on two Serine residues (Ser 177 and 181 for IKKβ, and Ser 176 and

180 for IKKα) located in an activation loop, similar to a large number of other kinases (Delhase et al. 1999; Mercurio et al. 1997). Mutation of these Serine residues to Alanine prevents activation of the kinases while mutation to Glutamic acid (phosphomimetic) renders them constitutively active, at least in the case of IKKβ. The search for an upstream kinase of IKKs has lead to the identification of TAK1, which at least in certain situations and in response to certain stimuli behaves as a *bona fide* IKKK (Ninomiya-Tsuji et al. 1999; Wang et al. 2001). Indeed, it has been shown that TAK1, which is also an upstream kinase for the JNK pathway, can phosphorylate IKKβ in the activation loop, that its downregulation interferes with IKK activation and that mutations in the TAK1 gene in drosophila interfere with the NF-κB and JNK pathways (Silverman et al. 2003). However, it has also been shown that tissue-specific deletion of the TAK1 gene in the mouse does not lead to a defect in the NF-κB response to B cell antigen (Sato et al. 2005). TAK1 is normally associated with the cofactors TAB 1 and TAB 2 (or TAB 3). While TAB 2 or TAB 3 seem to be involved in NF-κB activation, this does not seem to be the case for TAB 1 (Shim et al. 2005). Another kinase, MEKK3, has also been suggested to act upstream of the IKK complex, as cells lacking MEKK3 are partially defective in NF-κB activation in response to certain stimuli (Huang et al. 2004; Yang et al. 2001). In addition, it has been suggested that two pathways, dependent on either TAK1 or MEKK3, diverge downstream of TRAF6/IRAK1 in the NF-κB response to IL-1β (Qin et al. 2006; Yamazaki et al. 2009; Yao et al. 2007).

3 The NEMO/IKKγ Regulatory Subunit: Structure and Function

The third subunit of the IKK complex is a non-catalytic 48 kDa protein, called NEMO/IKKγ (Fig. 1). Although devoid of catalytic activity, NEMO is absolutely required for the canonical NF-κB activation pathway. Recent X-ray crystallography data indicate that it is essentially a long parallel dimeric intermolecular coiled coil, except for the C-terminus. The N-terminal part of NEMO (aa 47–120 in human NEMO) is responsible for interaction with the kinase subunits (May et al. 2000). The X-ray structure of aminoacids 44-111 of NEMO bound to amino acids 701–746 of IKKβ has been reported recently (Rushe et al. 2008): it forms an asymmetrical four helix bundle made of a parallel NEMO dimer, each monomer being a crescent shape alpha-helix, associated with two mainly helical IKKβ peptides which do not interact with each other.

Interestingly replacement of a phosphoacceptor Ser at position 68 by a phosphomimetic Glu decreases NEMO dimerization and reduces IKKβ binding (Palkowitsch et al. 2008). IKKβ has been suggested to be responsible for the phosphorylation of Ser 68.

The rest of the molecule contains a first coiled-coil (CC1: aa 91–194), a second one (CC2: aa 260–292) followed by a Leucine Zipper (LZ: aa 322–347 in Fig. 1), and a C-terminal ZF (aa 397–419).

Another recent report describes the X-ray structure of the central region of NEMO associated with a fragment of the viral protein vFLIP (Bagnéris et al. 2008). vFLIP is a transactivator encoded by the Kaposi's sarcoma herpes virus (KSHV) whose interaction with NEMO constitutively activates NF-κB. The structure indicates that the region encompassing aa 192–252 also folds into a parallel intermolecular coiled coil. How vFLIP activates NF-κB cannot, however, be deduced from this co-structure.

A breakthrough in understanding the function of NEMO came when it was realized that non-degradative polyubiquitination of the Lys63-linked type played an important role in the NF-κB cascade. It was in 1996 that the requirement of non-degradative protein ubiquitination for IKK activation was first demonstrated (Chen et al. 1996). Later on, biochemical purification and a reconstituted in vitro IKK activation system allowed to demonstrate that TRAF6, an E3 ligase and a component of the NF-κB cascade downstream of proinflammatory molecules such as IL-1β or LPS, associates with a dimeric E2 complex (Ubc13/Uev1a) to generate K63-linked polyubiquitin chains (Deng et al. 2000). This activity seems to be necessary for IKK activation. Another necessary component of TRAF6-dependent NF-κB activation turned out to be a complex containing the kinase TAK1 and its two cofactors TAB 1 and TAB 2 (Wang et al. 2001). This complex is able to phosphorylate IKK in a manner dependent on TRAF6 and Ubc13/Uev1a (although the role of Ubc13 in IKK activation has been challenged (Habelhah et al. 2004; Yamamoto et al. 2006)). Later on, it was demonstrated that Lys63-linked polyubiquitination of several components of the cascade seems to be a general feature of the response to different types of stimuli (Chen 2005). This is in particular the case for RIP1, a kinase and adaptor in the NF-κB response to TNF-α. This modification serves to recruit proteins or protein complexes to polyubiquitinated substrates. Recently, it was demonstrated that NEMO can specifically recognize Lys63-linked polyubiquitin chains, and becomes itself polyubiquitinated following activation of the NF-κB cascade (Ea et al. 2006; Tang et al. 2003; Wu et al. 2006a). While the ability of NEMO to bind polyubiquitin chains is clearly required for its activity, its own polyubiquitination remains poorly understood, and more specifically the function of this modification.

More recently, two publications challenged this relatively unified model: it was first demonstrated, using an in vitro system, that free K63 polyubiquitin chains generated by TRAF6 + Ubc13/Uev1a directly activate TAK1 by binding to TAB 2 (Xia et al. 2009). In addition, unanchored polyubiquitin chains synthesized by TRAF6 and UBCH5C (which are not (exclusively) of the K63 or K48 type) directly activate the IKK complex by binding to NEMO, while autoubiquitinated TRAF6 is unable to do so. Thus TAK1 can be activated by free K63 chains through the ubiquitin-binding domain of its TAB 2 cofactor, while IKK can be activated by free chains of an unknown type, through the ubiquitin-binding domain of NEMO.

Another report (Xu et al. 2009), using an ex vivo ubiquitin replacement strategy, suggests that K63 chains and Ubc13 are required for NF-κB activation by IL-1β, but surprisingly not by TNF-α. TNF-α activation seems to require Ubc5 and the E3 ligase cIAP1, which induce polyubiquitination of RIP1 (see Fig. 3), not restricted to K63-linked chains.

As an example the TNF-α cascade leading to NF-κB activation is shown in Fig. 2: TNF-α induces trimerisation of the TNF receptor, and leads to the recruitment of a number of adaptor molecules including the E3 ubiquitin-ligases TRAF2 (and/or TRAF5) and cIAP, and the kinase RIP1 (other molecules may be recruited but will not be discussed here). Polyubiquitination of RIP1 on Lys 377, by an

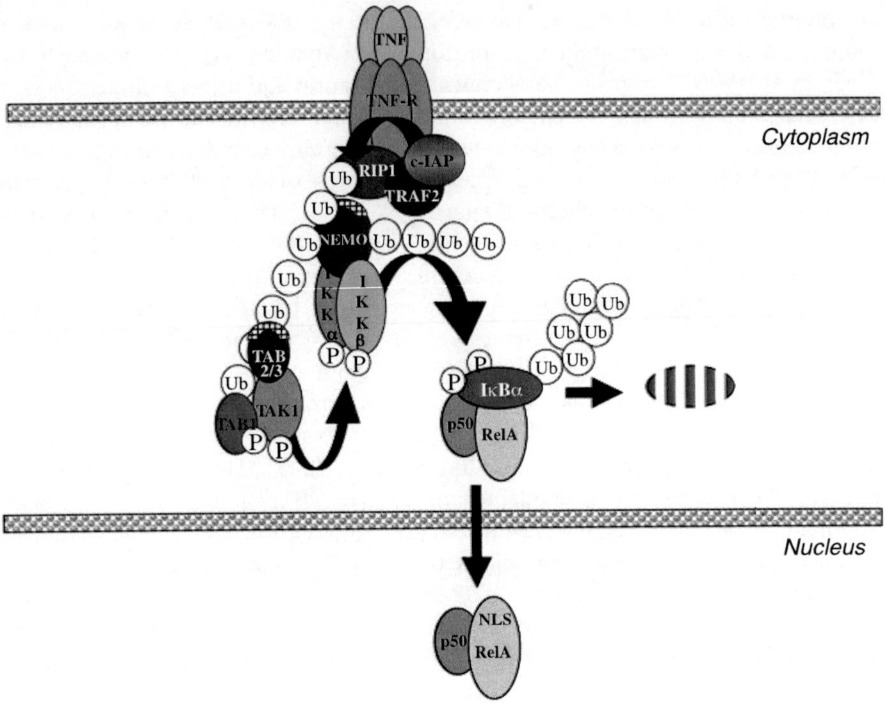

Fig. 2 The NF-κB response to TNF-α, TNF induces trimerisation of the TNF receptor, leading to the recruitment of a series of adaptors including the E3 ubiquitin-ligases TRAF2 (and/or TRAF5) and cIAP, and the kinase RIP1 (other recruited molecules have been omitted for simplicity). Polyubiquitination of RIP1 on Lys 377, possibly mediated by cIAP (*curved arrow*), leads to the recruitment of the TAK1/TAB 1/TAB 2 (or TAB 3) complex, through the ubiquitin-binding Zinc Finger of TAB 2. Through an unknown mechanism this leads to the activation of the TAK1 kinase. The IKK complex is also recruited to these K63 polyubiquitin chains through the ubiquitin-binding domain of NEMO, allowing TAK1 to phosphorylate and activate the IKKs. K63-linked polyubiquitination of NEMO has been observed, but its actual role is currently unclear. One possibility is that it allows recruitment of the TAK1 complex in close proximity to the IKK kinase subunits, allowing their activation by TAK1; alternatively it might allow NEMO oligomerization through cross-recognition by its own ubiquitin binding domain. Irrespective of the exact mechanism of activation of the IKKs, they eventually phosphorylate the IκB inhibitory subunit of NF-κB. IκB is then polyubiquitinated through Lys48-linked polyubiquitin chains by the β-TrCP E3 ubiquitin ligase, leading to its degradation by the proteasome and to nuclear translocation of free NF-κB dimers, ultimately ending in activation of NF-κB target genes

uncharacterized type of chain, possibly mediated by TRAF2/5 or by cIAP1, leads to the recruitment of the TAK1/TAB 1/TAB 2 complex, through the ubiquitin-binding Zinc Finger of TAB 2. Through an unknown mechanism, this leads to the activation of the TAK1 kinase. The IKK complex is also recruited to these K63 polyubiquitin chains through the specific ubiquitin-binding domain of NEMO. Alternatively, NEMO ubiquitination might directly recruit the TAK1 complex, allowing it to phosphorylate and activate the IKKs. Irrespective of the precise mechanism, activated TAK1 phosphorylates IKKβ in its activation loop, leading to its activation and to phosphorylation of the inhibitor IκBα. IκBα is then polyubiquitinated through Lys48-linked polyubiquitin chains and degraded by the proteasome.

The importance of the ability of NEMO to bind ubiquitin has been confirmed by mutagenesis, as well as by the analysis of the mutations found associated with human pathologies (see below). Indeed, mutations in the domain of NEMO allowing recognition of polyubiquitin chains (at aminoacids 311, 315, 319) have been found in patients affected with anhidrotic ectodermal dysplasia with immunodeficiency (EDA-ID) (see below). Database search allowed to narrow down the region of NEMO involved in binding to ubiquitin to a small 30–40 aminoacids domain located in the LZ domain, through identification of four other proteins that contain a similar region and also bind K63 linked polyubiquitin chains; optineurin, and ABIN-1,2,3 (Sebban et al. 2006; Wagner et al. 2008). This region has been termed NOA/UBAN/NUB. Mutations in conserved residues interfere with binding of these proteins to ubiquitin, but the functional consequences are unclear in the case of ABINs as their actual function is still a matter of debate. Regarding optineurin, it has been shown recently that it acts as a negative regulator of TNF-α -induced NF-κB activation by competing with NEMO for binding to polyubiquitin chains (Zhu et al. 2007).

Very recently a combination of X-ray and NMR analysis allowed to characterize the structural basis for recognition of polyubiquitin by the NOA domain (Lo et al. 2009). The data show that the region encompassing aa 265–330 forms a parallel intermolecular coiled coil, with a kink at residue Pro299, which marks the boundary between the CC2 and LZ domains. A combination of mutagenesis and NMR analysis of a NOA-K63 diubiquitin complex reveals that diubiquitin is positioned perpendicular to the coiled-coil and that each ubiquitin contacts both chains of a NEMO dimer. In addition, each ubiquitin interacts asymmetrically with NEMO. A more recent paper presents the crystal structure of the 249–343 region of murine NEMO complexed with K63-linked diubiquitin (Yoshikawa et al. 2009), and shows that two distinct dimers bind only one K63-linked diubiquitin. It is, however, unclear whether such a complex with a 1:4 stoichiometry exists in solution. Finally, another paper proposes a model, based on NMR and mutagenesis, whereby a dimeric NEMO molecule binds two K63-linked polyubiquitination chains which run parallel to the NEMO coiled coil (Grubisha et al. 2009).

Interestingly it has also been shown that NEMO can bind linear chains of polyubiquitin with a high affinity (Iwai and Tokunaga 2009; Lo et al. 2009; Rahighi et al. 2009). The crystal structure of the 250–339 region of murine NEMO with linear diubiquitin (Rahighi et al. 2009) indicates that a coiled coiled NEMO dimer interacts with two diubiquitins and contacts the four ubiquitin moieties, contrary to what is seen with K63-linked diubiquitin (Yoshikawa et al. 2009), where only one ubiquitin moiety per diubiquitin makes contact with NEMO, explaining the higher affinity of linear diubiquitin for the NOA domain. In addition, some of the mutations that specifically affect the binding of NEMO to linear chains interfere with NF-κB activation.

The physiological significance of NEMO binding to linear chains is currently unclear, as is the exact function of this type of chains in cellular metabolism (Iwai and Tokunaga 2009). However, it must be noted that a recent report (Tokunaga et al. 2009) describes the characterization of a dimeric E3 ligase made of two Ring Finger proteins, HOIP and HOIL-1L, which is able to generate linear polyubiquitin chains and to attach them to NEMO, onto Lys 285 and 309. This E3 ligase activity seems to be necessary for an NF-κB pathway which is independent of Ubc13.

To complicate matters further it was shown recently that the C-terminal Zinc Finger of NEMO is also able to bind ubiquitin (Cordier et al. 2009), and that the specificity and affinity of NEMO for K63 chains do not depend on NOA or ZF alone, but require both domains (Laplantine et al. 2009). Therefore, the C-terminal half of NEMO seems to represent a new type of bipartite K63-specific ubiquitin binding domain. Determination of the X-ray structure of a complex between this bipartite module and a K63-linked polyubiquitin chain will be necessary to understand how the specificity is achieved. Interestingly this bipartite module is conserved in two other proteins, ABIN2 and optineurin. These results suggest that the main function of NEMO is to bring its associated kinases to polyubiquitinated targets. This, however, requires some level of specificity and a basal level of affinity between NEMO and its targets, as has been demonstrated for RIP1 (Zhang et al. 2000).

While the role of the ubiquitin binding ability of NEMO is reasonably clear, the role of NEMO polyubiquitination is far less obvious. NEMO ubiquitination, possibly through K63-linked chains, in response to multiple stimuli has been observed (see for example Tang et al. 2003; Yamamoto et al. 2006; Zhou et al. 2004), but the kinetics of this ubiquitination with regard to IKK activation remains unclear: is it an early event required for activation of the IKK complex, or a late event involved in turning down NF-κB activation? It could for example be imagined that NEMO ubiquitination allows direct recruitment of the TAK1 complex (instead of IKK and TAK1 complexes being co-recruited to polyubiquitinated RIP1; see Fig. 2), which could then phosphorylate and activate the NEMO-associated kinases. Alternatively, ubiquitinated NEMO might allow to recruit deubiquitinases such as CYLD or A20, which have been described as negative regulators of NF-κB, through the use of adaptor proteins such as the ABINs or TAX1BP1, which recognize K63-linked polyubiquitin chains (Mauro et al. 2006). From that point of view one interesting observation is the fact that Ubc13-deficient cells are only mildly affected in NF-κB activation, while NEMO ubiquitination is strongly impaired (Yamamoto et al. 2006). The identification of the Lysine residues which are targeted would probably help, but so far only a single site has been unambiguously identified by mass spectrometry: Lys285 is ubiquitinated in response to the NOD2-RIP2 pathway (Abbott et al. 2004). A Lys residue located in the Zinc Finger at position 399 has also been postulated to be an important site of ubiquitination, essentially on the basis of mutagenesis experiments, but has never been confirmed by mass spectrometry analysis. Interestingly this site is located in the middle of the ubiquitin binding surface of the Zinc Finger and its ubiquitination would interfere with NEMO binding to ubiquitin.

NEMO ubiquitination probably implies that it somehow needs to be deubiquitinated. A K63-specific deubiquitinase, CYLD, has been found to interact with NEMO and to behave as a negative regulator of the NF-κB pathway (Sun 2008). CYLD can deubiquitinate NEMO in vitro. Therefore it was postulated that CYLD inhibits the NF-κB cascade by deubiquitinating specific substrates, such as NEMO, RIP1 or others. Unfortunately at the moment the identity of the physiological substrates of CYLD is still unclear. Incidently, other deubiquitinases, such as A20 or Cezanne, exhibit the same K63 specificity and downregulate the NF-κB pathway, but their exact substrates have not been identified yet (Sun 2008).

Although NEMO seems to be essentially dedicated to the NF-κB pathway, it has been shown recently that it also seems to bridge the NF-κB and the interferon regulatory factor (IRF) signaling pathways (Zhao et al. 2007). The IRF3/IRF7 pathway of the innate response to virus infection relies on two IKK-related kinases (TBK1 and IKKε) which phosphorylate the IRF3 and IRF7 transcription factors and allow their nuclear translocation and subsequent activation of their target genes. These two kinases belong to a complex that has been described to include one of three known additional subunits, TANK, NAP1 or SINTBAD (Chau et al. 2008). Zhao et al. (2007) demonstrated that virus-induced activation of IRF3 and IRF7 requires NEMO, which acts upstream of the kinases TBK1 and IKKε. The authors also demonstrate that NEMO does not directly interacts with the two kinases, but binds TANK. The exact role of NEMO in this cascade remains, however, unclear.

4 Other Post-translational Modifications of NEMO

While NEMO ubiquitination has been extensively discussed, few reports deal with NEMO phosphorylation. IKK-dependent phosphorylation of NEMO on Ser 31, 43, 68 and 376 have been suggested to regulate NF-κB activity, but these phosphorylation events have never been confirmed by mass spectrometric analysis (Carter et al. 2003; Palkowitsch et al. 2008). On the other hand, some other phosphorylation sites have been identified by global proteome-wide mass spectrometric analysis, but their actual significance remains unclear.

In parallel a specific NF-κB activating signal, DNA damage, has been studied in details and has revealed the role of a further modification of NEMO, sumoylation. It was first demonstrated that double strand breaks induce NF-κB through an ATM-IKK pathway, raising the question of how a nuclear signal could trigger a cytoplasmic response (Wu and Miyamoto 2007). The conclusion of a series of studies is now that NF-κB activation by DNA-damaging agents is probably mediated by the conjunction of two convergent pathways: DNA damage-induced ATM activation and a parallel stress pathway that causes SUMO-1 modification of NEMO to permit NF-κB activation. Indeed, it was shown that a sumoylated form of NEMO accumulated in the nucleus in response to genotoxic stress, and that this form of NEMO was apparently free (Huang et al. 2003). The sites of sumoylation have been identified as Lys 277 and 309. Additional proteins, PIDD (p53 induced protein with a death domain) and RIP1, were found to associate with NEMO in the nucleus, and to favor its sumoylation, although their exact role remains unclear (Janssens et al. 2005; Wu et al. 2006b). NEMO sumoylation is ATM-independent, but in order to allow NF-κB activation, NEMO must then be phosphorylated by ATM on Lys 85, leading to its monoubiquitination and to the export of a NEMO-ATM complex out of the nucleus (Huang et al. 2003). How this leads to activation of the IKK complex remains, however, unclear, although it might involve the ELKS protein (see below). More recently the SUMO ligase responsible for NEMO sumoylation has been identified as PIASy (Mabb et al. 2006). The interaction between PIASy and NEMO is increased by genotoxic stress, and occurs in the nucleus; NEMO-PIASy and NEMO-IKK interactions are mutually exclusive. A more recent report establishes a link between double-strand breaks and NEMO modification, by demonstrating a critical role for the poly(ADP-ribose) polymerase PARP-1 in this process (Stilmann et al. 2010). The authors demonstrate that PARP-1 senses DNA strand breaks, becomes poly(ADP-ribosyl)ated and assembles a nuclear NEMO/ATM/PIASy complex through recruitment to poly (ADP-ribose) chains. How this event fits into the cascade identified so far is currently unclear. One may wonder what is the role of NF-κB activation in response to DNA damaging agents. A series of reports suggest that NF-κB activation inhibits cell death induced by DNA-damaging anticancer drugs and radiation and thus facilitates malignant cell survival and growth.

5 IKK-Related Genetic Diseases

So far, only one component of the IKK complex, NEMO, has been found to be associated with inherited diseases in humans. Characterization of these diseases and molecular analysis of NEMO mutations causing them, has provided a wealth of information concerning not only the function of this protein in IKK activation, but also the various roles, sometimes previously unsuspected, of the NF-κB signaling pathway in vivo.

5.1 *Incontinentia Pigmenti (IP)*

5.1.1 Main Features of IP

IP (OMIM # 308300) is an X-linked genetic disease which is lethal in males, before the second trimester, and affects females soon after their birth (Cohen 1994; Landy and Donnai 1993). The common feature of the disease, which is highly variable in presentation, is a severe dermatosis which usually starts within 2 weeks after birth and evolves according to a complicated sequence of events. The whole process, which covers months/years, can be divided in four distinct, but sometimes overlapping, stages. First, patients exhibit skin blisters and an inflammatory response, accompanied by a massive eosinophilic granulocytes infiltration into the epidermis (Vesicular Stage/Stage I). Subsequently, verrucous hyperkeratotic lesions develop (Verrucous Stage/Stage II) then disappear over time, leaving behind areas of hyperpigmentation due to melanin accumulation (Hyperpigmented Stage/Stage III). These areas, that follow the lines of Blaschko, generally disappear by the second decade (Atrophic Stage/Stage IV) but adults may still show areas of dermal scarring with lack of hair follicle.

In addition to skin abnormalities, IP patients can also suffer from ophtalmologic, odontological or neurological problems. Ophtalmological problems, which affect approximately 35% of patients, mostly represent abnormalities of the developing retinal vessels. Retinal detachment can be observed as a consequence of a neovascularization following retinal ischemia caused by abnormal peripheral retinal vessels. Odontological problems are characterized by delayed eruption, oligodontia, agenesis, peg-shaped or malformed teeth, supernumerary teeth and supplementary cusps and affect more than 80% of IP patients. Neurological abnormalities, observed in approximately 30% of IP cases, occur during the first weeks of life, which may correlate with the neonatal cutaneous eruption, and includes epilepsy, mental retardation, hemiparesis, spasticity, microcephaly and cerebellar ataxia (Mangano and Barbagallo 1993). In rare cases, the CNS manifestations can be fatal, when seizures lead to death due to severe vascular cerebral damages resulting in thalamic hemorrhage, ischemia and necrosis of both hemispheres. Very little is still known regarding the primary molecular/cellular event(s) causing CNS abnormalities in IP patients. It has been proposed that microvascular ischemia may be a trigger (Hennel et al. 2003), but developmental defects cannot be excluded.

5.1.2 Genetics of IP

The gene responsible for IP has been associated with chromosomal region Xq28, where *NEMO* is located. In 2000, it has been demonstrated that this gene was indeed responsible for the pathology since a PCR analysis of *NEMO* locus in cells derived from IP-affected male foetuses revealed an absence of amplified fragments corresponding to exons 4 to 10 (Smahi et al. 2000). This absence was shown to be caused by a recurrent genomic rearrangement affecting around 70–80% of IP patients. A detailed analysis of the IP rearrangement has demonstrated that it involves not only the gene coding for NEMO but also a *NEMO* pseudogene located nearby in a duplicated region (Aradhya et al. 2001a; Smahi et al. 2000). This inactive pseudogene, which has diverged from the *NEMO* gene quite recently, after the appearance of primates, contains strongly conserved exons (more than 99% identity) equivalent to exons 4–10 of *NEMO*. This sequence similarity, together with other duplicated portions of the *NEMO* region and the presence of repeated sequences located around the *NEMO* gene and pseudogene, favor recombination and causes the recurrent IP rearrangement.

NEMO rearrangement in IP results in the synthesis of a truncated version of NEMO (aa 1–133), which, if stable, would only be able to interact with IKK catalytic subunits (see above). As a consequence, the NF-κB activation process is totally abolished in response to classical inducers of the canonical pathway. Moreover, IP cells are very sensitive to TNF-induced apoptosis, a feature that has important consequences for the development of the disease (see below). Besides this rearrangement, other mutations such as nonsense mutations or frameshift mutations can also affect the *NEMO* gene. Usually, they result in synthesis of a very truncated form of NEMO but not always (see comment below). Interestingly, few missense mutations of *NEMO* have also been identified in IP patients (Fig. 3 and Fusco et al. 2008), suggesting that «discrete» molecular abnormalities are sufficient to generate a full-blown disease (see also below «Molecular characterization of NEMO mutations»).

Irrespective of the type of *NEMO* mutation occuring, an additional parameter impacts upon the phenotype developed by IP patients. X-inactivation skewing, caused by counter-selection of cells expressing the mutation, is often observed. Since the extent of this selection is variable, not only depending on the cell type but also within the same tissue, it has an impact on the final manifestations of the disease. As a striking example, IP patients carrying the same recurrent DNA rearrangement of *NEMO* can exhibit a phenotype ranging from mild dermatosis, without any additional problems, to the most severe form of the disease including abnormalities of the CNS.

5.1.3 Pathophysiology of IP

The sequence of events associated with IP dermatosis has been linked to perturbed cellular interplays whose causes combine both X-linked inactivation, NF-κB signaling in the skin and sensibility of NEMO (–) cells to apoptosis. This complexity has been somehow deconvoluted using various mouse models of the disease, which have allowed identification of several molecules and cell types participating in IP dermatosis.

Nemo invalidation in the whole mouse generates a phenotype very similar to the one observed in IP patients. In particular, males die from liver apoptosis at day E12 whereas females survive till birth but, soon after, develop a dermatosis displaying features typical of IP. Remarkably, similar skin manifestations have also been observed after invalidating *Nemo* or *Ikkβ* specifically in the epidermis, using conditional recombination (Makris et al. 2000; Nenci et al. 2006; Pasparakis et al. 2002). This suggests that keratinocyte dysfunction may be sufficient to trigger the disease. In both strains of mice, it has been shown that IL-1β and TNF-α are likely participants in dermatosis occurrence and development. At very early stages (P2/P3), before detecting any skin abnormalities, an increase of IL-1β synthesis was observed in the epidermis. Interestingly, such accumulation was not seen with *Ikkβ* KO keratinocytes cultured ex vivo. Later on, at P4/P7, an accumulation of TNF-α in the dermis was detected. This cytokine plays a key role in the dermatosis process since crossing the mice with *Tnfr-1* KO mice abolishes all its manifestations. On the cellular side, keratinocytes, as said above, but also macrophages (Stratis et al. 2006) appear to play an important function in IP dermatosis whereas B and T lymphocytes are dispensable.

From these observations, it has been proposed that the mosaic status of the neonatal skin/epidermis of IP females, composed of cells expressing either wild type or mutant NEMO, might be a trigger for the whole dermatosis process. Mutant cells, most likely keratinocytes, would start to over-express pro-inflammatory cytokines such as IL-1β after birth, the reason why remaining uncertain (necrosis of some cells? Dysregulated adaptation to the (bacterial) environment at birth?…). Then, IL-1β would induce TNF-α synthesis by neighbouring wild type cells, and this cytokine would in turn act on mutant NEMO-expressing cells, inducing their death and clearance. This sequence of events may explain the final atrophic stage of IP dermatosis linked to lesion disappearance.

In contrast to what starts to be deciphered concerning the skin abnormalities in IP patients, very little is still known concerning the events occuring in the eyes or CNS. Recently, analysis of the eyes of *Nemo* (−) mice, has revealed retinal arteriolar abnormalities, including luminal narrowing, endothelial cell hypertrophy and basement membrane thickening. Surprisingly, neither obvious vaso-occlusion nor neovascularization was observed (Oster et al. 2009).

5.2 Anhidrotic Ectodermal Dysplasia with Immunodeficiency

Hypomorphic mutations of *NEMO* which do not completely inhibit NF-κB activation have been found to cause another X-linked pathology, EDA-ID (OMIM # 300291) (Aradhya et al. 2001b; Döffinger et al. 2001; Jain et al. 2001; Zonana et al. 2000). This inherited disease affects exclusively males, although in rare occasions affected female relatives exhibit mild signs of IP, and is characterized by a severe immunodeficiency associated with impaired development of skin appendages (hair, teeth and sweat glands).

On the immunodeficiency side, patients suffer from recurrent and life-threatening bacterial and viral infections (Orange et al. 2004a; Puel et al. 2004). The most frequent pathogens are Gram-positive and Gram-negative pyogenic bacteria, such as *S. pneumoniae* and *S. aureus* but some patients also suffer from fungal and viral diseases, including HSV encephalitis. This is, for a large part, caused by impaired functioning of innate immunity receptors which are well known NF-κB activators, such as TLR4 which recognizes LPS from Gram-negative bacteria and other TLRs as well. In addition, adaptive immunity is also perturbed in EDA-ID patients but an homogenous clinical and molecular picture is still difficult to draw. A defect in specific antibody production is often observed, with decreased IgG and increased IgA synthesis, and some patients also exhibit an hyper-IgM syndrome. These B cell defects may be linked to impaired co-stimulation by CD40. In some rare patients, a T cell impairment has also been reported and some have claimed that it may explain high sensitivity to infections by mycobacteria. More consistently found is a problem of NK cell activation, despite a normal cell count and proper development (Orange et al. 2002). It has been proposed that this impairment may explain recurrent infections of EDA-ID patients with viruses, such as herpesvirus and papillomaviruses. In addition, a reduced response to virus exposure might result from defective interferon (IFN) synthesis. Indeed, as mentioned above, NEMO is an essential component of the pathway specifically responsible for IFN class 1 production. In this pathway, NEMO is a partner for TBK-1, the kinase which phosphorylates IRF3 and IRF7, through its interaction with the TBK-1-associated TANK protein.

EDA-ID patients also exhibit impaired development of skin appendages. This observation has provided the first demonstration, through genetic analysis and subsequently confirmed biochemically, that the ectodysplasin/EDAR signaling pathway, which is specifically dedicated to formation of hair, teeth and sweat glands and whose mutations are associated with EDA in humans (Mikkola 2009), is connected to IKK/NF-κB activation through NEMO. Since then, the EDAR receptor has been shown to interact with EDARADD, an adaptor molecule whose mutations can also cause EDA in humans (Headon et al. 2001; Yan et al. 2002), and TRAF6 and TAK1 have been reported to be additional components acting upstream of IKK (Morlon et al., 2005).

In rare cases, EDA-ID can be found associated with osteopetrosis, which is characterized by defective RANK signaling and excessive bone formation, and lymphedema, which is caused by impaired VEGFR3 signaling and development of lymphatic vessels (OL-EDA-ID; Karkkainen et al. 2000). Although NF-κB is a well-known participant in the RANK signaling pathway and is necessary for proper osteoclast function (Leibbrandt and Penninger 2008) it is still unclear how exactly NEMO/IKK participates in the development of lymphatic vessels, although its role in the survival and adhesion properties of endothelial cells composing blood vessels, a developmentaly related tissue, is well established.

In contrast to *NEMO* mutations causing IP, which usually result in severe truncations of the NEMO protein, frameshift or nonsense mutations causing EDA-ID often only remove the NEMO ZF. In addition, a large set of missense mutations have been identified (Fusco et al. 2008). The distinction between IP and EDA-ID, at the genetic level, remains nevertheless far from clear-cut. Indeed, similar truncations affecting the NEMO C-terminus can produce IP in one case and EDA-ID in the other (Fig. 3). Moreover, as mentioned above, missense mutations have also been identified as a cause of IP, while neighbouring ones result in EDA-ID. To further complicate the picture, several male patients suffering from an immunodeficiency syndrome, not associated with EDA, have been reported as mutated in *NEMO* (Niehues et al. 2004; Orange et al. 2004b; Tobin et al. 2003) (Fig. 3). In this case also, it is difficult to establish a clear link between a specific kind of mutations

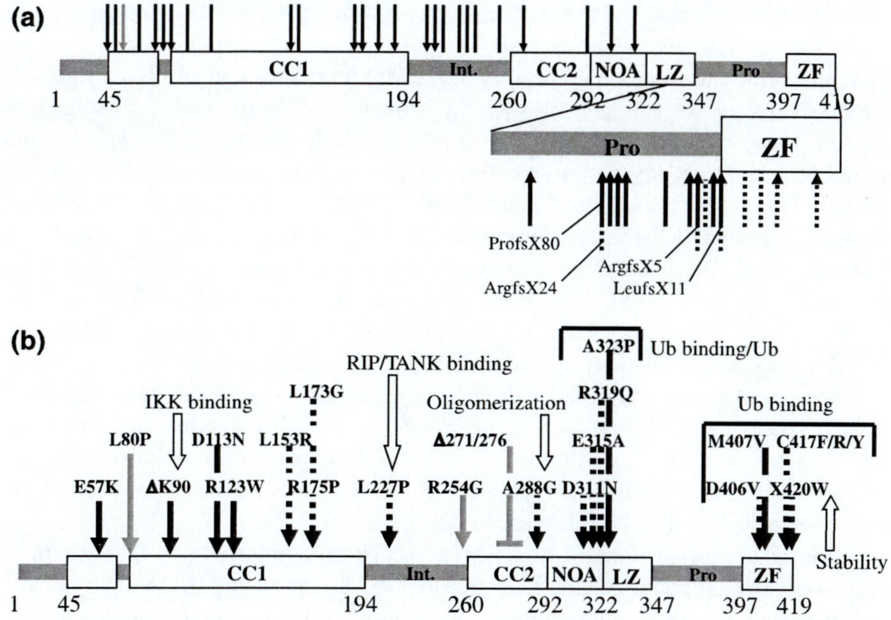

Fig. 3 Mutations of NEMO. **a** Frameshift and nonsense mutations of NEMO. All the mutations, except 110_111insC (ID-related mutation/*gray arrow*), result in C-terminal truncations. Since NEMO contains at its C-terminus a ZF playing an important role in signaling, activity of the protein is already compromised when only part of this domain is missing and EDA-ID is observed. In contrast, a complex clinical picture is observed when truncations affect the Pro-rich domain. Blunted deletions caused by nonsense mutations appear less deleterious than deletions resulting from frameshift mutations which append amino acid sequences of various length and proline content (several exemples are provided with an indication of the substituting residue and the length of the appended tail). Mutation 110_111insC results in the use of an alternative initiation codon located at aa 49, producing an N-terminal truncation of NEMO. *Bars* are for nonsense mutations and *arrows* for frameshift mutations. IP-related mutations are indicated in *black* whereas EDA-ID-related mutations are shown as *dotted lines* or *arrows*. Mutations were compiled by (Fusco et al. 2008) with additions from (Chang et al. 2008; Mancini et al. 2008; Zou and Zhao 2007). **b** Molecular defects associated with missense mutations and short truncations of NEMO. The impact of several IP- or EDA-ID-related mutations on NEMO function have been assessed based on their location within specific domains of the molecule. Analysis of A323P mutation has revealed a defect in NEMO ubiquitination which may be linked to an impaired interaction with TRAF6. Mutation X420W has been associated with destabilization of NEMO based on the direct analysis of protein expression in patient-derived fibroblasts. IP-related mutations are shown as *black arrows*, EDA-ID-related mutations as *dotted black arrows* and ID-related mutations as *gray arrows* or *bars*

and the phenotype displayed by these patients. All these observations provide a quite unique and fascinating example of how an X-linked abnormality affecting a pathway with widespread functions, such as the NF-κB pathway, can affect human physiology with a high level of complexity and diverse outcomes.

5.3 *Molecular Basis of NEMO-Related Pathologies*

The molecular and functional analysis of NEMO mutations causing IP or EDA-ID provides a way to validate in vivo in humans the postulated function(s) or mechanism(s) of action of NEMO. It should also help discovering new important domains and functions of this protein. Through this combined approach the defective step(s) and pathways causing IP and EDA-ID may be better defined, suggesting potential therapeutic options.

From what has been learned recently about the structure of NEMO, some previously uncategorized mutations can now be associated with a specific molecular defect. For instance, a single removal of the ZF occurs at high frequency in EDA-ID patients and can represent, in rare instances, a cause of IP (Fig. 3). In addition, a collection of missense mutations affecting the ZF have been identified in EDA-ID patients (Fig. 4). It has been shown that ZF deletions and mutations C417F, C417R, C417Y within the ZF affect NEMO interaction with polyubiquitinated chains, explaining the impaired NF-κB activation in response to multiple signals (Cordier et al. 2009; Laplantine et al. 2009).

Another important domain of NEMO, the NOA domain which also interacts with polyubiquitinated chains, is frequently mutated in EDA-ID patients (Döffinger et al. 2001; Filipe-Santos et al. 2006) (Fig. 3). Again, defective recognition of ubiquitin interferes with IKK activation following TNF-α stimulation (Rahighi et al. 2009). One mutation located within this part of NEMO, A323P, may in addition affect TRAF6-dependent NEMO ubiquitination (Sebban-Benin et al. 2007).

It has been reported that an EDA-ID-linked mutation, A288G, located in the CC2 region of NEMO, affects its oligomerization and impairs NF-κB activation in response to TNF-α and LPS (Vinolo et al. 2006). Worth noting, this Gly residue appears near Lys 285, which is modified through K63- and/or linear-linked polyubiquitination, suggesting that this process may also be affected.

A set of mutations causing EDA-ID are located in the intermediate domain. It is still unclear how they affect NEMO function but one of them, the L227P mutation, reduces interaction of NEMO with RIP and TANK without affecting the overall conformation of the protein (Sebban-Benin and Courtois, unpublished).

Until now, only one mutation associated with a severe form of IP, ΔK90, has been shown to reduce the interaction of NEMO with the catalytic subunits of IKK (Fusco et al. 2004). Interestingly, the published structure of the NEMO/IKK interaction domain has confirmed that K90 itself establishes contact with the 732 carbonyl of IKK1/IKK2. Nevertheless, a deletion of this residue may also have a broader deleterious impact by affecting neigbouring contact points (NEMO E89/IKKβ D738, NEMO F92/IKKβ T735 or NEMO L93/IKKβ F734).

Finally, the mutation associated with OL-EDA-ID, X420 W, which appends 27 aa at the C-terminus of NEMO, has been shown to strongly destabilize the protein (Döffinger et al. 2001). Nevertheless, it is still unclear whether a simple quantitative defect of NEMO expression is responsible for OL-EDA-ID since other mutations are also associated with reduced NEMO expression but do not generate osteopetrosis or lymphedema.

6 Are there other Components in the IKK Complex?

First, it is important to mention that several types of complexes most likely exist in cells, although this has not been systematically studied: it has already been mentioned that IKKα dimers exist in the absence of NEMO and IKKβ, but it is likely that complexes containing NEMO and a dimer of IKKβ also exist. In addition, free NEMO is also present in cells, independently of the DNA damage response (Fontan et al. 2007; Wu and Miyamoto 2007). The exact stoichiometry of the IKK complex has not been unambiguously determined, and its apparent molecular weight on sizing colums (600–800 kDa) does not help much, as it is essentially due to the elongated shape of NEMO. Based on the most recent structural data, the stoichiometry is probably one NEMO dimer for 2 kinase subunits, but higher order structures may exist. As the IKK complex needs relatively harsh conditions to be purified, one may wonder whether other components exist, besides NEMO and the kinases. The literature has described a large number of potential candidates (see Table 1 in Sebban et al. 2006), identified through two-hybrid screens or coimmunoprecipitation, but it is unclear whether any of these proteins is a bona fide permanent component of the IKK complex. Some of these proteins might just transiently interact with IKK, which would still make them important components of the cascade, but precludes their detailed description within the restricted space of this article. It is, however, worth mentioning the ELKS protein (Ducut-Sigala et al. 2004). Identified as a component of the IKK complex by purification and mass spectrometry, ELKS, a 105 kDa protein, is necessary for full NF-κB activation, and seems to be involved in recruiting IκBα to the IKK complex. As discussed above, ELKS also seems to be involved in the NF-κB response to DNA damaging agents (Wu et al. 2006b).

Chaperones such as hsp90 and hsp70 have also been described as components of the IKK complex (Salminen et al. 2008). Hsp70 seems to behave as a NEMO-interacting inhibitor of NF-κB signaling, while hsp90 associated with its co-chaperone cdc37 behaves as a stabilizing factor of IKK through interaction between cdc37 and the kinase domains of IKKα and IKKβ. However, hsp90 also interacts with other kinases and seems to be a general stabilizer of kinase domain folding.

References

Abbott DW, Wilkins A, Asara JM, Cantley LC (2004) The Crohn's disease protein, NOD2, requires RIP2 in order to induce ubiquitinylation of a novel site on NEMO. Curr Biol 14:2217–2227

Aradhya S, Courtois G, Rajkovic A, Lewis AL, Levy M, Israël A, Nelson DL (2001a) Atypical forms of Incontinentia Pigmenti in males result from mutations of a cytosine tract in exon 10 of NEMO (IKKg). Am J Hum Genet 68:765–771

Aradhya S, Woffendin H, Jakins T, Bardaro T, Esposito T, Smahi A, Shaw C, Levy M, Munnich A, D'Urso M, Lewis RA, Kenwrick S, Nelson DL (2001b) A recurrent deletion in the ubiquitously expressed NEMO (IKK-gamma) gene accounts for the vast majority of incontinentia pigmenti mutations. Hum Mol Genet 10:2171–2179

Bagnéris C, Ageichik AV, Cronin N, Wallace B, Collins M, Boshoff C, Waksman G, Barrett T (2008) Crystal structure of a vFlip-IKKgamma complex: insights into viral activation of the IKK signalosome. Mol Cell 30:620–631

Carter RS, Pennington KN, Ungurait BJ, Ballard DW (2003) In vivo identification of inducible phosphoacceptors in the IKK{gamma}/NEMO subunit of Human I{kappa}B Kinase. J Biol Chem 278:19642–19648

Chang TT, Behshad R, Brodell RT, Gilliam AC (2008) A male infant with anhidrotic ectodermal dysplasia/immunodeficiency accompanied by incontinentia pigmenti and a mutation in the NEMO pathway. J Am Acad Dermatol 58:316–320

Chau TL, Gioia R, Gatot JS, Patrascu F, Carpentier I, Chapelle JP, O'Neill LAJ, Beyaert R, Piette J, Chariot A (2008) Are the IKKs and IKK-related kinases TBK1 and IKK-epsilon similarly activated? Trends Biochem Sci 33:171–180

Chen ZJ (2005) Ubiquitin signalling in the NF-kappaB pathway. Nat Cell Biol 7:758–765

Chen ZJ, Parent L, Maniatis T (1996) Site-specific phosphorylation of IkBa by a novel ubiquitination-dependent protein kinase activity. Cell 84:853–862

Cohen P (1994) Incontinentia pigmenti: clinicopathologic characteristics and differential diagnosis. Cutis 54:161–166

Cordier F, Grubisha O, Traincard F, Véron M, Delepierre M, Agou F (2009) The zinc finger of NEMO is a functional ubiquitin-binding domain. J Biol Chem 284:2902–2907

Delhase M, Hayakawa M, Chen Y, Karin M (1999) Positive and negative regulation of I kappa B kinase activity through IKK beta subunit phosphorylation. Science 284:309–313

Deng L, Wang C, Spencer E, Yang LY, Braun A, You JX, Slaughter C, Pickart C, Chen ZJ (2000) Activation of the I kappa B kinase complex by TRAF6 requires a dimeric ubiquitin-conjugating enzyme complex and a unique polyubiquitin chain. Cell 103:351–361

Didonato JA, Hayakawa M, Rothwarf DM, Zandi E, Karin M (1997) A cytokine-responsive IkB kinase that activates the transcription factor NF-kB. Nature 388:548–554

Döffinger R, Smahi A, Bessia C, Geissmann F, Feinberg J, Durandy A, Bodemer C, Kenwrick S, Dupuis-Girod S, Blanche S, Wood P, Rabia SH, Headon DJ, Overbeek PA, Le Deist F, Holland SM, Belani K, Kumararatne DS, Fischer A, Shapiro R, Conley ME, Reimund E, Kalhoff H, Abinun M, Munnich A, Israël A, Courtois G, Casanova JL (2001) X-linked anhidrotic ectodermal dysplasia with immunodeficiency is caused by impaired NF-kappaB signaling. Nat Genet 27:277–285

Ducut-Sigala JL, Bottero V, Young DB, Shevchenko A, Mercurio F, Verma IM (2004) Activation of transcription factor NF-kappaB requires ELKS, an IkappaB kinase regulatory subunit. Science 304:1963–1967

Ea CK, Deng L, Xia ZP, Pineda G, Chen ZJ (2006) Activation of IKK by TNFalpha requires site-specific ubiquitination of RIP1 and polyubiquitin binding by NEMO. Mol Cell 22:1–13

Filipe-Santos O, Bustamante J, Haverkamp MH, Vinolo E, Ku CL, Puel A, Frucht DM, Christel K, von Bernuth H, Jouanguy E, Feinberg J, Durandy A, Senechal B, Chapgier A, Vogt G, de Beaucoudrey L, Fieschi C, Picard C, Garfa M, Chemli J, Bejaoui M, Tsolia MN, Kutukculer N, Plebani A, Notarangelo L, Bodemer C, Geissmann F, Israel A, Veron M, Knackstedt M,

Barbouche R, Abel L, Magdorf K, Gendrel D, Agou F, Holland SM, Casanova JL (2006) X-linked susceptibility to mycobacteria is caused by mutations in NEMO impairing CD40-dependent IL-12 production. J Exp Med 203:1745–1759

Fontan E, Traincard F, Levy SG, Yamaoka S, Veron M, Agou F (2007) NEMO oligomerization in the dynamic assembly of the IkappaB kinase core complex. Febs J 274:2540–2551

Fusco F, Bardaro T, Fimiani G, Mercadante V, Miano MG, Falco G, Israel A, Courtois G, D'Urso M, Ursini MV (2004) Molecular analysis of the genetic defect in a large cohort of IP patients and identification of novel NEMO mutations interfering with NF-kappaB activation. Hum Mol Genet 13:1763–1773

Fusco F, Pescatore A, Bal E, Ghoul A, Paciolla M, Lioi MB, D'Urso M, Rabia SH, Bodemer C, Bonnefont JP, Munnich A, Miano MG, Smahi A, Ursini MV (2008) Alterations of the IKBKG locus and diseases: an update and a report of 13 novel mutations. Hum Mutat 29:595–604

Greten FR, Arkan MC, Bollrath J, Hsu LC, Goode J, Miething C, Goktuna SI, Neuenhahn M, Fierer J, Paxian S, Van Rooijen N, Xu Y, O'Cain T, Jaffee BB, Busch DH, Duyster J, Schmid RM, Eckmann L, Karin M (2007) NF-kappaB is a negative regulator of IL-1beta secretion as revealed by genetic and pharmacological inhibition of IKKbeta. Cell 130:918–931

Grubisha O, Kaminska M, Duquerroy S, Fontan E, Cordier F, Haouz A, Raynal B, Chiaravalli J, Delepierre M, Israël A, Véron M, Agou F (2009) DARPin-assisted crystallography of the CC2-LZ domain of NEMO reveals a coupling between dimerization and ubiquitin binding. J Mol Biol (in press)

Habelhah H, Takahashi S, Cho SG, Kadoya T, Watanabe T, Ronai Z (2004) Ubiquitination and translocation of TRAF2 is required for activation of JNK but not of p38 or NF-kappaB. Embo J 23:322–332

Headon DJ, Emmal SA, Ferguson BM, Tucker AS, Justice MJ, Sharpe PT, Zonana J, Overbeek PA (2001) Gene defect in ectodermal dysplasia implicates a death domain adapter in development. Nature 414:913–916

Hennel SJ, Ekert PG, Volpe JJ, Inder TE (2003) Insights into the pathogenesis of cerebral lesions in incontinentia pigmenti. Pediatr Neurol 29:148–150

Huang Q, Yang J, Lin Y, Walker C, Cheng J, Liu ZG, Su B (2004) Differential regulation of interleukin 1 receptor and Toll-like receptor signaling by MEKK3. Nat Immunol 5:98–103

Huang TT, Wuerzberger-Davis SM, Wu ZH, Miyamoto S (2003) Sequential modification of NEMO/IKKgamma by SUMO-1 and ubiquitin mediates NF-kappaB activation by genotoxic stress. Cell 115:565–576

Iwai K, Tokunaga F (2009) Linear polyubiquitination: a new regulator of NF-kappaB activation. EMBO Rep 10:706–713

Jain A, Ma CA, Liu S, Brown M, Cohen J, Strober W (2001) Specific missense mutations in NEMO result in hyper-IgM syndrome with hypohydrotic ectodermal dysplasia. Nat Immunol 2:223–228

Janssens S, Tinel A, Lippens S, Tschopp J (2005) PIDD mediates NF-kappaB activation in response to DNA damage. Cell 123:1079–1092

Karkkainen MJ, Ferrell RE, Lawrence EC, Kimak MA, Levinson KL, McTigue MA, Alitalo K, Finegold DN (2000) Missense mutations interfere with VEGFR-3 signalling in primary lymphoedema. Nat Genet 25:153–159

Landy SJ, Donnai D (1993) Incontinentia Pigmenti (Bloch Sulzberger syndrom). J Med Genet 30:53–59

Laplantine E, Fontan E, Chiaravalli J, Lopez T, Lakisic G, Véron M, Agou F, Israël A (2009) NEMO specifically recognizes K63-linked poly-ubiquitin chains through a new bipartite ubiquitin-binding domain. EMBO J 28:2885–2895

Leibbrandt A, Penninger JM (2008) RANK/RANKL: regulators of immune responses and bone physiology. Ann N Y Acad Sci 1143:123–150

Lo YC, Lin SY, Rospigliosi CC, Conze DB, Wu CJ, Ashwell JD, Eliezer D, Wu H (2009) Structural basis for recognition of diubiquitins by NEMO. Mol Cell 33:602–615

Mabb AM, Wuerzberger-Davis SM, Miyamoto S (2006) PIASy mediates NEMO sumoylation and NF-kappaB activation in response to genotoxic stress. Nat Cell Biol 8:986–993

Makris C, Godfrey VL, Krahn-Senftleben G, Takahashi T, Roberts JL, Schwarz T, Feng LL, Johnson RS, Karin M (2000) Female mice heterozygous for IKK gamma/NEMO deficiencies develop a dermatopathy similar to the human X-linked disorder incontinentia pigmenti. Mol Cell 5:969–979

Mancini AJ, Lawley LP, Uzel G (2008) X-linked ectodermal dysplasia with immunodeficiency caused by NEMO mutation: early recognition and diagnosis. Arch Dermatol 144:342–346

Mangano S, Barbagallo A (1993) Incontinentia pigmenti: clinical and neuroradiologic features. Brain Dev 15:362–366

Mauro C, Pacifico F, Lavorgna A, Mellone S, Iannetti A, Acquaviva R, Formisano S, Vito P, Leonardi A (2006) ABIN-1 binds to NEMO/IKKgamma and co-operates with A20 in inhibiting NF-kappaB. J Biol Chem 281:18482–18488

May MJ, D'Acquisto F, Madge LA, Glockner J, Pober JS, Ghosh S (2000) Selective inhibition of NF-kappa B activation by a peptide that blocks the interaction of NEMO with the I kappa B kinase complex. Science 289:1550–1554

May MJ, Larsen SE, Shim JH, Madge LA, Ghosh S (2004) A novel ubiquitin-like domain in IkappaB kinase beta is required for functional activity of the kinase. J Biol Chem 279:45528–45539

Mercurio F, Murray BW, Shevchenko A, Bennett BL, Young DB, Li JW, Pascual G, Motiwala A, Zhu H, Mann M, Manning AM (1999) IkB kinase (IKK)-associated protein 1, a common component of the heterogeneous IKK complex. Mol Cell Biol 19:1526–1538

Mercurio F, Zhu H, Murray BW, Shevchenko A, Bennett BL, Li J, Young DB, Barbosa M, Mann M, Manning A, Rao A (1997) IKK-1 and IKK-2: cytokine-activated IkappaB kinases essential for NF-kappaB activation. Science 278:860–866

Mikkola ML (2009) Molecular aspects of hypohidrotic ectodermal dysplasia. Am J Med Genet A 149A:2031–2036

Morlon A, Munnich A, Smahi A (2005) TAB 2, TRAF6 and TAK1 are involved in NF-kappaB activation induced by the TNF-receptor, Edar and its adaptator Edaradd. Hum Mol Genet 14:3751–3757

Nenci A, Huth M, Funteh A, Schmidt-Supprian M, Bloch W, Metzger D, Chambon P, Rajewsky K, Krieg T, Haase I, Pasparakis M (2006) Skin lesion development in a mouse model of incontinentia pigmenti is triggered by NEMO deficiency in epidermal keratinocytes and requires TNF signaling. Hum Mol Genet 15:531–542

Niehues T, Reichenbach J, Neubert J, Gudowius S, Puel A, Horneff G, Lainka E, Dirksen U, Schroten H, Döffinger R, Casanova JL, Wahn V (2004) Nuclear factor kappaB essential modulator-deficient child with immunodeficiency yet without anhidrotic ectodermal dysplasia. J Allergy Clin Immunol 114:1456–1462

Ninomiya-Tsuji J, Kishimoto K, Hiyama A, Inoue J, Cao ZD, Matsumoto K (1999) The kinase TAK1 can activate the NF-kappaB as well as the MAP kinase cascade in the IL-1 signalling pathway. Nature 398:252–256

Orange JS, Brodeur SR, Jain A, Bonilla FA, Schneider LC, Kretschmer R, Nurko S, Rasmussen WL, Kohler JR, Gellis SE, Ferguson BM, Strominger JL, Zonana J, Ramesh N, Ballas ZK, Geha RS (2002) Deficient natural killer cell cytotoxicity in patients with IKK-gamma/NEMO mutations. J Clin Invest 109:1501–1509

Orange JS, Jain A, Ballas ZK, Schneider LC, Geha RS, Bonilla FA (2004a) The presentation and natural history of immunodeficiency caused by nuclear factor kappaB essential modulator mutation. J Allergy Clin Immunol 113:725–733

Orange JS, Levy O, Brodeur SR, Krzewski K, Roy RM, Niemela JE, Fleisher TA, Bonilla FA, Geha RS (2004b) Human nuclear factor kappa B essential modulator mutation can result in immunodeficiency without ectodermal dysplasia. J Allergy Clin Immunol 114:650–656

Oster SF, McLeod DS, Otsuji T, Goldberg MF, Lutty GA (2009) Preliminary ocular histopathological observations on heterozygous NEMO-deficient mice. Exp Eye Res 88:613–616

Palkowitsch L, Leidner J, Ghosh S, Marienfeld RB (2008) Phosphorylation of serine 68 in the IkappaB kinase (IKK)-binding domain of NEMO interferes with the structure of the IKK complex and tumor necrosis factor-alpha-induced NF-kappaB activity. J Biol Chem 283: 76–86

Pasparakis M, Courtois G, Hafner M, Schmidt-Supprian M, Nenci A, Toksoy A, Krampert M, Goebeler M, Gillitzer R, Israël A, Krieg T, Rajewsky K, Haase I (2002) TNF-mediated inflammatory skin disease in mice with epidermis-specific deletion of IKK2. Nature 417:861–866

Puel A, Picard C, Ku CL, Smahi A, Casanova JL (2004) Inherited disorders of NF-kappaB-mediated immunity in man. Curr Opin Immunol 16:34–41

Qin J, Yao J, Cui G, Xiao H, Kim TW, Fraczek J, Wightman P, Sato S, Akira S, Puel A, Casanova JL, Su B, Li X (2006) TLR8-mediated NF-kappaB and JNK activation are TAK1-independent and MEKK3-dependent. J Biol Chem 281:21013–21021

Rahighi S, Ikeda F, Kawasaki M, Akutsu M, Suzuki N, Kato R, Kensche T, Uejima T, Bloor S, Komander D, Randow F, Wakatsuki S, Dikic I (2009) Specific recognition of linear ubiquitin chains by NEMO is important for NF-kappaB activation. Cell 136:1098–1109

Rothwarf DM, Zandi E, Natoli G, Karin M (1998) IKK-g is an essential regulatory subunit of the IkB kinase complex. Nature 395:297–300

Rushe M, Silvian L, Bixler S, Chen LL, Cheung A, Bowes S, Cuervo H, Berkowitz S, Zheng T, Guckian K, Pellegrini M, Lugovskoy A (2008) Structure of a NEMO/IKK-associating domain reveals architecture of the interaction site. Structure 16:798–808

Salminen A, Paimela T, Suuronen T, Kaarniranta K (2008) Innate immunity meets with cellular stress at the IKK complex: regulation of the IKK complex by HSP70 and HSP90. Immunol Lett 117:9–15

Sato S, Sanjo H, Takeda K, Ninomiya-Tsuji J, Yamamoto M, Kawai T, Matsumoto K, Takeuchi O, Akira S (2005) Essential function for the kinase TAK1 in innate and adaptive immune responses. Nat Immunol 6:1087–1095

Schmidt-Supprian M, Bloch W, Courtois G, Addicks K, Israël A, Rajewsky K, Pasparakis M (2000) NEMO/IKK gamma-deficient mice model Incontinentia Pigmenti. Mol Cell 5:981–992

Sebban H, Yamaoka S, Courtois G (2006) Posttranslational modifications of NEMO and its partners in NF-kappaB signaling. Trends Cell Biol 16:569–577

Sebban-Benin H, Pescatore A, Fusco F, Pascuale V, Gautheron J, Yamaoka S, Moncla A, Ursini MV, Courtois G (2007) Identification of TRAF6-dependent NEMO polyubiquitination sites through analysis of a new NEMO mutation causing incontinentia pigmenti. Hum Mol Genet 16:2805–2815

Shim JH, Xiao C, Paschal AE, Bailey ST, Rao P, Hayden MS, Lee KY, Bussey C, Steckel M, Tanaka N, Yamada G, Akira S, Matsumoto K, Ghosh S (2005) TAK1, but not TAB 1 or TAB 2, plays an essential role in multiple signaling pathways in vivo. Genes Dev 19:2668–2681

Sil AK, Maeda S, Sano Y, Roop DR, Karin M (2004) IkappaB kinase-alpha acts in the epidermis to control skeletal and craniofacial morphogenesis. Nature 428:660–664

Silverman N, Zhou R, Erlich RL, Hunter M, Bernstein E, Schneider D, Maniatis T (2003) Immune activation of NF-kappaB and JNK requires Drosophila TAK1. J Biol Chem 278:48928–48934

Smahi A, Courtois G, Vabres P, Yamaoka S, Heuertz S, Munnich A, Israël A, Heiss NS, Klauck S, Kioschis P, Wiemann S, Poustka A, Esposito T, Bardaro T, Gianfrancesco F, Ciccodicola A, D'Urso M, Woffendin H, Jakins T, Donnai D, Stewart H, Kenwrick S, Aradhya S, Yamagata T, Levy M, Lewis RA, Nelson DL (2000) Genomic rearrangement in NEMO impairs NF-kB activation and is a cause of Incontinentia Pigmenti. Nature 405:466–472

Stilmann M, Hinz M, Arslan S, Zimmer A, Schreiber V, Scheidereit C (2010) A nuclear poly(ADP-Ribose)-dependent signalosome confers DNA damage-induced IkappaB kinase activation. Mol Cell 36:365–378

Stratis A, Pasparakis M, Rupec RA, Markur D, Hartmann K, Scharffetter-Kochanek K, Peters T, van Rooijen N, Krieg T, Haase I (2006) Pathogenic role for skin macrophages in a mouse model of keratinocyte-induced psoriasis-like skin inflammation. J Clin Invest 116:2094–2104

Sun SC (2008) Deubiquitylation and regulation of the immune response. Nat Rev Immunol 8:501–511

Tang ED, Wang CY, Xiong Y, Guan KL (2003) A role for NF-kappaB essential modifier/IkappaB kinase-gamma (NEMO/IKKgamma) ubiquitination in the activation of the IkappaB kinase complex by tumor necrosis factor-alpha. J Biol Chem 278:37297–37305

Tobin E, Rohwedder A, Holland SM, Philips B, Carlson JA (2003) Recurrent 'sterile' verrucous cyst abscesses and epidermodysplasia verruciformis-like eruption associated with idiopathic CD4 lymphopenia. Br J Dermatol 149:627–633

Tokunaga F, Sakata S, Saeki Y, Satomi Y, Kirisako T, Kamei K, Nakagawa T, Kato M, Murata S, Yamaoka S, Yamamoto M, Akira S, Takao T, Tanaka K, Iwai K (2009) Involvement of linear polyubiquitylation of NEMO in NF-kappaB activation. Nat Cell Biol 11:123–132

Vinolo E, Sebban H, Chaffotte A, Israel A, Courtois G, Veron M, Agou F (2006) A point mutation in NEMO associated with anhidrotic ectodermal dysplasia with immunodeficiency pathology results in destabilization of the oligomer and reduces lipopolysaccharide- and tumor necrosis factor-mediated NF-kappa B activation. J Biol Chem 281:6334–6348

Wagner S, Carpentier I, Rogov V, Kreike M, Ikeda F, Lohr F, Wu CJ, Ashwell JD, Dotsch V, Dikic I, Beyaert R (2008) Ubiquitin binding mediates the NF-kappaB inhibitory potential of ABIN proteins. Oncogene 27:3739–3745

Wang C, Deng L, Hong M, Akkaraju GR, Inoue J, Chen ZJ (2001) TAK1 is a ubiquitin-dependent kinase of MKK and IKK. Nature 412:346–351

Wu CJ, Conze DB, Li T, Srinivasula SM, Ashwell JD (2006a) NEMO is a sensor of Lys 63-linked polyubiquitination and functions in NF-kappaB activation. Nat Cell Biol 8:398–406

Wu ZH, Miyamoto S (2007) Many faces of NF-kappaB signaling induced by genotoxic stress. J Mol Med 85:1187–1202

Wu ZH, Shi Y, Tibbetts RS, Miyamoto S (2006b) Molecular linkage between the kinase ATM and NF-{kappa}B signaling in response to genotoxic stimuli. Science 311:1141–1146

Xia Z, Sun L, Chen X, Pineda G, Jiang X, Adhikari A, Zeng W, Chen Z (2009) Direct activation of protein kinases by unanchored polyubiquitin chains. Nature 461:114–120

Xu M, Skaug B, Zeng W, Chen ZJ (2009) A ubiquitin replacement strategy in human cells reveals distinct mechanisms of IKK activation by TNFalpha and IL-1beta. Mol Cell 36:302–314

Yamamoto M, Okamoto T, Takeda K, Sato S, Sanjo H, Uematsu S, Saitoh T, Yamamoto N, Sakurai H, Ishii KJ, Yamaoka S, Kawai T, Matsuura Y, Takeuchi O, Akira S (2006) Key function for the Ubc13 E2 ubiquitin-conjugating enzyme in immune receptor signaling. Nat Immunol 7:962–970

Yamaoka S, Courtois G, Bessia C, Whiteside ST, Weil R, Agou F, Kirk HE, Kay RJ, Israël A (1998) Complementation cloning of NEMO, a component of the IkB kinase complex essential for NF-kB activation. Cell 93:1231–1240

Yamazaki K, Gohda J, Kanayama A, Miyamoto Y, Sakurai H, Yamamoto M, Akira S, Hayashi H, Su B, Inoue J (2009) Two mechanistically and temporally distinct NF-kappaB activation pathways in IL-1 signaling. Sci Signal 2:ra66

Yan M, Zhang Z, Brady JR, Schilbach S, Fairbrother WJ, Dixit VM (2002) Identification of a novel death domain-containing adaptor molecule for ectodysplasin-A receptor that is mutated in crinkled mice. Curr Biol 12:409–413

Yang J, Lin Y, Guo Z, Cheng J, Huang J, Deng L, Liao W, Chen Z, Liu Z, Su B (2001) The essential role of MEKK3 in TNF-induced NF-kappaB activation. Nat Immunol 2:620–624

Yao J, Kim TW, Qin J, Jiang Z, Qian Y, Xiao H, Lu Y, Qian W, Gulen MF, Sizemore N, DiDonato J, Sato S, Akira S, Su B, Li X (2007) Interleukin-1 (IL-1)-induced TAK1-dependent versus MEKK3-dependent NFkappaB activation pathways bifurcate at IL-1 receptor-associated kinase modification. J Biol Chem 282:6075–6089

Yoshikawa A, Sato Y, Yamashita M, Mimura H, Yamagata A, Fukai S (2009) Crystal structure of the NEMO ubiquitin-binding domain in complex with Lys 63-linked di-ubiquitin. FEBS Lett 583:3317–3322

Zhang SQ, Kovalenko A, Cantarella G, Wallach D (2000) Recruitment of the IKK signalosome to the p55 TNF receptor: RIP and A20 bind to NEMO (IKKgamma) upon receptor stimulation. Immunity 12:301–311

Zhao T, Yang L, Sun Q, Arguello M, Ballard DW, Hiscott J, Lin R (2007) The NEMO adaptor bridges the nuclear factor-kappaB and interferon regulatory factor signaling pathways. Nat Immunol 8:592–600

Zhou H, Wertz I, O'Rourke K, Ultsch M, Seshagiri S, Eby M, Xiao W, Dixit VM (2004) Bcl10 activates the NF-kappaB pathway through ubiquitination of NEMO. Nature 427:167–171

Zhu G, Wu CJ, Zhao Y, Ashwell JD (2007) Optineurin negatively regulates TNFalpha-induced NF-kappaB activation by competing with NEMO for ubiquitinated RIP. Curr Biol 17:1438–1443

Zonana J, Elder ME, Schneider LC, Orlow SJ, Moss C, Golabi M, Shapira SK, Farndon PA, Wara DW, Emmal SA, Ferguson BM (2000) A novel X-linked disorder of immune deficiency and hypohidrotic ectodermal dysplasia is allelic to incontinentia pigmenti and due to mutations in IKK-gamma (NEMO). Am J Hum Genet 67:1555–1562

Zou CC, Zhao ZY (2007) Clinical and molecular analysis of NF-kappaB essential modulator in Chinese incontinentia pigmenti patients. Int J Dermatol 46:1017–1022

Control of NF-κB Activity by Proteolysis

Véronique Baud and Emmanuel Derudder

Abstract NF-κB transcription factors are critical regulators of many biological processes such as innate and adaptive immune responses, inflammation, cell proliferation and programmed cell death. This versatility necessitates a highly complex and tightly coordinated control of the signaling pathways leading to their activation. Here, we review the role of proteolysis in the regulation of NF-κB activity, more specifically the contribution of the well-known ubiquitin–proteasome system and the involvement of proteolytic activity of caspases and calpains.

Contents

V. Baud (✉)
Institut Cochin, Université Paris Descartes, CNRS (UMR 8104), Paris, France
e-mail: veronique.baud@inserm.fr

V. Baud
Inserm, U1016, Paris, France

E. Derudder
Program in Cellular and Molecular Medicine at Children's Hospital, Immune Disease Institute, Harvard Medical School, Boston, MA, USA

Current Topics Microbiology (2011) 349: 97-114
DOI: 10.1007/82_2010_101

Published Online: 26 January 2011

The NF-κB family of transcription factors was characterized as a constitutive DNA-binding activity that recognizes the intronic enhancer of the Immunoglobulin κ light chain locus in B cells (Sen and Baltimore 1986). Before long, it became apparent that this activity could be induced by the degradation of an inhibitory molecule named IκB (Inhibitor of NF-κB) (Baeuerle and Baltimore 1988; Davis et al. 1991; Haskill et al. 1991; Henkel et al. 1993; Mellits et al. 1993; Tewari et al. 1992). These original findings opened the way to the realization of the crucial and intricate role played by proteolysis in the regulation of NF-κB signaling.

1 Regulation of NF-κB Activity by the Proteasome

1.1 The Ubiquitin and Proteasome System

The 26S proteasome is a major regulator of protein degradation within a cell (Finley 2009; Navon and Ciechanover 2009; Schrader et al. 2009). This barrel-shaped complex is composed of a central 20S core particle flanked by one or two 19S regulatory particles. While the core particle is responsible for proteolysis due to the presence of caspase-, trypsin-, and chemotrypsin-like activities, the regulatory particle plays a role in recognition and unfolding of target proteins, as well as access of substrates to the core particle. The recognition of a protein by the proteasome requires its prior modification by ubiquitination on the ε-NH_2 group of a specific lysine (K). Ubiquitin is a polypeptide of 76 amino acids which contains seven lysines allowing the generation of ubiquitin chains with different regulatory properties, of which K48-linked polyubiquitination is key for proteasomal degradation (Navon and Ciechanover 2009; Schrader et al. 2009). The first step in the polyubiquitination process is the "activation" of ubiquitin by an ubiquitin-activating enzyme (E1). The E1 then passes ubiquitin to an ubiquitin-conjugating enzyme (E2). Finally, E2 cooperates with an E3 ubiquitin ligase to ubiquitinate target proteins. This cascade repeats itself until a full chain of ubiquitin is attached to the target. E3 ubiquitin ligases are divided into two families depending on the presence of a RING (Really Interesting New Gene) domain or an HECT (Homologous to E6-AP C-Terminus) domain (Jackson et al. 2000). E3 ligases of the RING family bring E2 and substrate together for a direct reaction, whereas ubiquitin is first transferred to E3 ligases of the HECT family before being covalently linked to a lysine residue of the substrate.

1.2 Degradation of "small" IκBs

In mammals, stimulation of various receptors, such as Tumor Necrosis Factor Receptor (TNFR) or Toll Like Receptors (TLRs), triggers the degradation of the

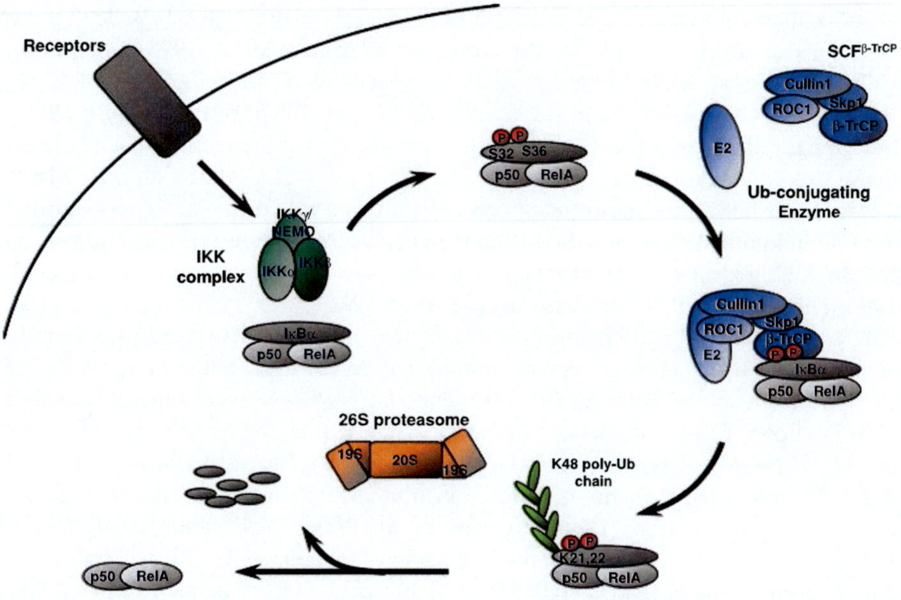

Fig. 1 IκBα degradation upon induction of the NF-κB canonical pathway. Activation of a specific set of receptors, including TNFR and TLRs, leads to the phosphorylation (P) of IκBα on serines 32 and 36 by the IKK complex, which comprises the structural protein IKKγ/NEMO and the two kinases IKKα and IKKβ. This modification creates a docking site for the E3 ligase SCF$^{β\text{-TrCP}}$, resulting in the recruitment to IκBα of an ubiquitin-conjugating enzyme (E2), such as CDC34 and members of the UbcH5 family. The E2 then catalyzes the addition of a K48-linked polyubiquitin chain on lysines 21 or 22 of IκBα. This promotes IκBα recognition and degradation by the 26S proteasome, thus releasing the prototypical p50:RelA dimer which in turn activates the transcription of its specific target genes

"small" IκB inhibitory proteins, IκBα, IκBβ, and IκBε (Fig. 1) (Vallabhapurapu and Karin 2009). A critical step in this process is the phosphorylation by the IκB kinase (IKK) complex of two specific serines within the N-terminal domain of the "small" IκBs, namely, serines 32 and 36 of IκBα, serines 29 and 23 of IκBβ, and serines 18 and 22 of IκBε (Brown et al. 1995; DiDonato et al. 1996, 1997; Mercurio et al. 1997; Regnier et al. 1997; Rothwarf et al. 1998; Weil et al. 1997; Whiteside et al. 1995, 1997; Woronicz et al. 1997; Yamaoka et al. 1998; Zandi et al. 1997). These phosphorylated serines are embedded in a DpSGXXpS (D aspartic acid; pS phospho-serine; G glycine; and X any residue) phosphodegron motif recognized by the multisubunit SCF$^{β\text{-TrCP}}$ E3 ligase (Fuchs et al. 1999; Hatakeyama et al. 1999; Kroll et al. 1999; Shirane et al. 1999; Spencer et al. 1999; Tan et al. 1999; Winston et al. 1999; Wu and Ghosh 1999; Yaron et al. 1998). The SCF$^{β\text{-TrCP}}$ complex comprises the substrate-interacting F-box β-TrCP1 or β-TrCP2, and the subunits Skp1, Cullin1, and ROC1 (Fig. 1). Skp1 links β-TrCP1/2 to Cullin1 which in cooperation with ROC1 recruits and activates the E2 ubiquitin-conjugating enzyme (Jackson et al. 2000). E2s, such as UbcH5 family members and

CDC34, then catalyze the addition of a polyubiquitin chain to the IκBs leading to their subsequent degradation by the proteasome (Alkalay et al. 1995; Chen et al. 1995; Gonen et al. 1999; Shirane et al. 1999; Spencer et al. 1999; Strack et al. 2000; Vuillard et al. 1999; Weil et al. 1997; Whiteside et al. 1997; Wu and Ghosh 1999). Intriguingly, the requirement of the DpSGXXpS motif for the recruitment of the E3 ligase may not be as stringent for IκBε as for IκBα and IκBβ. Indeed, an IκBε S18A, S22A (S serine; A alanine) mutant can still interact with $SCF^{\beta\text{-TrCP}}$, although the ensuing ubiquitination is impaired (Shirane et al. 1999). While IκBα is modified on K21 or K22, acceptor lysine residues are still elusive for IκBβ and IκBε (Baldi et al. 1996; DiDonato et al. 1996; Scherer et al. 1995; Weil et al. 1997; Whiteside et al. 1997). Of note, the participation of E2s in the degradation of IκBs was mainly characterized using in vitro reconstitution assays. However cellular expression of catalytically inactive mutants of UbcH5 and CDC34 E2s impaired the degradation of IκBα upon TNFα stimulation, thus supporting a role for these enzymes in the control of NF-κB activity in vivo (Gonen et al. 1999). Interestingly, β-TrCP1 and β-TrCP2 both contribute to IκBα degradation in spite of their distinct nucleo-cytoplasmic distribution (Guardavaccaro et al. 2003; Nakayama et al. 2003). β-TrCP1 is predominantly detected in the nucleus, whereas β-TrCP2 is described as a cytoplasmic protein (Davis et al. 2002). It suggests, in agreement with the ability of IκBα and IκBε to shuttle between the nucleus and cytoplasm, that "small" IκB polyubiquitination may take place in different cellular compartments (Hayden and Ghosh 2004).

Cactus, the "small" IκB homologue in drosophila, contains five serines (S74, S78, S82, S83, and S116) that are all required for optimal signal-induced Cactus degradation (Fernandez et al. 2001; Reach et al. 1996). Serines 78 and 82 are embedded in a phosphodegron motif similar to that of IκBα. In addition, Slimb, the drosophila β-TrCP, has been reported to participate in Cactus degradation, thus implying again proteasome-mediated proteolysis (Spencer et al. 1999). This evolutionary conserved mechanism underscores the crucial role played by "small" IκBs in the regulation of NF-κB activity.

1.3 Processing and Degradation of NF-κB1 and NF-κB2 Precursors

NF-κB1 and NF-κB2, the precursors of p50 and p52, respectively, are atypical NF-κB molecules that also belong to the IκB family, owing to the presence of an ankyrin domain in their C-terminus (Vallabhapurapu and Karin 2009).

In resting cells, constitutive generation of p50 occurs concurrently to its mRNA translation (Lin et al. 1998). Two regions, the acidic region (residues 446–454) and the glycine-rich region (residues 372–404) of the nascent protein regulate its proteolysis into p50 (Orian et al. 1999, 2000). While the acidic region promotes the addition of polyubiquitin chains onto lysines 441 and 442, the glycine-rich region acts as a stop signal for the proteasome (Orian et al. 1999). Remarkably, the association of NF-κB molecules with the nascent p105 polypeptide favors the synthesis of the full precursor, hence, generating a pool of inactive NF-κB (Cohen et al. 2001; Lin et al. 1998). Although constitutive processing of NF-κB1 into p50 seems to generate the major pool of p50, a mechanism of inducible processing was also reported via the activation of the IKK complex (Cohen et al. 2004).

NF-κB2 processing to p52 shares many features with the generation of p50. Basal level of p52 generation was also reported to depend on proteasome activity in a co-translational manner, the glycine rich region acting as a stop signal to prevent complete degradation (Heusch et al. 1999). Nonetheless, in contrast to p50, generation of p52 seems to be primarily inducible upon engagement of receptors such as CD40, BAFF- and lymphotoxin-β receptors (Vallabhapurapu and Karin 2009). While the sequence of events leading to NF-κB2 processing into p52 is not fully elucidated, it seems that NIK binding to NF-κB2 facilitates the recruitment and subsequent activation of IKKα (Dejardin et al. 2002; Ling et al. 1998; Senftleben et al. 2001; Xiao et al. 2004), which in turn phosphorylates several serine residues within NF-κB2. Serines 866 and 870 appear to be essential for the regulation of NF-κB2 processing as mutations of these two serines in alanines prevent the generation of p52 (Xiao et al. 2001, 2004). Once phosphorylated, NF-κB2 interacts with $SCF^{\beta\text{-TrCP}}$, which promotes the addition of degradative K48-polyubiquitin chain onto lysine 855 by an E2, possibly of the UbcH5 family (Amir et al. 2004; Fong and Sun 2002; Xiao et al. 2004). This leads to the degradation of the C-terminal ankyrin domain of the precursor and the generation of p52-containing dimers such as RelB:p52. NF-κB2 has also been shown to control the activity of RelA:p50 and RelB:p50 dimers, the release from NF-κB2 inhibition being activated in response to lymphotoxin-β receptor signaling by a still unclear mechanism (Basak et al. 2007; Derudder et al. 2003).

Beyond processing, the activity of NF-κB can also be regulated by complete degradation of the precursors. Upon cell stimulation by TNFα or IL-1, NF-κB1 is phosphorylated by the IKK complex on serines 923, 927, and 932 within its C-terminal PEST domain (Beinke et al. 2002; Heissmeyer et al. 1999, 2001; Lang et al. 2003; Salmeron et al. 2001). These three serines are embedded in two motifs that are much similar to the phosphodegron present in IκBα. Their phosphorylation promotes the recruitment of $SCF^{\beta\text{-TrCP}}$ and subsequent ubiquitination and degradation of NF-κB1 by the proteasome (Cohen et al. 2004; Heissmeyer et al. 2001; Lang et al. 2003; Orian et al. 2000). Remarkably, the 30 lysine residues present in the C-terminal half of NF-κB1 all contribute to the ubiquitination of the precursor, which is in clear contrast with the only two specific lysines involved in IκBα degradation (Cohen et al. 2004).

1.4 Degradation of Mediators of the NF-κB Signaling Cascades

Proteasomal degradation of IκBs is surely a critical step in the activation of NF-κB. However, the proteasome is also involved in the regulation of NF-κB

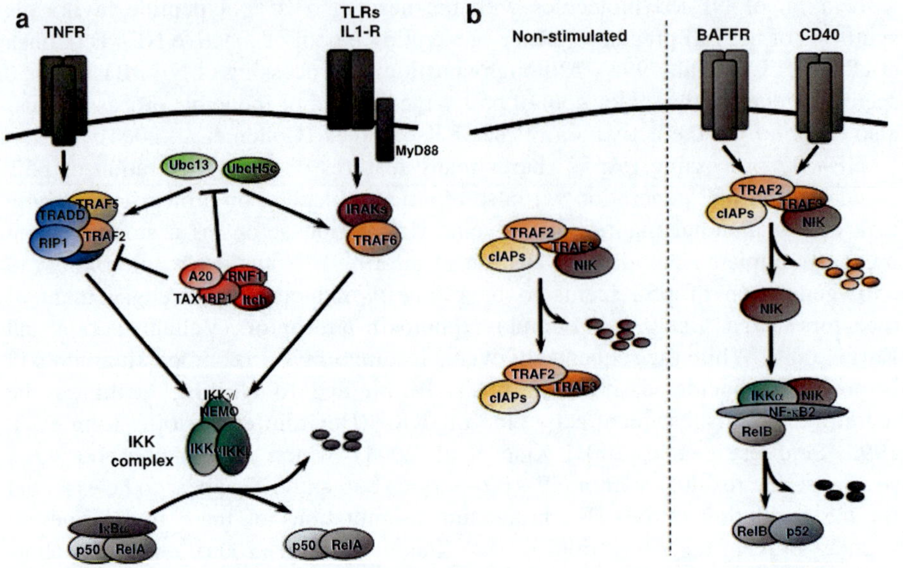

Fig. 2 Role of the ubiquitin–proteasome system in the regulation of NF-κB signaling pathways. **a** Activation of the canonical pathway upon TNFR engagement requires the formation of a complex containing TRADD, TRAF2, TRAF5, and the kinase RIP1 at the receptor cytoplasmic tail. Stimulation of TLRs and IL1-R leads to the recruitment of members of the IRAK family and TRAF6 to the adaptor MyD88. In both cases, termination of the canonical signaling necessitates the intervention of a complex including the ubiquitin-editing enzyme A20, two additional E3 ligases, RNF11 and Itch, and TAX1BP1, which recruits A20 to its substrates. This complex contributes to the inhibition of RIP1 by removing activating K63-polyubiquitin chains and mediating the addition of K48-polyubiquitin, thus tagging RIP1 for degradation. A20 also promotes the addition of K48-polyubiquitin chains and subsequent proteasomal degradation of Ubc13 and UbcH5c, the E2 enzymes that catalyze TRAF2 and TRAF6 non-degradative K63 polyubiquitination which is required for optimal canonical NF-κB activation in response to TNFα and IL-1, respectively. **b** In non-stimulated cells, NIK is associated with the adaptors TRAF2 and TRAF3 together with the E3 ligases cIAP1 and cIAP2. Within this complex, cIAP1 and cIAP2 target NIK for degradation, keeping NIK activity at low basal level. Upon receptor engagement, such as BAFFR and CD40, cIAPs catalyze the degradative K48-polyubiquitination of TRAF3, thus releasing NIK from degradation. Stabilized NIK, together with IKKα, then induces the processing of NF-κB2 to p52 leading to the activation of RelB:p52 dimers

activity by controlling the stability of important mediators of the NF-κB-signaling cascades.

TNFAIP3 is a NF-κB target gene that encodes the ubiquitin-editing enzyme A20 (Krikos et al. 1992; Wertz et al. 2004). A20 inhibits the function of several intermediate molecules of the canonical pathway as part of a negative feedback loop leading to the termination of the signal via its non-degradative-K63-deubiquitinase- and degradative-K48-ubiquitin ligase activities (Fig. 2a). In response to TNFα, A20 first removes the K63-linked polyubiquitin chain from RIP1, impairing its adaptor function in the TNFR-associated complex

(Vallabhapurapu and Karin 2009; Wertz et al. 2004). In a second step, A20, together with two other E3 ligases, Itch and RNF11, promotes the addition of K48-linked polyubiquitin chain and subsequent degradation of TNFR-associated RIP1 (Fig. 2a) (Shembade et al. 2008, 2009; Wertz et al. 2004). A20 also contributes to the addition of K48-polyubiquitin chains and subsequent proteasomal degradation of Ubc13 and UbcH5c, the E2 enzymes that catalyze TRAF2 and TRAF6 non-degradative K63 polyubiquitination, which is required for optimal canonical NF-κB activation in response to TNFα and IL-1, respectively (Fig. 2a) (Shembade et al. 2010). Of note, A20 also participates in the removal of K63-linked polyubiquitin chains from TRAF2 and TRAF6, hence inhibiting their activity (Boone et al. 2004; Shembade et al. 2010).

Bcl10, another intermediate molecule of the canonical NF-κB-signaling cascade (Vallabhapurapu and Karin 2009), is degraded by both proteasome-dependent and proteasome-independent mechanisms upon antigen-receptor engagement in lymphocytes (Hu et al. 2006; Lobry et al. 2007; Scharschmidt et al. 2004). Phosphorylation of Bcl10 by the IKK complex at threonine 81 and serine 85, two residues present in a phosphodegron motif, promotes its association with the E3 ligase $SCF^{\beta\text{-TrCP}}$, thus leading to Bcl10 ubiquitination and subsequent degradation by the proteasome (Lobry et al. 2007). In addition, TCR engagement leads to Bcl10 ubiquitination by the two HECT family E3 ligases, NEDD4 and Itch. However, in that context Bcl10 subsequent degradation occurs in a proteasome-independent manner (Scharschmidt et al. 2004). Finally, it has been shown that cIAP2 E3 ligase activity contributes to Bcl10 polyubiquitination and degradation in stimulated lymphocytes (Hu et al. 2006).

Proteasomal degradation also appears to be required for the maintenance of physiologic level of IKKβ. Indeed expression knock-down of the E3 ligase KEAP1 results in a marked increase in IKKβ protein expression levels both in resting and TNFα-stimulated cells (Lee et al. 2009).

Activation of the NF-κB alternative signaling pathway is also regulated by proteasome-mediated proteolysis. In non-stimulated cells, NIK is rapidly degraded keeping NIK activity at a low basal level (He et al. 2006, 2007; Liao et al. 2004). NIK degradation depends on its interaction with TRAF3 which bridges NIK to a complex comprising TRAF2 and the E3 ligases cIAP1 and cIAP2 (Fig. 2b) (Vallabhapurapu et al. 2008; Zarnegar et al. 2008). Within this complex, cIAP1 and cIAP2 promote the degradative K48-linked polyubiquitination of NIK (Varfolomeev et al. 2007; Vince et al. 2007). Receptor engagement, such as LTβR, BAFFR, or CD40, leads to the recruitment of the NIK-containing complex to the receptor and stimulation of TRAF2-E3 ligase activity. This in turn enables the induction of non-degradative-K63-linked polyubiquitination of cIAP1/2 and thereby enhances their ubiquitin ligase activity, which is now directed toward TRAF3. This then leads to the addition of a K48-linked polyubiquitin chain to TRAF3 and its subsequent proteasomal degradation (Vallabhapurapu et al. 2008; Zarnegar et al. 2008). Once TRAF3 is degraded, NIK is relieved from its association with the TRAF2–cIAPs complex, resulting in the stabilization of newly synthesized NIK and its eventual autophosphorylation and activation which triggers the alternative NF-κB-signaling pathway.

1.5 Degradation of NF-κB Proteins

Initially, the proteasome–ubiquitin system was reported to be responsible for constitutive c-Rel turnover in non-stimulated cells (Chen et al. 1998). Recent study clearly indicates that proteasomal proteolysis also controls NF-κB protein stability upon cell stimulation. In macrophages, LPS treatment leads to K48-linked polyubiquitination, and subsequent degradation of p50. Importantly, such a mechanism requires its intact DNA binding domain (Carmody et al. 2007). Bcl-3 deficiency leads to a more pronounced K48-ubiquitination of p50, thereby resulting in an additional decrease in p50 stability. As a consequence, recruitment of RelA and c-Rel to endogenous promoter of a subset of NF-κB target genes (e.g. TNFα and CXCL2) is increased, thus leading to their enhanced mRNA expression. Taken together, these data suggest that upon receptor stimulation, transcriptionally inactive p50:p50 homodimers bound to DNA are degraded, thereby allowing transcriptionally active NF-κB dimers (e.g. RelA and c-Rel containing dimers) to bind to the now freed κB binding sites. Bcl-3 interaction with p50 protects it from degradation and limits the access of RelA or c-Rel to promoters allowing a fine-tuned control of a subset of NF-κB target gene expression.

Inducible proteasomal degradation of the nuclear pool of RelA was reported in response to several inducers of the canonical NF-κB signaling pathway (e.g. TNFα and LPS) (Saccani et al. 2004; Tanaka et al. 2007). Remarkably, RelA binding to DNA is a prerequisite to its degradative K48-linked polyubiquitination. Moreover, RelA phosphorylation on serine 536 by IKKα is critical for proper control of its stability in response to LPS (Lawrence et al. 2005; Saccani et al. 2004). Beyond phosphorylation, other post-translational modifications control RelA stability. TNFα-induced methylation of RelA K314 and K315 by the methyltransferase Set9 triggers proteasome-mediated proteolysis of DNA-bound RelA (Yang et al. 2009). Cell stimulation with TNFα induces the association of RelA with the histone acetyltransferase GCN5, which depends on RelA serine 468 phosphorylation by the IKK complex (Mao et al. 2009). This in turn promotes nuclear RelA polyubiquitination and subsequent degradation. GCN5 also binds to the ubiquitin ligase of the RING family ECS^{SOCS1} (Elongins, Cullin2, and SOCS-box) and COMMD1, a complex previously shown to contribute to RelA degradation, thus suggesting that GCN5 may bring RelA and ECS^{SOCS1} in close proximity (Maine et al. 2009; Mao et al. 2009; Ryo et al. 2003). Another ubiquitin ligase, PDLIM2 (PDZ and LIM domain 2), was also shown to contribute to nuclear RelA stability (Tanaka et al. 2005, 2007). Notably, RelA polyubiquitination was impaired in PDLIM2 deficient $CD11c^{+}$ splenic cells upon LPS stimulation.

Altogether, these data suggest that proteasomal degradation of DNA-bound NF-κB proteins defines a regulatory mechanism that modulates NF-κB target gene expression.

2 Regulation of NF-κB Activity by Caspases

Cysteine proteases, caspases, form a family of enzymes that cleave their substrates usually after an aspartate residue (Li and Yuan 2008). These enzymes are present in cells as inactive zymogens that are activated by proteolytic cleavage upon cellular stimulation.

Remarkably, caspases can act both as activator or inhibitor of the NF-κB-signaling cascades. The most striking example for the positive role of caspases in the induction of NF-κB activity has been reported in drosophila during the anti-microbial response (Ferrandon et al. 2007). Upon peptidoglycan stimulation, DREDD, the drosophila homologue of caspase 8, removes the first thirty amino acids of IMD, a protein most similar to RIP1 (Fig. 3), and creates a docking site for DIAP2, the drosophila IAP2, which directs its ubiquitin ligase activity to non-degradative K63-polyubiquitination of IMD (Georgel et al. 2001; Paquette et al. 2010). This in turn leads to activation of the drosophila IKK complex DmIKK, and eventual phosphorylation of Relish, the drosophila homologue of NF-κB1 and NF-κB2 (Dushay et al. 1996; Erturk-Hasdemir et al. 2009; Silverman et al. 2000; Stoven et al. 2003). DREDD is now responsible for direct cleavage of phosphorylated Relish, releasing its N-terminal active form p68 that in turn induces the expression of anti-bacterial peptides (Fig. 3) (Erturk-Hasdemir et al. 2009; Stoven et al. 2000, 2003). It is worth noting that this mechanism drastically differs from the proteasome-mediated processing of NF-κB1 and NF-κB2 observed in mammalian cells. In support of the positive roles played by DREDD in the activation of NF-κB in drosophila, caspase 8 also catalyzes the processing of c-FLIP$_L$, an inhibitor of apoptosis, into a cleaved form that contributes to T-cell-antigen-receptor- and Fas-induced NF-κB activation in mammals (Kataoka et al. 2000; Kataoka and Tschopp 2004; Misra et al. 2007). Upon death receptor 4 engagement, caspase 8 also cleaves IκBα, leading to its degradation and subsequent activation of NF-κB (Rathore et al. 2004). Recently, the proteolytic activity of the caspase-related MALT1 has been shown to contribute to the induction of NF-κB downstream of B- and T-cell-antigen receptors (Coornaert et al. 2008; Ferch et al. 2009; Hailfinger et al. 2009; Rebeaud et al. 2008). MALT1 cleaves the ubiquitin-editing enzyme A20 within its C-terminal zinc finger domain (Coornaert et al. 2008). This generates two fragments that are no more able to inhibit the NF-κB canonical signaling cascade, most likely ensuring the optimal induction of this activation pathway (Coornaert et al. 2008).

Caspases can also act as inhibitors of NF-κB activity. Several proteins throughout the NF-κB-signaling cascades are cleaved by caspases in response to inducers of programmed cell death, thus leading to impaired NF-κB activation

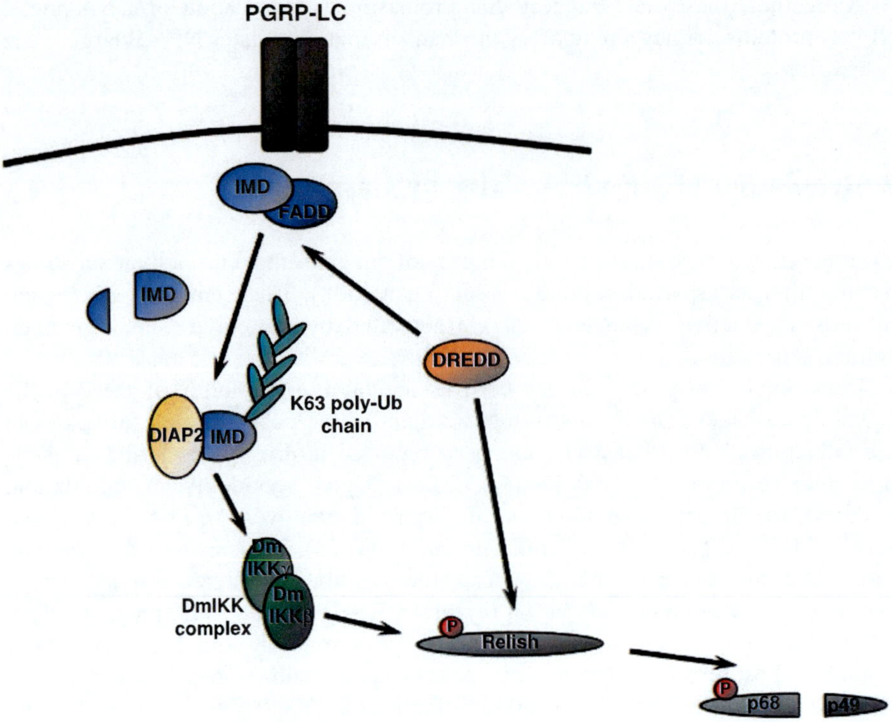

Fig. 3 DREDD functions in the anti-bacterial IMD pathway. Activation of the surface peptidoglycan recognition protein receptor (PGRP-LC) results in the engagement of DREDD, the drosophila homologue of caspase 8. This enzyme cleaves the N-terminus of the adaptor protein IMD thereby promoting its association with DIAP2 and its subsequent non-degradative K63-polyubiquitination. This in turn leads to the activation of the drosophila IKK complex (DmIKK), and eventual phosphorylation of Relish. DREDD is now responsible for direct cleavage of phosphorylated Relish, releasing its N-terminal active form p68 that in turn induces the expression of anti-bacterial peptides

(Frelin et al. 2008; Lin et al. 1999; Ravi et al. 1998; Reuther and Baldwin 1999; Tang et al. 2001). While the resulting cleaved fragments of positive regulators (e.g. IKKβ and RIP1) are defective in their ability to induce NF-κB activity, the cleavage of negative regulators (e.g. IκBα) generates dominant-negative molecules that impair further activation of the NF-κB-signaling pathways. Indeed, TNFα-induced apoptosis leads to IKKβ cleavage by caspases 3 and 7 at multiple sites, thus generating several fragments carrying no kinase activity (Tang et al. 2001). It also directs caspase 8 to cleave RIP1 after aspartate 324, thereby generating two truncated proteins unable to mediate NF-κB activation (Lin et al. 1999). Caspases 3 and 7 proteolytic activity also generate an IκBα dominant-negative mutant that lacks the two K48-linked polyubiquitin chain acceptor sites (lysines 21 and 22), thus preventing inducible IκBα degradation (Reuther and Baldwin 1999).

3 Regulation of NF-κB Activity by Calpains

Calcium-dependent cysteine protease calpains were also shown to control IκBα stability and thereby NF-κB activity (Chen et al. 1997; Han et al. 1999; Shen et al. 2001; Shumway et al. 1999; Teranishi et al. 2003). Induction of IκBα proteolysis by calpains depends on its C-terminus PEST domain (Shumway et al. 1999). Interestingly, CK2 was shown to phosphorylate several residues within the PEST domain of IκBα (e.g. serines 283, 289, and 293; threonines 291 and 299), thereby facilitating calpain binding to IκBα and its subsequent degradation (Barroga et al. 1995; Lin et al. 1996; McElhinny et al. 1996; Shen et al. 2001; Shumway et al. 1999). Treatment of cells with calpain and CK2 inhibitors as well as expression of CK2 kinase inactive mutants result in both increased IκBα stability and reduced NF-κB activity (Pianetti et al. 2001; Romieu-Mourez et al. 2002; Shen et al. 2001). Similarly, CK2 and calpain A participate in the regulation of Cactus gradient in drosophila embryo, an important event in the establishment of the dorso-ventral pattern (Fontenele et al. 2009; Liu et al. 1997).

4 Conclusion

Proteolysis is an essential mode of regulation of NF-κB activity acting at various levels throughout the signaling cascades. As reviewed here, it is well illustrated that proteolysis is critical for the regulation of "small"-IκB degradation, maturation of NF-κB precursors, and stability of several critical mediators of the canonical and the alternative NF-κB-signaling pathways. As this area of research is moving at such a rapid pace, future study will likely uncover new targets and mechanisms of action involved in the complex regulation of NF-κB activity by protein stability.

References

Alkalay I, Yaron A, Hatzubai A, Jung S, Avraham A, Gerlitz O, Pashut-Lavon I, Ben-Neriah Y (1995) In vivo stimulation of I kappa B phosphorylation is not sufficient to activate NF-kappa B. Mol Cell Biol 15:1294–1301

Amir RE, Haecker H, Karin M, Ciechanover A (2004) Mechanism of processing of the NF-kappa B2 p100 precursor: identification of the specific polyubiquitin chain-anchoring lysine residue and analysis of the role of NEDD8-modification on the SCF(beta-TrCP) ubiquitin ligase. Oncogene 23:2540–2547

Baeuerle PA, Baltimore D (1988) I kappa B: a specific inhibitor of the NF-kappa B transcription factor. Science 242:540–546

Baldi L, Brown K, Franzoso G, Siebenlist U (1996) Critical role for lysines 21 and 22 in signal-induced, ubiquitin-mediated proteolysis of I kappa B-alpha. J Biol Chem 271:376–379

Barroga CF, Stevenson JK, Schwarz EM, Verma IM (1995) Constitutive phosphorylation of I kappa B alpha by casein kinase II. Proc Natl Acad Sci USA 92:7637–7641

Basak S, Kim H, Kearns JD, Tergaonkar V, O'Dea E, Werner SL, Benedict CA, Ware CF, Ghosh G, Verma IM, Hoffmann A (2007) A fourth IkappaB protein within the NF-kappaB signaling module. Cell 128:369–381

Beinke S, Belich MP, Ley SC (2002) The death domain of NF-kappa B1 p105 is essential for signal-induced p105 proteolysis. J Biol Chem 277:24162–24168

Boone DL, Turer EE, Lee EG, Ahmad RC, Wheeler MT, Tsui C, Hurley P, Chien M, Chai S, Hitotsumatsu O, McNally E, Pickart C, Ma A (2004) The ubiquitin-modifying enzyme A20 is required for termination of Toll-like receptor responses. Nat Immunol 5:1052–1060

Brown K, Gerstberger S, Carlson L, Franzoso G, Siebenlist U (1995) Control of I kappa B-alpha proteolysis by site-specific, signal-induced phosphorylation. Science 267:1485–1488

Carmody RJ, Ruan Q, Palmer S, Hilliard B, Chen YH (2007) Negative regulation of toll-like receptor signaling by NF-kappaB p50 ubiquitination blockade. Science 317:675–678

Chen Z, Hagler J, Palombella VJ, Melandri F, Scherer D, Ballard D, Maniatis T (1995) Signal-induced site-specific phosphorylation targets I kappa B alpha to the ubiquitin-proteasome pathway. Genes Dev 9:1586–1597

Chen F, Lu Y, Kuhn DC, Maki M, Shi X, Sun SC, Demers LM (1997) Calpain contributes to silica-induced I kappa B-alpha degradation and nuclear factor-kappa B activation. Arch Biochem Biophys 342:383–388

Chen E, Hrdlickova R, Nehyba J, Longo DL, Bose HR Jr, Li CC (1998) Degradation of proto-oncoprotein c-Rel by the ubiquitin-proteasome pathway. J Biol Chem 273:35201–35207

Cohen S, Orian A, Ciechanover A (2001) Processing of p105 is inhibited by docking of p50 active subunits to the ankyrin repeat domain, and inhibition is alleviated by signaling via the carboxyl-terminal phosphorylation/ubiquitin-ligase binding domain. J Biol Chem 276:26769–26776

Cohen S, Achbert-Weiner H, Ciechanover A (2004) Dual effects of IkappaB kinase beta-mediated phosphorylation on p105 Fate: SCF(beta-TrCP)-dependent degradation and SCF(beta-TrCP)-independent processing. Mol Cell Biol 24:475–486

Coornaert B, Baens M, Heyninck K, Bekaert T, Haegman M, Staal J, Sun L, Chen ZJ, Marynen P, Beyaert R (2008) T cell antigen receptor stimulation induces MALT1 paracaspase-mediated cleavage of the NF-kappaB inhibitor A20. Nat Immunol 9:263–271

Davis N, Ghosh S, Simmons DL, Tempst P, Liou HC, Baltimore D, Bose HR Jr (1991) Rel-associated pp40: an inhibitor of the rel family of transcription factors. Science 253:1268–1271

Davis M, Hatzubai A, Andersen JS, Ben-Shushan E, Fisher GZ, Yaron A, Bauskin A, Mercurio F, Mann M, Ben-Neriah Y (2002) Pseudosubstrate regulation of the SCF(beta-TrCP) ubiquitin ligase by hnRNP-U. Genes Dev 16:439–451

Dejardin E, Droin NM, Delhase M, Haas E, Cao Y, Makris C, Li ZW, Karin M, Ware CF, Green DR (2002) The lymphotoxin-beta receptor induces different patterns of gene expression via two NF-kappaB pathways. Immunity 17:525–535

Derudder E, Dejardin E, Pritchard LL, Green DR, Korner M, Baud V (2003) RelB/p50 dimers are differentially regulated by tumor necrosis factor-alpha and lymphotoxin-beta receptor activation: critical roles for p100. J Biol Chem 278:23278–23284

DiDonato J, Mercurio F, Rosette C, Wu-Li J, Suyang H, Ghosh S, Karin M (1996) Mapping of the inducible IkappaB phosphorylation sites that signal its ubiquitination and degradation. Mol Cell Biol 16:1295–1304

DiDonato JA, Hayakawa M, Rothwarf DM, Zandi E, Karin M (1997) A cytokine-responsive IkappaB kinase that activates the transcription factor NF-kappaB. Nature 388:548–554

Dushay MS, Asling B, Hultmark D (1996) Origins of immunity: Relish, a compound Rel-like gene in the antibacterial defense of Drosophila. Proc Natl Acad Sci USA 93:10343–10347

Erturk-Hasdemir D, Broemer M, Leulier F, Lane WS, Paquette N, Hwang D, Kim CH, Stoven S, Meier P, Silverman N (2009) Two roles for the Drosophila IKK complex in the activation of Relish and the induction of antimicrobial peptide genes. Proc Natl Acad Sci USA 106:9779–9784

Ferch U, Kloo B, Gewies A, Pfander V, Duwel M, Peschel C, Krappmann D, Ruland J (2009) Inhibition of MALT1 protease activity is selectively toxic for activated B cell-like diffuse large B cell lymphoma cells. J Exp Med 206:2313–2320

Fernandez NQ, Grosshans J, Goltz JS, Stein D (2001) Separable and redundant regulatory determinants in Cactus mediate its dorsal group dependent degradation. Development 128:2963–2974

Ferrandon D, Imler JL, Hetru C, Hoffmann JA (2007) The Drosophila systemic immune response: sensing and signalling during bacterial and fungal infections. Nat Rev Immunol 7:862–874

Finley D (2009) Recognition and processing of ubiquitin-protein conjugates by the proteasome. Annu Rev Biochem 78:477–513

Fong A, Sun SC (2002) Genetic evidence for the essential role of beta-transducin repeat-containing protein in the inducible processing of NF-kappa B2/p100. J Biol Chem 277:22111–22114

Fontenele M, Carneiro K, Agrellos R, Oliveira D, Oliveira-Silva A, Vieira V, Negreiros E, Machado E, Araujo H (2009) The Ca2+-dependent protease Calpain A regulates Cactus/I kappaB levels during Drosophila development in response to maternal Dpp signals. Mech Dev 126:737–751

Frelin C, Imbert V, Bottero V, Gonthier N, Samraj AK, Schulze-Osthoff K, Auberger P, Courtois G, Peyron JF (2008) Inhibition of the NF-kappaB survival pathway via caspase-dependent cleavage of the IKK complex scaffold protein and NF-kappaB essential modulator NEMO. Cell Death Differ 15:152–160

Fuchs SY, Chen A, Xiong Y, Pan ZQ, Ronai Z (1999) HOS, a human homolog of Slimb, forms an SCF complex with Skp1 and Cullin1 and targets the phosphorylation-dependent degradation of IkappaB and beta-catenin. Oncogene 18:2039–2046

Georgel P, Naitza S, Kappler C, Ferrandon D, Zachary D, Swimmer C, Kopczynski C, Duyk G, Reichhart JM, Hoffmann JA (2001) Drosophila immune deficiency (IMD) is a death domain protein that activates antibacterial defense and can promote apoptosis. Dev Cell 1:503–514

Gonen H, Bercovich B, Orian A, Carrano A, Takizawa C, Yamanaka K, Pagano M, Iwai K, Ciechanover A (1999) Identification of the ubiquitin carrier proteins, E2s, involved in signal-induced conjugation and subsequent degradation of IkappaBalpha. J Biol Chem 274:14823–14830

Guardavaccaro D, Kudo Y, Boulaire J, Barchi M, Busino L, Donzelli M, Margottin-Goguet F, Jackson PK, Yamasaki L, Pagano M (2003) Control of meiotic and mitotic progression by the F box protein beta-Trcp1 in vivo. Dev Cell 4:799–812

Hailfinger S, Lenz G, Ngo V, Posvitz-Fejfar A, Rebeaud F, Guzzardi M, Penas EM, Dierlamm J, Chan WC, Staudt LM, Thome M (2009) Essential role of MALT1 protease activity in activated B cell-like diffuse large B-cell lymphoma. Proc Natl Acad Sci USA 106:19946–19951

Han Y, Weinman S, Boldogh I, Walker RK, Brasier AR (1999) Tumor necrosis factor-alpha-inducible IkappaBalpha proteolysis mediated by cytosolic m-calpain. A mechanism parallel to the ubiquitin-proteasome pathway for nuclear factor-kappab activation. J Biol Chem 274:787–794

Haskill S, Beg AA, Tompkins SM, Morris JS, Yurochko AD, Sampson-Johannes A, Mondal K, Ralph P, Baldwin AS Jr (1991) Characterization of an immediate-early gene induced in adherent monocytes that encodes I kappa B-like activity. Cell 65:1281–1289

Hatakeyama S, Kitagawa M, Nakayama K, Shirane M, Matsumoto M, Hattori K, Higashi H, Nakano H, Okumura K, Onoe K, Good RA, Nakayama K (1999) Ubiquitin-dependent degradation of IkappaBalpha is mediated by a ubiquitin ligase Skp1/Cul 1/F-box protein FWD1. Proc Natl Acad Sci USA 96:3859–3863

Hayden MS, Ghosh S (2004) Signaling to NF-kappaB. Genes Dev 18:2195–2224

He JQ, Zarnegar B, Oganesyan G, Saha SK, Yamazaki S, Doyle SE, Dempsey PW, Cheng G (2006) Rescue of TRAF3-null mice by p100 NF-kappa B deficiency. J Exp Med 203:2413–2418

He JQ, Saha SK, Kang JR, Zarnegar B, Cheng G (2007) Specificity of TRAF3 in its negative regulation of the noncanonical NF-kappa B pathway. J Biol Chem 282:3688–3694

Heissmeyer V, Krappmann D, Wulczyn FG, Scheidereit C (1999) NF-kappaB p105 is a target of IkappaB kinases and controls signal induction of Bcl-3-p50 complexes. Embo J 18:4766–4778

Heissmeyer V, Krappmann D, Hatada EN, Scheidereit C (2001) Shared pathways of IkappaB kinase-induced SCF(betaTrCP)-mediated ubiquitination and degradation for the NF-kappaB precursor p105 and IkappaBalpha. Mol Cell Biol 21:1024–1035

Henkel T, Machleidt T, Alkalay I, Kronke M, Ben-Neriah Y, Baeuerle PA (1993) Rapid proteolysis of I kappa B-alpha is necessary for activation of transcription factor NF-kappa B. Nature 365:182–185

Heusch M, Lin L, Geleziunas R, Greene WC (1999) The generation of nfkb2 p52: mechanism and efficiency. Oncogene 18:6201–6208

Hu S, Du MQ, Park SM, Alcivar A, Qu L, Gupta S, Tang J, Baens M, Ye H, Lee TH, Marynen P, Riley JL, Yang X (2006) cIAP2 is a ubiquitin protein ligase for BCL10 and is dysregulated in mucosa-associated lymphoid tissue lymphomas. J Clin Invest 116:174–181

Jackson PK, Eldridge AG, Freed E, Furstenthal L, Hsu JY, Kaiser BK, Reimann JD (2000) The lore of the RINGs: substrate recognition and catalysis by ubiquitin ligases. Trends Cell Biol 10:429–439

Kataoka T, Tschopp J (2004) N-terminal fragment of c-FLIP(L) processed by caspase 8 specifically interacts with TRAF2 and induces activation of the NF-kappaB signaling pathway. Mol Cell Biol 24:2627–2636

Kataoka T, Budd RC, Holler N, Thome M, Martinon F, Irmler M, Burns K, Hahne M, Kennedy N, Kovacsovics M, Tschopp J (2000) The caspase-8 inhibitor FLIP promotes activation of NF-kappaB and Erk signaling pathways. Curr Biol 10:640–648

Krikos A, Laherty CD, Dixit VM (1992) Transcriptional activation of the tumor necrosis factor alpha-inducible zinc finger protein, A20, is mediated by kappa B elements. J Biol Chem 267:17971–17976

Kroll M, Margottin F, Kohl A, Renard P, Durand H, Concordet JP, Bachelerie F, Arenzana-Seisdedos F, Benarous R (1999) Inducible degradation of IkappaBalpha by the proteasome requires interaction with the F-box protein h-betaTrCP. J Biol Chem 274:7941–7945

Lang V, Janzen J, Fischer GZ, Soneji Y, Beinke S, Salmeron A, Allen H, Hay RT, Ben-Neriah Y, Ley SC (2003) BetaTrCP-mediated proteolysis of NF-kappaB1 p105 requires phosphorylation of p105 serines 927 and 932. Mol Cell Biol 23:402–413

Lawrence T, Bebien M, Liu GY, Nizet V, Karin M (2005) IKKalpha limits macrophage NF-kappaB activation and contributes to the resolution of inflammation. Nature 434:1138–1143

Lee DF, Kuo HP, Liu M, Chou CK, Xia W, Du Y, Shen J, Chen CT, Huo L, Hsu MC, Li CW, Ding Q, Liao TL, Lai CC, Lin AC, Chang YH, Tsai SF, Li LY, Hung MC (2009) KEAP1 E3 ligase-mediated downregulation of NF-kappaB signaling by targeting IKKbeta. Mol Cell 36:131–140

Li J, Yuan J (2008) Caspases in apoptosis and beyond. Oncogene 27:6194–6206

Liao G, Zhang M, Harhaj EW, Sun SC (2004) Regulation of the NF-kappaB-inducing kinase by tumor necrosis factor receptor-associated factor 3-induced degradation. J Biol Chem 279:26243–26250

Lin R, Beauparlant P, Makris C, Meloche S, Hiscott J (1996) Phosphorylation of IkappaBalpha in the C-terminal PEST domain by casein kinase II affects intrinsic protein stability. Mol Cell Biol 16:1401–1409

Lin L, DeMartino GN, Greene WC (1998) Cotranslational biogenesis of NF-kappaB p50 by the 26S proteasome. Cell 92:819–828

Lin Y, Devin A, Rodriguez Y, Liu ZG (1999) Cleavage of the death domain kinase RIP by caspase-8 prompts TNF-induced apoptosis. Genes Dev 13:2514–2526

Ling L, Cao Z, Goeddel DV (1998) NF-kappaB-inducing kinase activates IKK-alpha by phosphorylation of Ser-176. Proc Natl Acad Sci USA 95:3792–3797

Liu ZP, Galindo RL, Wasserman SA (1997) A role for CKII phosphorylation of the Cactus PEST domain in dorsoventral patterning of the Drosophila embryo. Genes Dev 11:3413–3422

Lobry C, Lopez T, Israel A, Weil R (2007) Negative feedback loop in T cell activation through IkappaB kinase-induced phosphorylation and degradation of Bcl10. Proc Natl Acad Sci USA 104:908–913

Maine GN, Mao X, Muller PA, Komarck CM, Klomp LW, Burstein E (2009) COMMD1 expression is controlled by critical residues that determine XIAP binding. Biochem J 417:601–609

Mao X, Gluck N, Li D, Maine GN, Li H, Zaidi IW, Repaka A, Mayo MW, Burstein E (2009) GCN5 is a required cofactor for a ubiquitin ligase that targets NF-kappaB/RelA. Genes Dev 23:849–861

McElhinny JA, Trushin SA, Bren GD, Chester N, Paya CV (1996) Casein kinase II phosphorylates I kappa B alpha at S-283, S-289, S-293, and T-291 and is required for its degradation. Mol Cell Biol 16:899–906

Mellits KH, Hay RT, Goodbourn S (1993) Proteolytic degradation of MAD3 (I kappa B alpha) and enhanced processing of the NF-kappa B precursor p105 are obligatory steps in the activation of NF-kappa B. Nucl Acids Res 21:5059–5066

Mercurio F, Zhu H, Murray BW, Shevchenko A, Bennett BL, Li J, Young DB, Barbosa M, Mann M, Manning A, Rao A (1997) IKK-1 and IKK-2: cytokine-activated IkappaB kinases essential for NF-kappaB activation. Science 278:860–866

Misra RS, Russell JQ, Koenig A, Hinshaw-Makepeace JA, Wen R, Wang D, Huo H, Littman DR, Ferch U, Ruland J, Thome M, Budd RC (2007) Caspase-8 and c-FLIPL associate in lipid rafts with NF-kappaB adaptors during T cell activation. J Biol Chem 282:19365–19374

Nakayama K, Hatakeyama S, Maruyama S, Kikuchi A, Onoe K, Good RA, Nakayama KI (2003) Impaired degradation of inhibitory subunit of NF-kappa B (I kappa B) and beta-catenin as a result of targeted disruption of the beta-TrCP1 gene. Proc Natl Acad Sci USA 100:8752–8757

Navon A, Ciechanover A (2009) The 26 S proteasome: from basic mechanisms to drug targeting. J Biol Chem 284:33713–33718

Orian A, Schwartz AL, Israel A, Whiteside S, Kahana C, Ciechanover A (1999) Structural motifs involved in ubiquitin-mediated processing of the NF-kappaB precursor p105: roles of the glycine-rich region and a downstream ubiquitination domain. Mol Cell Biol 19:3664–3673

Orian A, Gonen H, Bercovich B, Fajerman I, Eytan E, Israel A, Mercurio F, Iwai K, Schwartz AL, Ciechanover A (2000) SCF(beta)(-TrCP) ubiquitin ligase-mediated processing of NF-kappaB p105 requires phosphorylation of its C-terminus by IkappaB kinase. Embo J 19:2580–2591

Paquette N, Broemer M, Aggarwal K, Chen L, Husson M, Erturk-Hasdemir D, Reichhart JM, Meier P, Silverman N (2010) Caspase-mediated cleavage, IAP binding, and ubiquitination: linking three mechanisms crucial for Drosophila NF-kappaB signaling. Mol Cell 37:172–182

Pianetti S, Arsura M, Romieu-Mourez R, Coffey RJ, Sonenshein GE (2001) Her-2/neu overexpression induces NF-kappaB via a PI3-kinase/Akt pathway involving calpain-mediated degradation of IkappaB-alpha that can be inhibited by the tumor suppressor PTEN. Oncogene 20:1287–1299

Rathore N, Matta H, Chaudhary PM (2004) An evolutionary conserved pathway of nuclear factor-kappaB activation involving caspase-mediated cleavage and N-end rule pathway-mediated degradation of IkappaBalpha. J Biol Chem 279:39358–39365

Ravi R, Bedi A, Fuchs EJ, Bedi A (1998) CD95 (Fas)-induced caspase-mediated proteolysis of NF-kappaB. Cancer Res 58:882–886

Reach M, Galindo RL, Towb P, Allen JL, Karin M, Wasserman SA (1996) A gradient of Cactus protein degradation establishes dorsoventral polarity in the Drosophila embryo. Dev Biol 180:353–364

Rebeaud F, Hailfinger S, Posevitz-Fejfar A, Tapernoux M, Moser R, Rueda D, Gaide O, Guzzardi M, Iancu EM, Rufer N, Fasel N, Thome M (2008) The proteolytic activity of the paracaspase MALT1 is key in T cell activation. Nat Immunol 9:272–281

Regnier CH, Song HY, Gao X, Goeddel DV, Cao Z, Rothe M (1997) Identification and characterization of an IkappaB kinase. Cell 90:373–383

Reuther JY, Baldwin AS Jr (1999) Apoptosis promotes a caspase-induced amino-terminal truncation of IkappaBalpha that functions as a stable inhibitor of NF-kappaB. J Biol Chem 274:20664–20670

Romieu-Mourez R, Landesman-Bollag E, Seldin DC, Sonenshein GE (2002) Protein kinase CK2 promotes aberrant activation of nuclear factor-kappaB, transformed phenotype, and survival of breast cancer cells. Cancer Res 62:6770–6778

Rothwarf DM, Zandi E, Natoli G, Karin M (1998) IKK-gamma is an essential regulatory subunit of the IkappaB kinase complex. Nature 395:297–300

Ryo A, Suizu F, Yoshida Y, Perrem K, Liou YC, Wulf G, Rottapel R, Yamaoka S, Lu KP (2003) Regulation of NF-kappaB signaling by Pin1-dependent prolyl isomerization and ubiquitin-mediated proteolysis of p65/RelA. Mol Cell 12:1413–1426

Saccani S, Marazzi I, Beg AA, Natoli G (2004) Degradation of promoter-bound p65/RelA is essential for the prompt termination of the nuclear factor kappaB response. J Exp Med 200:107–113

Salmeron A, Janzen J, Soneji Y, Bump N, Kamens J, Allen H, Ley SC (2001) Direct phosphorylation of NF-kappaB1 p105 by the IkappaB kinase complex on serine 927 is essential for signal-induced p105 proteolysis. J Biol Chem 276:22215–22222

Scharschmidt E, Wegener E, Heissmeyer V, Rao A, Krappmann D (2004) Degradation of Bcl10 induced by T-cell activation negatively regulates NF-kappa B signaling. Mol Cell Biol 24:3860–3873

Scherer DC, Brockman JA, Chen Z, Maniatis T, Ballard DW (1995) Signal-induced degradation of I kappa B alpha requires site-specific ubiquitination. Proc Natl Acad Sci USA 92:11259–11263

Schrader EK, Harstad KG, Matouschek A (2009) Targeting proteins for degradation. Nat Chem Biol 5:815–822

Sen R, Baltimore D (1986) Inducibility of kappa immunoglobulin enhancer-binding protein Nf-kappa B by a posttranslational mechanism. Cell 47:921–928

Senftleben U, Cao Y, Xiao G, Greten FR, Krahn G, Bonizzi G, Chen Y, Hu Y, Fong A, Sun SC, Karin M (2001) Activation by IKKalpha of a second, evolutionary conserved, NF-kappa B signaling pathway. Science 293:1495–1499

Shembade N, Harhaj NS, Parvatiyar K, Copeland NG, Jenkins NA, Matesic LE, Harhaj EW (2008) The E3 ligase Itch negatively regulates inflammatory signaling pathways by controlling the function of the ubiquitin-editing enzyme A20. Nat Immunol 9:254–262

Shembade N, Parvatiyar K, Harhaj NS, Harhaj EW (2009) The ubiquitin-editing enzyme A20 requires RNF11 to downregulate NF-kappaB signalling. Embo J 28:513–522

Shembade N, Ma A, Harhaj EW (2010) Inhibition of NF-kappaB signaling by A20 through disruption of ubiquitin enzyme complexes. Science 327:1135–1139

Shen J, Channavajhala P, Seldin DC, Sonenshein GE (2001) Phosphorylation by the protein kinase CK2 promotes calpain-mediated degradation of IkappaBalpha. J Immunol 167:4919–4925

Shirane M, Hatakeyama S, Hattori K, Nakayama K, Nakayama K (1999) Common pathway for the ubiquitination of IkappaBalpha, IkappaBbeta, and IkappaBepsilon mediated by the F-box protein FWD1. J Biol Chem 274:28169–28174

Shumway SD, Maki M, Miyamoto S (1999) The PEST domain of IkappaBalpha is necessary and sufficient for in vitro degradation by mu-calpain. J Biol Chem 274:30874–30881

Silverman N, Zhou R, Stoven S, Pandey N, Hultmark D, Maniatis T (2000) A Drosophila IkappaB kinase complex required for Relish cleavage and antibacterial immunity. Genes Dev 14:2461–2471

Spencer E, Jiang J, Chen ZJ (1999) Signal-induced ubiquitination of IkappaBalpha by the F-box protein Slimb/beta-TrCP. Genes Dev 13:284–294

Stoven S, Ando I, Kadalayil L, Engstrom Y, Hultmark D (2000) Activation of the Drosophila NF-kappaB factor Relish by rapid endoproteolytic cleavage. EMBO Rep 1:347–352

Stoven S, Silverman N, Junell A, Hedengren-Olcott M, Erturk D, Engstrom Y, Maniatis T, Hultmark D (2003) Caspase-mediated processing of the Drosophila NF-kappaB factor Relish. Proc Natl Acad Sci USA 100:5991–5996

Strack P, Caligiuri M, Pelletier M, Boisclair M, Theodoras A, Beer-Romero P, Glass S, Parsons T, Copeland RA, Auger KR, Benfield P, Brizuela L, Rolfe M (2000) SCF(beta-TRCP) and phosphorylation dependent ubiquitination of I kappa B alpha catalyzed by Ubc3 and Ubc4. Oncogene 19:3529–3536

Tan P, Fuchs SY, Chen A, Wu K, Gomez C, Ronai Z, Pan ZQ (1999) Recruitment of a ROC1-CUL1 ubiquitin ligase by Skp1 and HOS to catalyze the ubiquitination of I kappa B alpha. Mol Cell 3:527–533

Tanaka T, Soriano MA, Grusby MJ (2005) SLIM is a nuclear ubiquitin E3 ligase that negatively regulates STAT signaling. Immunity 22:729–736

Tanaka T, Grusby MJ, Kaisho T (2007) PDLIM2-mediated termination of transcription factor NF-kappaB activation by intranuclear sequestration and degradation of the p65 subunit. Nat Immunol 8:584–591

Tang G, Yang J, Minemoto Y, Lin A (2001) Blocking caspase-3-mediated proteolysis of IKKbeta suppresses TNF-alpha-induced apoptosis. Mol Cell 8:1005–1016

Teranishi F, Liu ZQ, Kunimatsu M, Imai K, Takeyama H, Manabe T, Sasaki M, Okamoto T (2003) Calpain is involved in the HIV replication from the latently infected OM10.1 cells. Biochem Biophys Res Commun 303:940–946

Tewari M, Dobrzanski P, Mohn KL, Cressman DE, Hsu JC, Bravo R, Taub R (1992) Rapid induction in regenerating liver of RL/IF-1 (an I kappa B that inhibits NF-kappa B, RelB-p50, and c-Rel-p50) and PHF, a novel kappa B site-binding complex. Mol Cell Biol 12:2898–2908

Vallabhapurapu S, Karin M (2009) Regulation and function of NF-kappaB transcription factors in the immune system. Annu Rev Immunol 27:693–733

Vallabhapurapu S, Matsuzawa A, Zhang W, Tseng PH, Keats JJ, Wang H, Vignali DA, Bergsagel PL, Karin M (2008) Nonredundant and complementary functions of TRAF2 and TRAF3 in a ubiquitination cascade that activates NIK-dependent alternative NF-kappaB signaling. Nat Immunol 9:1364–1370

Varfolomeev E, Blankenship JW, Wayson SM, Fedorova AV, Kayagaki N, Garg P, Zobel K, Dynek JN, Elliott LO, Wallweber HJ, Flygare JA, Fairbrother WJ, Deshayes K, Dixit VM, Vucic D (2007) IAP antagonists induce autoubiquitination of c-IAPs, NF-kappaB activation, and TNFalpha-dependent apoptosis. Cell 131:669–681

Vince JE, Wong WW, Khan N, Feltham R, Chau D, Ahmed AU, Benetatos CA, Chunduru SK, Condon SM, McKinlay M, Brink R, Leverkus M, Tergaonkar V, Schneider P, Callus BA, Koentgen F, Vaux DL, Silke J (2007) IAP antagonists target cIAP1 to induce TNFalpha-dependent apoptosis. Cell 131:682–693

Vuillard L, Nicholson J, Hay RT (1999) A complex containing betaTrCP recruits Cdc34 to catalyse ubiquitination of IkappaBalpha. FEBS Lett 455:311–314

Weil R, Laurent-Winter C, Israel A (1997) Regulation of IkappaBbeta degradation. Similarities to and differences from IkappaBalpha. J Biol Chem 272:9942–9949

Wertz IE, O'Rourke KM, Zhou H, Eby M, Aravind L, Seshagiri S, Wu P, Wiesmann C, Baker R, Boone DL, Ma A, Koonin EV, Dixit VM (2004) De-ubiquitination and ubiquitin ligase domains of A20 downregulate NF-kappaB signalling. Nature 430:694–699

Whiteside ST, Ernst MK, LeBail O, Laurent-Winter C, Rice N, Israel A (1995) N- and C-terminal sequences control degradation of MAD3/I kappa B alpha in response to inducers of NF-kappa B activity. Mol Cell Biol 15:5339–5345

Whiteside ST, Epinat JC, Rice NR, Israel A (1997) I kappa B epsilon, a novel member of the I kappa B family, controls RelA and cRel NF-kappa B activity. Embo J 16:1413–1426

Winston JT, Strack P, Beer-Romero P, Chu CY, Elledge SJ, Harper JW (1999) The SCFbeta-TRCP-ubiquitin ligase complex associates specifically with phosphorylated destruction motifs in IkappaBalpha and beta-catenin and stimulates IkappaBalpha ubiquitination in vitro. Genes Dev 13:270–283

Woronicz JD, Gao X, Cao Z, Rothe M, Goeddel DV (1997) IkappaB kinase-beta: NF-kappaB activation and complex formation with IkappaB kinase-alpha and NIK. Science 278:866–869

Wu C, Ghosh S (1999) Beta-TrCP mediates the signal-induced ubiquitination of IkappaBbeta. J Biol Chem 274:29591–29594

Xiao G, Harhaj EW, Sun SC (2001) NF-kappaB-inducing kinase regulates the processing of NF-kappaB2 p100. Mol Cell 7:401–409

Xiao G, Fong A, Sun SC (2004) Induction of p100 processing by NF-kappaB-inducing kinase involves docking IkappaB kinase alpha (IKKalpha) to p100 and IKKalpha-mediated phosphorylation. J Biol Chem 279:30099–30105

Yamaoka S, Courtois G, Bessia C, Whiteside ST, Weil R, Agou F, Kirk HE, Kay RJ, Israel A (1998) Complementation cloning of NEMO, a component of the IkappaB kinase complex essential for NF-kappaB activation. Cell 93:1231–1240

Yang XD, Huang B, Li M, Lamb A, Kelleher NL, Chen LF (2009) Negative regulation of NF-kappaB action by Set9-mediated lysine methylation of the RelA subunit. Embo J 28:1055–1066

Yaron A, Hatzubai A, Davis M, Lavon I, Amit S, Manning AM, Andersen JS, Mann M, Mercurio F, Ben-Neriah Y (1998) Identification of the receptor component of the IkappaBalpha-ubiquitin ligase. Nature 396:590–594

Zandi E, Rothwarf DM, Delhase M, Hayakawa M, Karin M (1997) The IkappaB kinase complex (IKK) contains two kinase subunits, IKKalpha and IKKbeta, necessary for IkappaB phosphorylation and NF-kappaB activation. Cell 91:243–252

Zarnegar BJ, Wang Y, Mahoney DJ, Dempsey PW, Cheung HH, He J, Shiba T, Yang X, Yeh WC, Mak TW, Korneluk RG, Cheng G (2008) Noncanonical NF-kappaB activation requires coordinated assembly of a regulatory complex of the adaptors cIAP1, cIAP2, TRAF2 and TRAF3 and the kinase NIK. Nat Immunol 9:1371–1378

NF-κB and Innate Immunity

Anurupa Dev, Shankar Iyer, Bahram Razani and Genhong Cheng

Abstract Members of the NF-κB transcription factor family play a critical role in the development of innate immunity. Upon recognition of pathogen infections or tissue damage, the NF-κB pathway is strongly activated by cellular pattern recognition receptors, including Toll-like receptors and multiple cytosolic receptors such as RIG-I-like helicases and NOD family proteins. NF-κB is required not only for the expression, but also for subsequent signal transduction of numerous downstream cytokines. NF-κB-responsive genes affect a diverse array of cellular processes including apoptosis and cell survival, and often directly control the course of a pathogen infection. In this review, we will examine signaling pathways leading to NF-κB activation during the innate immune response and mechanisms of pathogen-modulation of these pathways; the specifics of NF-κB-dependent gene programs, and the physiological consequences for the immune system caused by the absence of individual NF-κB subunits.

Abbreviations

PRR	Pattern recognition receptor
PAMP	Pathogen associated molecular pattern
TLR	Toll-like receptor
RLR	RIG-I-like receptor
NLR	NOD-like receptor

A. Dev, S. Iyer, B. Razani and G. Cheng (✉)
Department of Microbiology, Immunology & Molecular Genetics,
University of California Los Angeles, 615 Charles Young Dr S.,
210A BSRB, Los Angeles, CA 90095, USA
e-mail: gcheng@mednet.ucla.edu

Current Topics Microbiology (2011) 349: 115-143
DOI: 10.1007/82_2010_102

Published Online: 17 September 2010

IFN	Interferon
IFNAR	Interferon α/β receptor
NF-κB	Nuclear factor-kappaB
LPS	Lipopolysaccharide
TIR	Toll/IL-1R
TRIF	TIR domain-containing adaptor gene inducing IFN-β
MyD88	Myeloid differentiation primary response gene 88
MAPK	Mitogen activated protein kinase
TNF	Tumor necrosis factor
TRAF	TNF receptor-associated factor
TIRAP	TIR-domain containing adaptor protein
IRAK	IL-1 receptor associated kinase
TAK1	Transforming growth factor-activated protein kinase 1
IKK	ikappaB kinase
IRF	Interferon regulatory factor
Poly(I:C)	Polyinosinic:polycytidylic acid
RIP	Receptor interacting protein
RHIM	RIP homotypic interaction motif
IL	Interleukin
TANK	TRAF-family member-associated NF-κB activator
TBK1	TANK-binding kinase-1
VSV	Vesicular stomatitis virus
ISRE	Interferon stimulated response element
RIG-I	Retinoic acid inducible gene-I
pDC	Plasmacytoid dendritic cell
NIK	NF-κB inducing kinase
PI-3K	Phosphatidylinositol 3-kinase
NDV	Newcastle disease virus
CARD	Caspase recruitment domain
Mda5	Melanoma differentiation-associated gene 5
FADD	Fas-associated protein with death domain
DAI	DNA-dependent activator of IFN-regulatory factors
ZBP-1	Z-DNA binding protein-1
NOD	Nucleotide-binding oligomerization domain
HIV-1	Human immunodeficiency virus-1
LTR	Long terminal repeat
HSV-1	Herpes simplex virus-1
ASFV	African swine flu virus
Th1	Type I helper T cell
PRD	Positive regulatory domain

Contents

1 Introduction

The body's first line of defense against invading pathogens is the innate immune system, which generates an immediate, non-specific response against foreign components such as microbial proteins and nucleic acids. When a cell is infected by a virus or bacteria, it undergoes rapid changes, both through pathogen modulation of cellular components as well as activation of the cell's own innate immune response. Activation of the innate immune system is mediated by diverse families of pattern recognition receptors (PRRs) that recognize microbial components known as pathogen associated molecular patterns (PAMPs). Cellular receptors such as Toll-like receptors (TLRs), RIG-I-like receptors (RLRs), and Nod-like receptors (NLRs) are among the array of PRRs that the cell employs to recognize signs of infection.

Once these cellular receptors bind their distinct ligands, specific signal transduction pathways are activated, resulting in the induction of numerous cytokine and chemokine genes. A critical component of the innate immune response is the nuclear factor—kappaB (NF-κB) family of transcription factors. There are five NF-κB family members (NF-κB1, NF-κB2, c-Rel, RelA, and RelB), all of which contain a DNA-binding Rel-homology domain. These transcription factors are sequestered in the cytoplasm by inhibitor of kappaB (IκB) proteins, until upstream signals cause their release into the nucleus, where they bind to ubiquitous NF-κB response elements. Numerous cellular processes are regulated by NF-κB-responsive genes, including inflammation, apoptosis/cell survival, and initiation of the adaptive immune response.

NF-κB is strongly induced downstream of most PRRs, and a number of NF-κB pathway components are also utilized in the development of the innate immune response. Accordingly, viruses and other invading pathogens will often attempt to modulate cellular NF-κB to their own advantage. Among the genes induced by NF-κB itself is the functionally important IFN-β as well as a number of inflammatory chemokines and interleukins. In this chapter, we will review NF-κB signaling and gene regulation during the innate immune response, as well as investigate immune system defects caused by deficiencies in NF-κB family members.

2 Activation of NF-κB by Toll-Like Receptors

Toll-like receptors (TLRs) are a major class of membrane-bound pattern recognition receptors (PRRs) belonging to the IL-1R family. TLRs function as sentinels of the innate immune system and are critical in the induction of long-term acquired immunity. Each TLR is able to recognize distinct PAMPs found in bacteria, viruses, fungi, and protozoa. TLR1, 2, 4, and 6 recognize lipids, with TLR4 specifically detecting lipopolysaccharide (LPS) found in gram-negative bacteria. TLR5 and 11 bind to microbacterial protein components. The final class of TLRs is intracellularly located and able to recognize viral and bacterial nucleic acids which are internalized during an infection via endocytosis of viral particles. TLR3 responds to double-stranded RNA, while TLR7 and 8 recognize single-stranded RNA. Finally, TLR9 binds to double-stranded CpG motifs in pathogen DNA (Kawai and Akira 2007).

2.1 MyD88 and TRIF-Dependent Signaling

TLR signaling is mediated through interactions between the cytoplasmic Toll/IL-1R (TIR) homology domain with downstream adaptor molecules, mainly TRIF (TIR domain-containing adaptor gene inducing IFN-β) and MyD88 (myeloid differentiation primary response gene 88). TLRs, along with other members of the IL-1 receptor (IL-IR) family, such as IL-1R and IL-18R, are potent activators of the mitogen-activated protein kinase (MAPK) and the canonical NF-κB pathway. These receptors are all defined by a common structure consisting of a leucine rich region (LRR) for PAMP recognition or a domain for cytokine binding and the shared cytoplasmic TIR signaling domain.

A critical family of adaptor proteins downstream of MyD88 and TRIF in the innate response is the tumor necrosis factor (TNF) receptor-associated factors (TRAFs). There are six proteins in this family (TRAF1-6), and each contains a conserved C-terminal domain able to interact with a number of different receptors, including TNF receptors, CD40, and TLRs. While many TRAFs were originally identified as required for activation of NF-κB and AP-1, TRAF3 has recently been identified as a positive regulator in the IFN response in a number of cell types (Häcker et al. 2006; Oganesyan et al. 2006).

TLR3 utilizes TRIF to activate both IRF3 and NF-κB (Yamamoto et al. 2002a, b). The other TLRs appear to be MyD88-dependent, with the exception of TLR4 which utilizes TRIF for late-phase IRF3 and NF-κB activation (Fitzgerald et al. 2003a, b; Yamamoto et al. 2003). TLR2 and TLR4 also require the use of an additional adaptor Mal/TIRAP (TIR-domain containing adaptor protein) for MyD88 recruitment (Horng et al. 2002; Yamamoto et al. 2002a, b; Fitzgerald et al. 2001). Mal directly recruits TRAF6 and is essential for NF-κB production downstream of TLR2 and 4 (Verstak et al. 2009). MyD88 recruits members of the IRAK (IL-1 receptor associated kinase) family through its death domain, followed by binding of IRAK1 to TRAF6, which functions as an E3 ubiquitin ligase. TRAF6 ubiquitinates itself as well as TAK1 (transforming growth factor-activated protein kinase 1) and the downstream protein NEMO (Mogensen 2009).

Many of the signal-induced NF-κB pathways converge at the level of IKK activation. The IKK (IkappaB kinase) complex is made up of two catalytic subunits, IKKα and IKKβ, as well as a regulatory subunit IKKγ/NEMO. (Häcker and Karin 2006). The IKK complex sequesters NF-κB in the cytoplasm, until upstream activation signals lead to IKK activation and phosphorylation of the IκB proteins, targeting them for proteasomal degradation (Scheidereit 2006). This degradation is followed by predominant release of c-Rel and RelA-containing dimers to the nucleus (Hayden et al. 2006).

While TRIF activates IRF3 through a TRAF3-dependent pathway, TRIF-dependent activation of NF-κB is separately regulated. TRIF recruits TRAF6 and TAK1 (Sato et al. 2003) as well as the serine–threonine kinase RIP1 (receptor interacting protein 1) to activate NF-κB. TRIF has a RIP homotypic interaction motif (RHIM) through which it interacts with RIP1, and RIP1-deficient MEFs are deficient in NF-κB production upon stimulation with poly(I:C), a synthetic dsRNA ligand for TLR3 (Meylan et al. 2004). TRIF signaling downstream of TLR4 also involves the protein TRAM (TRIF-related adaptor molecule), which interacts with TRIF, TIRAP, and TLR4 and is specifically required for LPS signaling and induction of NF-κB transactivation and subsequent induction of downstream genes IL-6 and TNFα (Fitzgerald et al. 2003a, b; Yamamoto et al. 2003).

2.2 IKK-Related Kinases: TBK1 and IKK-i

In addition to the canonical IKK kinases, there are two IKK-related kinases, TBK1 (TANK binding kinase-1) and IKKε/IKK-i (Peters and Maniatis 2001). TBK1 and IKK-i phosphorylate the interferon regulatory factors IRF3 and IRF7, which are critical in the activation of the IFN response (Fitzgerald et al. 2003a, b; Sharma et al. 2003; McWhirter et al. 2004). Cells deficient in TBK1 displayed a delayed or ablated IFN response to challenge with LPS, poly(I:C), or Sendai virus. However, TBK1 and IKK-i are not essential for TLR-dependent NF-κB activation, as stimulation with these ligands in wildtype and TBK1 deficient cells show no significant difference in NF-κB nuclear localization or DNA-binding activity (Perry et al. 2004; Hemmi et al. 2004; McWhirter et al. 2004).

TANK (TRAF family member-associated NF-κB activator) is a NEMO-interacting protein which links to upstream signals to the IKK complex to activate NF-κB. A NEMO construct lacking the TANK-binding site was not able to fully recapitulate NF-κB activation in $NEMO^{-/-}$ cells. TBK1 and IKK-i are able to promote TANK-IKK complex formation (Chariot et al. 2002). It was later found that TANK also interacts with TRIF as well as IRF3 and that targeted knockdown of TANK leads to a decrease in IFN production and increased viral titers upon Sendai virus infection. This suggests that TANK works as a link between upstream adaptors and TBK1/IKK-i activation in the type I IFN pathway (Guo and Cheng 2007).

2.3 Canonical IKK Kinases in IRF Activation

Recent studies have shown that in addition to inducing NF-κB, members of the canonical IKK signaling complex play a role in regulating IRF phosphorylation and activation. In addition to its involvement in NF-κB activation (Yamaoka et al. 1998), the regulatory IKK subunit NEMO bridges both interferon and NF-κB signaling. MEFs deficient in NEMO have an impaired ability to clear an infection by Sendai virus or VSV (vesicular stomatitis virus), correlated with a decrease in IRF3 and IRF7 activation and interferon-stimulated regulatory element (ISRE) reporter gene activation. NEMO is also able to interact with TANK and recruit the IKK-related kinases TBK-1 and IKK-i to the RNA-virus retinoic acid inducible gene I (RIG-I) signaling complex (Zhao et al. 2007). Additionally, IKKα was shown to be a critical component of interferon signaling downstream of TLR7 and 9 in plasmacytoid dendritic cells (pDCs). IKKα interacts with and directly phosphorylates IRF7, connecting the MyD88 adaptor protein to downstream IFN-α production (Hoshino et al. 2006).

2.4 IFN-Regulated Induction of NF-κB

While PAMP recognition in cells initiates signaling pathways leading to NF-κB induction, as a product of a primary response gene IFN itself can activate NF-κB, acting to amplify the initial inflammatory response and promote cell survival. There are two known mechanisms by which this occurs—first, through phosphatidylinositol 3-kinase (PI3K) and Akt, with STAT3 directly coupling PI3K to IFNAR. Activation of the alternative NF-κB pathway also occurs downstream of IFNAR through a NIK (NF-κB inducing kinase) and TRAF2-dependent mechanism (Du et al. 2007).

3 Intracellular Pattern Recognition Receptors

While certain specialized immune cells such as macrophages and pDCs have high expression of Toll-like receptors, it is clear that many other cells—even those with little to no TLR expression—are able to produce type I IFNs and activate inflammatory pathways. Additionally, MEF cells which are lacking in TLR3, 7, 9, or both TLR adaptors MyD88 and TRIF are still able to produce IFN-β and IL-6 upon Newcastle disease virus (NDV) infection (Kato et al. 2005). Therefore, it was proposed that there is an alternate system of PAMP recognition which functions in fibroblastoid cells.

3.1 Cytoplasmic RIG-I Like Receptors

The mounting of an antiviral response to double-stranded RNA in fibroblastoid cells involves the CARD (caspase recruitment domain)-containing DExD/H-box helicases RIG-I and melanoma differentiation-associated gene 5 (Mda5) (Yoneyama et al. 2005). RIG-I specifically binds to uncapped 5$'$ triphosophate RNA, a characteristic of numerous viral nucleic acids (Hornung et al. 2006). RIG-I deficient MEFs show a reduction in ISRE and NF-κB activation upon Newcastle disease virus (NDV) infection. RIG-I functions upstream of TBK1 and IKK-i to induce IRF3 phosphorylation and IFN-β production (Kato et al. 2005). The CARD domain of RIG-I is essential for RIG-I signaling activity, as its expression alone activates IRF3 and causes constitutive NF-κB DNA-binding activity (Yoneyama et al. 2005). It was subsequently found that RIG-I interacts with another CARD-containing downstream adaptor molecule CARDIF/VISA/MAVS/IPS-1 (Meylan et al. 2005;

Seth et al. 2005; Xu et al. 2005; Kawai et al. 2005). Cardif is able to recruit the classical IKK kinases via its C-terminal region (Meylan et al. 2005) and also interacts with TRIF and TRAF6, indicating a branching point for both IRF and NF-κB activation (Xu et al. 2005). CARDIF also directly and specifically interacts with the critical TLR adaptor TRAF3 via a TRAF-interaction motif, linking it to downstream kinases TBK1 and IKK-i and subsequent IFN-β production (Saha et al. 2006). Intracellular RNA also induces interferon through a TLR3-independent, RIP1/Fas-associated protein with death domain (FADD)/TBK1-dependent mechanism, highlighting the existence of numerous cellular proteins which are utilized in the cytosolic antiviral response (Balachandran et al. 2004).

3.2 Intracellular DNA Recognition

Much like the cellular response to non-self RNAs, infection with a DNA virus or stimulation with synthetic DNAs also causes activation of immune and inflammatory responses. Double-stranded B-form DNA ((poly(dA–dT)·poly(dA–dT)) or *Listeria monocytogenes* bacterial DNA triggers an antiviral response independently of TLRs (Ishii et al. 2006; Stetson and Medzhitov 2006). While the IFN response to DNA was originally thought to be independent of the RIG-I pathway, recent papers have shown that viral and bacterial DNA can be converted into 5′-triphosphate RNA via DNA-dependent RNA Polymerase III pathway to produce ligands for RIG-I, thereby causing the production of NF-κB and type IFNs (Ablasser et al. 2009; Chiu et al. 2009).

The first putative receptor to be identified within the cytosolic DNA pathway was DAI (DNA-dependent activator of IFN-regulatory factors), previously known as ZBP1, or Z-DNA binding protein 1. DAI binds directly to double-stranded DNA, which enhances its association with TBK1 and IRF3 (Takaoka et al. 2007). DAI-dependent activation of NF-κB is dependent on recruitment of RIP1 and RIP3 through the RHIM, and the RHIM-containing viral protein M45 from Murine cytomegalovirus is able to abolish this interaction. The involvement of the RIP kinases in this intracellular pathway mirrors TRIF-dependent activation of NF-κB downstream of TLR3 (Rebsamen et al. 2009; Kaiser et al. 2008). However, it was later shown that DAI is not essential for the type I IFN response, as multiple immune cell types derived from DAI knockout mice had no deficiency in either IFN-β or IL-6 production upon B-DNA stimulation (Ishii et al. 2008).

3.3 NF-κB Activation Downstream of Cytoplasmic Receptors

As previously noted, Toll-like receptor-mediated production of NF-κB involves activation of TAK1 and the IKK complex by TRAF6. TRAF6 is also essential in for NF-κB activation by Sendai virus and NDV in MEF cells, but instead forms a complex with TANK, TBK1, IKK-I, and IRF7. TRAF6 deficient MEFs also are defective in the production of IFN-α, IFN-β, and IL-6 when stimulated with B-DNA (Konno et al. 2009).

3.4 Nod-Like Receptors

Another major class of PRRs is the nod-like receptors (NLRs), cytosolic proteins which are able to mount a response against invading bacteria. NLRs are composed of an N-terminal effector domain, commonly a Pyrin domain (PYD) or caspase recruitment domain (CARD) domain, as well as a nucleotide binding domain (NBD) and C-terminal LRRs. The NLRs NOD1 and NOD2 specifically recognize peptidoglycan fragments contained in a bacterial cell wall. Like TLRs, these two receptors activate MAPK proteins as well as NF-κB and NF-κB-responsive genes IL-18 and IL-1β, key events in the production of an inflammatory response (Creagh and O'Neill 2006). Once an NLR is activated, it self-associates and oligomerizes through the NBD, leading to recruitment of RIP (receptor interacting protein)2 via a homophilic CARD-CARD interaction (Bertin et al. 1999; Ogura et al. 2001). RIP2 interacts directly with NEMO, promoting its ubiquitination and leading to activation of the catalytic IKK complex (Inohara et al. 2000; Abbott et al. 2004). NOD1 and NOD2 activate overlapping gene programs to those activated by TLRs and it is hypothesized this may promote a stronger antibacterial innate immune response (Franchi et al. 2009).

4 Viral Modulation of NF-κB Activity

While NF-κB can play a central role in promoting host cell immunity, NF-κB pathways are also routinely hijacked by pathogens to their own advantage. Viruses are able to block NF-κB to regulate the innate response or in order to induce apoptosis to promote the release and spread of viral progeny. However, viruses also frequently activate NF-κB to enhance cell survival and block apoptosis to further viral replication. Finally, a number of viruses benefit from direct or indirect NF-κB activation as they possess NF-κB binding sequences in their genome. Here, we will discuss some specific examples of how viruses modulate cellular NF-κB pathways during the course of an infection.

4.1 Viral Genomes Containing NF-κB Elements

There are a number of viruses which contain NF-κB response elements in their genomes, thus co-opting the activation of NF-κB to their own advantage

(Hiscott et al. 2006). Human immunodeficiency virus-1 (HIV-1) was found to contain two consensus NF-κB binding sites in the enhancer region which are necessary for viral transcription from the HIV-1 long terminal repeat (LTR) (Nabel and Baltimore 1987). Induction of NF-κB is also required for activation of latent HIV-1 in T cells, specifically by binding of p65 to the LTR and subsequent Pol II recruitment (Williams et al. 2007). Correlated with this role for NF-κB, myeloid cells infected with HIV-1 demonstrate constitutive activation of the IKK complex. If NF-κB signaling is blocked at the level of IκBα, viral RNA levels decrease and HIV-1 multiplication is drastically inhibited (Kwon et al. 1998). While HIV-1 may benefit in this instance from host cell signaling pathways, there are a number of viral-dependent mechanisms of NF-κB activation. These include the HIV-1 envelope protein gp120 binding to the CD4 receptor, or induction through the regulatory protein Tat (Hiscott et al. 2001).

Herpes simplex virus-1 (HSV-1) also contains NF-κB binding sequences in the ICP0 gene region, a key intermediate-early gene in viral replication (Rong et al. 1992). HSV-1 causes persistent nuclear translocation of NF-κB, which is accompanied by a decrease in levels of IκBα and IκBβ (Patel et al. 1998). An active HSV-1 infection is able to redirect nuclear NF-κB from the IκBα gene to consensus sequences in the ICP0 promoter, leading to several hours of sustained transcription of ICP0. Consequently, if virus-induced NF-κB activation is blocked by an IKK inhibitor or a constitutive repressor form of IκBα, there is a significant decrease in viral RNA production as well as HSV-1 replication (Patel et al. 1998; Amici et al. 2006). Thus, the activation of NF-κB can be a critical step for the viral life cycle, particularly when viral gene expression is NF-κB dependent.

4.2 Modulation of Apoptotic Pathways

A host cell can induce apoptosis upon infection to curb viral replication and slow the spread of viral growth. NF-κB is vital in this process, as it is able to transcriptionally activate a number of anti-apoptotic factors such as the inhibitor of apoptosis (IAP) genes as well as Bcl-2 and Bcl-X. These NF-κB signaling pathways can be altered during the course of an infection by interaction with viral proteins, sometimes benefiting viral replication and other times the host innate immune response (reviewed in Roulston et al. 1999). The single-stranded RNA Coxsackie virus has a protease 3Cpro which cleaves IκBα to create a nuclear IκBα fragment able to bind to NF-κB and block its downstream gene activation. The resulting increase in apoptosis also leads to a decrease in viral replication, beneficial to the infected host cell (Zaragoza et al. 2006).

4.3 *Bi-Phasic Control of NF-κB During Viral Infection*

A striking example of the interplay between viruses and NF-κB can be found in the African swine flu virus (ASFV), a large double-stranded DNA virus which differentially regulates NF-κB during the course of an infection. ASFV contains a protein called A238L which is extremely homologous to the IκB proteins but lacks the residues necessary for phosphorylation by IKK and subsequent degradation, thus blocking NF-κB release into the nucleus (Tait et al. 2000). This viral mechanism may be essential in subverting the initial host IFN response. However, in later stages of infection, the IKK-activating late protein A244L is expressed, turning on NF-κB transcriptional activity. A244L is also an IAP-like protein with anti-apoptotic functions, which can further allow for viral replication (Rodríguez et al. 2002). This bi-phasic model of NF-κB control allows the virus to utilize the cellular machinery to gain advantages in carrying out its life cycle and producing viral progeny.

5 NF-κB: Transcriptional Regulation and Gene Targets in the Innate Response

NF-κB acts as a critical mediator of inflammatory responses by directing a transcriptional program of gene expression that leads to the production of antimicrobial effector molecules and factors that promote the recruitment and survival of leukocytes in the inflammatory milieu. Importantly, this transcriptional profile differs depending on the inducing stimuli as well as the cell type mediating the response. In this section, we discuss the molecular mechanisms by which cells in the innate immune system utilize NF-κB to generate and regulate transcriptional gene programs to generate an appropriate inflammatory response.

5.1 *Induction of PAMP-Specific Cytokines and Chemokines*

Stimulation of distinct TLRs exhibits differential cellular responses in various cell types of the innate immune system. TLR function is dictated primarily by ligand specificity, engagement of specific cellular adaptors and finally, activation of differential subsets of transcription factors. Transcriptional specificity is achieved via combinatorial control of signaling pathways. Coordinated signaling events allow for the coincidence of multiple transcription factors on target promoters, which then serve as a platform for dynamic regulation of transcription activation. The result is the induction of distinct gene expression profiles that can be characterized by three major attributes: identity of the genes induced, the potency of induction, and the temporal regulation of induction.

In fact, to some degree one can infer specific PAMP stimulation based on the pattern of cytokine and chemokine expression (Ramirez-Carrozzi et al. 2009). We can reconcile the selectivity of specific gene targets in the inflammatory response through an understanding of the signaling modules that generate the response and characterization of the promoter architecture that regulates gene expression. Below we discuss three major aspects of gene regulation that define the functional specificity of NF-κB targets.

5.1.1 NF-κB Sequence Diversity and Dimerization

NF-κB, similar to other transcription factor families, recognizes DNA binding sites that are widely dispersed throughout the genome. Studies using a systematic panel of single and double NF-κB gene knockouts have confirmed hundreds of NF-κB target genes, and as high throughput technologies become refined, it is becoming more evident that the vast majority of the inflammatory gene expression program is NF-κB dependent (Hoffmann et al. 2003; Hoffmann and Baltimore 2006). Interestingly, while NF-κB site sequences are diverse, the different dimers have broad sequence recognition that largely overlap (Ghosh and Hayden 2008). Still, it remains apparent that individual NF-κB dimers often fulfill distinct physiological roles. For instance, while p65/RelA is expressed ubiquitously, expression of c-Rel is limited to monocytic and lymphocytic lineages (Liou et al. 1994). The functional consequence is demonstrated in the regulation of IL-12/p40 which is dependent on c-Rel but not p65 (Sanjabi et al. 2000).

5.1.2 Stimulus Specific Gene Expression via NF-κB Dynamic Control

Though many receptor modules of the innate immune system utilize similar components and activate common downstream transcriptional activators including NF-κB, AP-1, and C/EBP, they do so with disparate amplifying power. For instance, canonical IKK proteins can be activated by members of the TLR and TNF-R1 superfamilies. Remarkably, cell stimulation by LPS or TNF to activate TLR4 and TNF-R1, respectively, produces characteristically distinct IKK induction profiles independent of stimulus concentration (Werner et al. 2005; Cheong et al. 2006).

While the exact mechanisms responsible for stimulus specific IKK activity is not known, initial studies suggest differential feedback mechanisms modulate IKK activity over time. TNF-induced IKK is subject to negative regulation by A20, whereas LPS-induced IKK is amplified by a feed-forward autocrine TNF loop (Lee et al. 2000; Werner et al. 2005). Importantly, feedback mechanisms on IKK activity differentially alter NF-κB activation and result in distinct transcriptional profiles.

Stimulus specific gene expression is also subject to desensitization of immune cells to subsequent agonist treatment in a phenomenon known as "endotoxin tolerance." One of the main characteristics of LPS tolerance is a change in the pattern of inflammatory gene expression in cells of myeloid lineage when the response to one or two sequential LPS exposures are compared (Henricson et al. 1991). For example, re-stimulation of monocytes and macrophages previously exposed to LPS fails to elicit TNF-α, IL-1β, IL-6, IL-12, and Jun B gene expression although other genes including IL-10 and TNFRII are expressed at normal or elevated levels (Dobrovolskaia and Vogel 2002). While disruption of major signaling components leading to NF-κB activation and translocation are observed in LPS-pretreated macrophages, including IRAK-1 and IκBα, a global suppression of all LPS response genes is not observed. Instead, there appears to be locus specific control that leads to diametric suppression and over-expression of certain gene sets.

5.1.3 Temporal Recruitment of NF-κB Members

Generation of the inflammatory response relies on a shared subset of transcription factors recruited to the promoters of inflammatory cytokines. Most prominent are NF-κB, AP-1, and C/EBP family members. Although the induction of pro-inflammatory genes is accelerated in response to microbial infection, there is still a level of temporal regulation.

Before most transcriptional activator factors access their binding sites, DNA transitions from a condensed to a decondensed chromatin structure. The activation of transcription is preceded by the remodeling of specific nucleosomes. As a major determinant of cell identity and cell memory, chromatin structure is a particularly significant contributor to gene regulation, in that it serves to mark genes that are expressed constitutively versus those that are poised for expression upon exposure to a stimulus.

However, even groups of genes that exhibit inducible expression are subject to diverse kinetic and temporal regulation. For instance, upon LPS stimulation, NFκB is rapidly recruited to the CXCL2 and TNFα promoters, whereas the IL-6, CCL5, and CCL2 promoters display delayed NFκB association (Ramirez-Carrozzi et al. 2006).

Accessibility of NFκB to its target sequences is dependent on the chromatin architecture of the enhancer regions and promoters that regulate gene expression. As a result we can define classes of inflammatory genes as primary or secondary response genes based on the kinetics of their expression. Interestingly, categorizing gene subsets in this manner correlates with requirements for locus specific recruitment of ATP-dependent nucleosome remodeling complexes, such as SWI/SNF. IL-6, CCL5, CCL2, and other secondary response genes are dependent on SWI/SNF recruitment and enzymatic activity, whereas CXCL2 and TNFα expression are not (Ramirez-Carrozzi et al. 2006). It has been proposed that SWI/SNF is required to establish accessibility and maintenance of transcription promoting chromatin structure in macrophages.

Furthermore, many secondary response genes require the de novo synthesis of transcription factors induced rapidly as part of the primary response gene set. For instance, LPS induces IκBζ, which is essential for the induction of IL-12/p40 and IL-6, but not for the induction of primary response gene TNF (Yamamoto et al.

2004). Interestingly, the regulation of innate response genes can differ depending on cell type. For example, IL-6 displays a secondary response gene expression profile in macrophages, but a primary response profile in fibroblasts in response to LPS (Kishimoto 2006).

5.2 NF-κB Regulation of Specific Genes

Transcriptional specificity is achieved via combinatorial control of signaling pathways. Though the heterogeneity of gene induction precludes generalization of inducible gene expression, a number of transcriptional systems have been studied that provide a model for the types of molecular events regulating the activation of inflammatory cytokines in the innate immune system. Below we discuss two prominently studied genes, the *IFN-β enhanceosome* that regulates the expression of IFN-β, a critical mediator of anti-viral response and the *IL-12β/p40* locus which is involved in initiating the type I helper T cell (Th1) response.

5.2.1 Regulation of the IFN-β Enhanceosome

Cis-regulatory DNA sequences, such as promoters and enhancers, integrate and process regulatory circuits created by complex signaling pathways. Many *cis*-regulatory elements contain multiple binding sites for distinct transcription factors that co-assemble into higher order multi-factorial complexes on the enhancer DNA. Fully assembled enhancer complexes, or enhanceosomes, modify the local chromatin architecture and recruit the RNA Polymerase II machinery to the promoter to initiate transcription of the target gene.

One of the best characterized higher eukaryotic enhancers is that of the Interferon-β (IFN-β) gene. Expression of the IFNβ gene requires the coordinate activation and direct contact of three dimeric transcription factor families: ATF-2/c-Jun, IRF-3/IRF-7, NF-κB, and the architectural protein HMGA1 to a 55 base pair region, termed the enhancer, immediately upstream of the transcription initiation site of the IFN-β promoter (Thanos and Maniatis 1995; Merika and Thanos 2001). The IFNβ enhancer operates as a platform for the coordinate recruitment and assembly of the aforementioned activator transcription factors into a highly stable protein complex, named the enhanceosome (Kim and Maniatis 1997; Munshi et al. 1999).

Following assembly, the enhanceosome directs the modification and repositioning of nucleosomes on the IFN-β promoter that sterically block the formation of a transcriptional pre-initiation complex on the IFN-β promoter. Importantly, the expression of IFN-β is dependent on the coincident presence of all required transcription factors on the enhancer. That is, individual factors do not activate IFN-β gene expression by themselves, and failure to mobilize any one of the factors abrogates IFN-β transcription entirely (Kim and Maniatis 1997; Munshi et al. 1999). Thus, the enhanceosome functions as a single regulatory unit in which the enhancer forms a composite binding module of overlapping cis elements.

Though the enhanceosome functions as a single composite integrative unit, it can be divided into four structural positive regulatory domains (PRD I-IV) characterized by specific overlapping protein interaction motifs. The enhancer region spans a nucleosome-free interval from -102 to -47 relative to the transcription start site. Virus infection leads to the activation of ATF-2/c-Jun, IRF-3/7, and NF-κB and their binding to the nucleosome-free enhancer. Structural mapping of three sets of overlapping crystal structures reveal ATF-2/c -Jun complexed with two IRF-3 molecules on the PRDIII-IV regions of the enhancer, while NF-κB complexes with IRF-7 and IRF-3 across PRDI-II (Panne et al. 2004; Panne et al. 2007). The structure shows that this combinatorial specificity is encoded not just in the various binding sites but also in their overlap and in their positions with respect to each other. HMGA1, while required for enhanceosome assembly, is not present in the functional enhanceosome complex, suggesting a role as a scaffolding protein or molecular chaperone (Panne et al. 2007).

Unlike ATF-2/c-Jun or the two IRF dimers, NF-κB binds a 12 bp site that does not overlap with its neighbors. In vivo studies suggest that a p50:p65 heterodimer predominately constitutes the NF-κB component of the enhanceosome complex, but that other NF-κB dimer combinations can exist (Ghosh et al. 1995; Berkowitz et al. 2002; Escalante et al. 2002). In theory, the inclusion of differential NF-κB components in the enhanceosome can contribute to allosteric conformational changes that can modulate or fine-tune IFN-β expression, but that possibility has not been studied in extensive detail as of yet.

Thus, cooperative binding and major contributions from the architectural activities of HMGA1, elicits the formation of a highly stable enhanceosome complex. Two nucleosomes flank the IFN-β enhancer, including a highly positioned nucleosome that masks a downstream TATA box required for the recruitment of basal transcription factors, such as TATA-binding protein (TBP) and transcription factor IID (TFIID), necessary for the formation of the transcription pre-initiation complex and activation of RNA Polymerase II. Remodeling of the two flanking nucleosomes is mediated by the sequential recruitment and activation of CBP/p300 and GCN5, both of which possess histone acetyl-transferase (HAT) activity. CBP/p300 is recruited to the interface of the IFN-β enhanceosome complex and makes contacts with all four transcription factor dimers, which may explain why IFN-β expression only occurs when all enhanceosome components are assembled on the enhancer in the correct conformation. Acetylation of the flanking histones recruits the ATP-dependent nucleosome remodeling complex SWI/SNF, which displaces the nucleosome from the proximal IFN-β promoter (Agalioti et al. 2000). After remodeling, the pre-initiation complex gains access to the IFN-β promoter via the recruitment of TFIID, which contains TBP, allowing for stability of the RNA Polymerase II holoenzyme and subsequent transcription initiation (Agalioti et al. 2000).

5.2.2 Regulation of the Interleukin 12 p40 Locus

Interleukin 12 (IL-12) is a heterodimeric cytokine secreted by macrophages and other antigen presenting cells upon microbial infection that serves to stimulate the development of the Th1 response. As a result, IL-12 serves as a bridge between the innate and adaptive immune response and consequently its activity and regulation has been studied quite extensively.

IL-12 (p70) comprises a heterodimer of p35 and p40, each of which is regulated in distinct fashions. The p35 subunit is expressed ubiquitously and is regulated primarily at the post-transcriptional level (Kelly and Locksley 2000). In contrast, the p40 gene is regulated at the transcriptional level and is highly inducible by microbial products. The production of IL-12 is induced via two different mechanism. First, innate immune cells, exposed to microorganisms or microbial products, such as *Listeria monocytogenes* or LPS stimulation, generate IL-12. IL-12 can also be produced upon the engagement of CD40 stimulation during T lymphocyte-antigen-presenting cell interactions (Ellwood et al. 1998).

Within the innate immune system, IL-12p40 expression is regulated by both positive and negative signaling cascades. IL-12p40 is induced by IFN-γ, TNFα, GM-CSF as well as stimulation via TLRs (Weintraub and Groudine 1976; Hebbes et al. 1994; Schübeler et al. 2000). Constitutive activation of IL-12 is associated with a number of auto-immune diseases, and so a number of negative regulators of IL-12 exist, including IL-10, IL-4, IL-11, IL-13, transforming growth factor-β, and IFN-α/β (Wu et al. 1979; Takemoto et al. 1998; Agarwal and Rao 1998; Kubo et al. 1997; Riggs and Pfeifer 1992).

Transcriptional regulation of IL-12p40 is best understood in the upon engagement of TLR4 signaling via LPS stimulation (Kubo et al. 1997; Riggs and Pfeifer 1992; Kim et al. 1999). TLR activation leads to both IKK activation as well as p38 MAPK activity to activate downstream transcription factor targets including NF-κB, AP-1, C/EBP, and IRF-1, all of which bind to the proximal IL-12p40 promoter at distinct sites.

Activation of IL-12p40 differs mechanistically from IFN-β gene expression in a number of ways. First, IL-12p40 induction has a specific requirement for c-Rel containing NF-κB dimers. Subsequently, c-rel$^{-/-}$ mice exhibit defective IL-12p40 expression and this impairment cannot be rescued by ectopic expression of NF-κB dimers containing p65 but not c-Rel. Also, IL-12p40 induction is limited primarily to lymphoid tissues which specifically express the c-Rel subunit (Sanjabi et al. 2000).

In addition, while the expression of IFN-β features the coordinate assembly of an enhanceosome directly upstream of the proximal promoter, induction of IL-12p40 involves activation of a distal enhancer element located approximately 10 kb upstream of the IL-12p40 promoter. This region is specifically remodeled upon TLR stimulation prior to the recruitment of NF-κB, AP-1, and C/EBP to the IL-12p40 (Weinmann et al. 2001). While the specific events involved in remodeling this distal enhancer are not known, studies have shown that they occur in an

NF-κB-independent fashion and are required to provide accessibility DNA target sites to transcription factors by initiating nucleosome remodeling at the proximal promoter (Weinmann et al. 2001).

Importantly, IL-12p40 induction is contextual and modulated differentially with respect to different stimuli. It follows that IL-12p40 expression can be synergistically induced by TLR and IFN-γ stimulation (Bell et al. 2001). Presumably this is a result of both the increased potency of signaling as well as differential combinations of transcription factors recruited to the promoter.

6 Negative Regulation of NF-κB

Overall, the mechanisms underlying transcriptional termination of the NF-κB response are poorly understood compared to our understanding of the regulatory mechanisms that lead to its activation. Still, it is apparent that NF-κB plays an active role in the modulation of inflammatory response through a number of feedback mechanisms.

6.1 Induction of IκB Family Members

IκB proteins function to sequester NF-κB dimers in the cytosol, preventing gene target activation. IκB family members also represent potent targets of NF-κB transcription that are immediately induced upon activation of inflammatory pathways. Thus, de novo synthesis of IκB members in the cytosol acts as a "molecular sponge" to prevent sustained activation of NF-κB targets by preventing further nuclear translocation of NF-κB dimers over time. Additionally, p65/RelA and c-Rel bound to a promoter NF-κB element can be ubiquitinated and degraded in an IKKα-dependent manner (Carmody and Chen 2007). IKKα also negatively regulates c-Rel and RelA by accelerating promoter clearance of these subunits at pro-inflammatory genes, possibly through a phosphorylation-dependent mechanism (Lawrence et al. 2005).

6.2 Negative Regulators Upstream of the IKK Complex

There are a number of signaling components upstream of the IKK complex which are also involved in dampening NF-κB-activating pathways. The kinase-deficient IRAK molecule IRAK-M is able to block signal-induced association of IRAK1 and TRAF6, cutting off TLR-induced NF-κB. TOLLIP, another protein which complexes with IRAK1 (Burns et al. 2000) as well as TLR2 and TLR4, inhibits

IRAK1 phosphorylation and kinase activity by acting as a direct IRAK1 substrate (Zhang and Ghosh 2002). SOCS1 (suppressor of cytokine signaling-1) acts through a different mechanism, targeting the TLR2/4 adaptor Mal for polyubiquitination and degradation. A deficiency in SOCS1 leads to a sustained increase in p65 phosphorylation and transactivation, as well as expression of the pro-inflammatory genes IL-6 and TNFα (Mansell et al. 2006).

A protein which has been found to downregulate NF-κB signaling downstream of a number of different receptors is the LPS-induced ubiquitin modifying enzyme A20. While originally found to limit TNF-induced NF-κB activation, A20 also deubiquitinates TRAF6 and RIP1 and is necessary for the termination of NF-κB activity and proinflammatory cytokine production downstream of TLRs (Boone et al. 2004; Wertz et al. 2004). A20 similarly functions as a negative regulator in the RIG-I pathway, blocking signaling to NF-κB and IRF3 (Lin et al. 2006). Finally, A20 inhibits RIP2 ubiquitination and NF-κB activation downstream of NOD1 and NOD2 (Hasegawa et al. 2008; Hitotsumatsu et al. 2008).

6.3 Induction of Anti-Inflammatory Cytokines

Interleukin 10 (IL-10) is a potent anti-inflammatory cytokine that suppresses the induction of pro-inflammatory cytokine genes, including IL12p40. IL-10 is secreted primarily by activated macrophages and T cells and its impaired expression is associated with the development of a number of auto-immune diseases including Crohn's disease, rheumatoid arthritis, and multiple sclerosis. Importantly, IL-10 is induced in part through an NF-κB-dependent pathway, although the mechanisms are not known (Wessells et al. 2004). Logically, IL-10 production is under temporal control, usually occurring subsequent to the induction of primary NF-κB inflammatory targets.

6.4 NF-κB Induced Tolerance

Tolerance refers to the phenomenon by which prior exposure to a specific inflammatory insult leads a reduced inflammatory response to subsequent challenge of the same stimulus. It represents one way by which host response prevents excessive inflammation and endotoxin shock (Beeson 1947). Tolerance is normally attributed to decreased receptor sensitivity and attenuation of signaling cascades. NF-κB can play a major role in dampening response by the accumulation of p50 containing dimers on transcriptional targets. These dimers lack a transactivation domain (TAD) and are unable to direct gene transcription. Alternatively, in some cases, RelB can act as a transcriptional repressor in LPS-induced tolerance. RelB is induced by LPS at later timepoints and can act to specifically suppress pro-inflammatory cytokines like IL-1 and TNF (Saccani et al. 2003; El Gazzar et al. 2007).

7 Physiological Roles of NF-κB in Innate Immunity

Determining the precise physiological role of NF-κB in innate host defense is challenging given the multifarious functions these transcription factors play in multiple tissues. Therefore, while a large number of studies have shown that deficiency of particular NF-κB subunits results in increased or decreased susceptibility to a variety of pathogens, it has been difficult to dissect whether the cause was due to defects in immune cell development, immune organ development, innate or adaptive cell functionality, or cell survival. These challenges lie on top of the fact that our understanding of how infections are ultimately controlled on an organismal scale is still developing. In the section below, we review studies where mice deficient in particular subunits of NF-κB have been challenged with bacterial or viral infection and defects in innate host defense have been observed.

*7.1 RelA (*rela*)*

As RelA-deficient mice are embryonic lethal at day 14, the physiological role of RelA in innate host defense has been addressed through the use of chimeric mice and in vivo administration of antisense oligonucleotides or adenoviral vectors prior to infection (Doi et al. 1997). Adoptive transfer of *rela*$^{-/-}$ fetal liver cells into lethally irradiated hosts results in dramatically increased susceptibility to *Leishmania major* (Mise-Omata et al. 2009). While no differences are observed between *rela*$^{-/-}$ and *rela*$^{-++}$ chimeric mice in the T-cell response to *Leishmania* infection, macrophages from *rela*$^{-/-}$ chimeras display reduced expression of NOS2 and Fas in response to infection and in vivo expression of these genes is also reduced. Overexpression of RelA using intratracheal injection of adenoviral vectors results in reduced pulmonary load of *Pseudomonas aeruginosa* in wildtype mice (Sadikot et al. 2006). However, no increased resistance with RelA-overexpression is observed in *tnfα*$^{-/-}$ mice, suggesting that RelA-induced synthesis of TNF-α is responsible for this phenomenon. Finally, gastric administration of antisense oligonucleotides targeting RelA results in reduced production of TNF-α and IL-1b in gastric tissues in response to *Helicobacter pylori* infection in the absence of any major histopathological changes (Kim et al. 2005).

*7.2 RelB (*relb*)*

Unlike RelA, RelB-deficient mice live to adulthood; however, they display histopathological abnormalities in a number of immune tissues and inflammatory changes in several organs (Weih et al. 1995). *Relb*$^{-/-}$ mice are highly susceptible to in vivo *Listeria monocytogenes* infection yet recruitment of neutrophils to sites of infection is not affected, neither is the phagocytic ability or NO production of *relb*$^{-/-}$ macrophages reduced (Weih et al.1997). However, macrophages from *relb*$^{-/-}$ mice show a reduced ability to express TNFα in reponse to in vitro treatment with LPS or IFN-γ and *relb*$^{-/-}$ neutrophils show defects in phagocytic ability. In addition to *Listeria*, RelB-deficient mice have also been shown to be significantly more susceptible to *Toxoplasma gondii* infection which was associated with a severe defect in IFN-γ production from splenocytes which was thought to result in reduced natural killer cell function (Caamaño et al. 1999). Although these deficiencies correlate with increased susceptibility to these infectious agents, further studies will have to be done to demonstrate that they are the cause of reduced resistance seen in *relb*$^{-/-}$ animals.

7.3 *c-Rel* (rel)

Rel-deficient mice develop to adulthood and display significant susceptibility to *Leishmania major* infection (Grigoriadis et al. 1996). Interestingly, while development and migration of *rel*$^{-/-}$ macrophages are completely normal, resident but not elicited *rel*$^{-/-}$ peritoneal macrophages have a significant defect in the cytotoxic activity. This defect is associated with a deficiency in iNOS induction and subsequent NO_2^- production by resident but not elicited *rel*$^{-/-}$ peritoneal macrophages. Furthermore, TNFα production is defective in both resident and elicited *rel*$^{-/-}$ peritoneal macrophages upon in vitro infection with *Listeria monocytogenes* (Mason et al. 2002). *Rel*-deficient macrophages also show a defect in IL-12 production in response to infection with *Corynebacterium parvum*; however, this deficiency does not exist when macrophages are stimulated with *Toxoplasma gondii* and *rel*$^{-/-}$ mice do not show any increased susceptibility to this pathogen (Mason et al. 2002). Rel also appears to play an important role in the inflammatory response to infection as *rel*$^{-/-}$ mice on a RAG background develop significantly more colitis than RAG mice when infected with *Helicobacter hepaticus* (Wang et al. 2008). Finally, although *Rel*-deficient mice display a slight delay in clearance of influenza infection, this has been associated with defects in the adaptive immune response to the virus (Harling-McNabb et al. 1999).

7.4 *p50/p105 (NF-κB1)*

The absence of the p50 NF-κB subunit has been most extensively studied in the context of innate host defense. Mice deficient in p50 have significant difficulty controlling acute infections with the intracellular bacterium *L. monocytogenes* and the gram positive pathogen *S. pneumoniae*, resulting in greater bacterial titer and a wider systemic distribution of bacteria (Sha et al. 1995). As the authors found normal numbers of phagocytes which displayed unaltered phagocytic activity, they concluded that the increased bacterial susceptibility is likely due to defective cytokine-mediated activation of the phagocytes. This study also found that $p50^{-/-}$ mice display no differences in susceptibility to the gram-negative bacteria *E. coli* K1 or *H. Influenzae*, possibly because sufficient NF-κB-independent host defenses were triggered by LPS to control the infections. In contrast, later studies demonstrated the importance of p50 for control of the natural gram-negative murine gastrointestinal pathogen *Citrobacter rodentium* (Dennis et al. 2008). In this model, the time and extent of *Citrobacter* colonization is markedly increased in $p50^{-/-}$ mice as compared to wildtype mice. Although levels of major inflammatory cytokines are equivalent between wildtype and p50-deficient mice, a significant defect in leukocyte recruitment to the site of the infection is observed in $p50^{-/-}$ mice (Dennis et al. 2008). Finally, using a more specific gene knockout approach, Ishikawa and colleagues specifically deleted the c-terminus of p105, leaving only the p50 subunit intact (Ishikawa et al. 1998). Interestingly, these mice are highly susceptible to opportunistic bacterial infections which may be due to the reduced cytokine production from macrophages. Taken together, these studies demonstrate the critical importance of p50 in host defense against a variety of different bacteria.

The role of p50 in the control of viral infections has also been studied to some extent. Sha et al. first reported that $p50^{-/-}$ mice display increased resistance to infection with the picornavirus Encephalomyocarditis virus (EMCV) possibly due to increased production of IFN-β(12). However, a later study suggested that the increased resistance of $p50^{-/-}$ mice is not IFNAR-dependent and instead is likely due to rapid infection-induced apoptosis of $p50^{-/-}$ cells thus precluding viral release (Schwarz et al. 1998). In contrast, a role for p50 in control of in vivo viral replication through modulation of IFN production has been demonstrated for reovirus. Although reovirus replication is not affected by the absence of p50 in most organs, the hearts of $p50^{-/-}$ mice have significantly higher viral titers resulting in substantially greater cardiac pathology (O'Donnell et al. 2005). This heart-specific defect in control of reovirus in $p50^{-/-}$ mice is associated with significantly reduced levels of cardiac IFN-β induction and the myocarditis observed in p50-deficient animals can be corrected with treatment of exogenous IFN-β.

Table 1 Increased pathogen susceptibility in NF-κB knockout mice

NF-κB subunit	Organism
RelA	*H. pylori*, *P. aeruginosa*, *L. major*
RelB	*L. monocytogenes*, *T. gondii*, LCMV
c-Rel	*L. major*, *H. hepaticus*, *T. gondii*, Influenza
p50/p105	*L. monocytogenes*, *S. pneumoniae*, *E. coli*, *H. Influenzae*, *C. rodentium*, *M. Tuberculosis*, Encephalomyocarditis Virus, Reovirus, H5N1
p52/p100	*L. major*, *T. gondii*, Influenza

7.5 p52/p100 (NF-κB2)

Investigations into the role of p52/p100 in innate host defense have been quite limited possibly because the major phenotypes of *p100*$^{-/-}$ mice largely concern the adaptive immune system such as lymphoid organ microarchitecture and lymphocyte maintenance. However, when Speirs and colleagues used a *Leishmania major* infection model, they found the increased susceptibility of p100-deficient mice to this pathogen is not due to an intrinsic T-cell defects but rather due to decreased IL-12 production by *p100*$^{-/-}$ macrophages (Speirs et al. 2002). This was most likely a result of the critical role of p52/p100 in transmitting signaling through CD40-receptor on macrophages which is required for IL-12 transactivation. Although p52/p100 knockout mice have been observed during a number of different infections, any deficiencies in host defense have been attributed to defects in adaptive immunity (Franzoso et al. 1998; Caamaño et al. 2000).

In addition to genetic deficiency of NF-κB transcription factors, NF-κB activity of multiple dimers can also be generically inhibited through transgenic overexpression of a degradation-resistant mutant of IκB. When this has been done in the liver, mice are rendered highly susceptible to *Listeria monocytogenes* infection possibly through defective induction of protective cytokines (Lavon et al. 2000). Determining the precise role that NF-κB plays has been difficult given the complexity of how infections are cleared and the diverse roles that NF-κB subunits play in immune function and cell survival. However, taken together, all of these studies clearly demonstrate the important role of NF-κB in innate host defense against bacterial and viral pathogens (see Table 1).

8 Conclusion

Significant advances have been made in delineating the role of the NF-κB family of transcription factors in regulating inflammation and the innate immune response. Activation of NF-κB is essential for production of the antiviral cytokine IFN-β, as well as an inflammatory response which leads to the recruitment and activation of immune effector cells. Numerous pathogens hijack cellular NF-κB proteins to suppress innate immune responses and modulate apoptotic pathways to their own benefit. Many specific regulatory mechanisms have been identified, but it is clear that there are a number of undiscovered instances of pathogen-mediated modulation of the NF-κB pathway, which should continue to be examined in both in vitro and in vivo infection models. While in vivo models of mice lacking NF-κB subunits generally exhibit defects in pathogen clearance, the mechanism leading to this impaired host defense is not always clear given the complexity of the immune response and diversity of immunological systems involved. Studies have historically focused on the role of NF-κB in hematopoetic cells in orchestrating the innate and adaptive host immune response. However, it is becoming increasingly clear that NF-κB activation in epithelial cells which encounter pathogens is also critically important (Lavon et al. 2000; Zaph et al. 2007; Nenci et al. 2007). Future studies of NF-κB and related signaling components in specific cell types will help dissect their roles in the development of successful immune responses against a wide array of pathogen infections.

References

Abbott DW, Wilkins A, Asara JM, Cantley LC (2004) The Crohn's disease protein, NOD2, requires RIP2 in order to induce ubiquitinylation of a novel site on NEMO. Curr Biol 14: 2217–2227

Ablasser A, Bauernfeind F, Hartmann G, Latz E, Fitzgerald KA et al (2009) RIG-I-dependent sensing of poly(dA:dT) through the induction of an RNA polymerase III-transcribed RNA intermediate. Nat Immunol 10: 1065–1072

Agarwal S, Rao A (1998) Modulation of chromatin structure regulates cytokine gene expression during T cell differentiation. Immunity 9:765–775

Agalioti T, Lomvardas S, Parekh B, Yie J, Maniatis T et al (2000) Ordered recruitment of chromatin modifying and general transcription factors to the IFN-beta promoter. Cell 103:667–678

Amici C, Rossi A, Costanzo A, Ciafrè S, Marinari B et al (2006) Herpes simplex virus disrupts NF-kappaB regulation by blocking its recruitment on the IkappaBalpha promoter and directing the factor on viral genes. J Biol Chem 281:7110–7117

Balachandran S, Thomas E, Barber GN (2004) A FADD-dependent innate immune mechanism in mammalian cells. Nature 432:401–405

Beeson PB (1947) Tolerance to bacterial pyrogens: I. Factors influencing its development. J Exp Med 86:29–38

Bell AC, West AG, Felsenfeld G (2001) Insulators and boundaries: versatile regulatory elements in the eukaryotic genome. Science 291:447–450

Berkowitz B, Huang D, Chen-Park FE, Sigler PB, Ghosh G (2002) The x-ray crystal structure of the NF-kappa B p50.p65 heterodimer bound to the interferon beta-kappa B site. J Biol Chem 277:24694–24700

Bertin J, Nir WJ, Fischer CM, Tayber OV, Errada PR et al (1999) Human CARD4 protein is a novel CED-4/Apaf-1 cell death family member that activates NF-kappaB. J Biol Chem 274:12955–12958

Boone DL, Turer EE, Lee EG, Ahmad R, Wheeler MT et al (2004) The ubiquitin-modifying enzyme A20 is required for termination of Toll-like receptor responses. Nat Immunol 5:1052–1060

Burns K, Clatworthy J, Martin L, Martinon F, Plumpton C et al (2000) Tollip, a new component of the IL-1RI pathway, links IRAK to the IL-1 receptor. Nat Cell Biol 2:346–351

Caamaño J, Alexander J, Craig L, Bravo R, Hunter CA (1999) The NF-kappa B family member RelB is required for innate and adaptive immunity to *Toxoplasma gondii.* J Immunol 163:4453–4461

Caamaño J, Tato C, Cai G, Villegas EN, Speirs K et al (2000) Identification of a role for NF-kappa B2 in the regulation of apoptosis and in maintenance of T cell-mediated immunity to *Toxoplasma gondii.* J Immunol 165:5720–5728

Carmody RJ, Chen YH (2007) Nuclear factor-kappaB: activation and regulation during toll-like receptor signaling. Cell Mol Immunol 4:31–41

Chariot A, Leonardi A, Muller J, Bonif M, Brown K et al (2002) Association of the adaptor TANK with the I kappa B kinase (IKK) regulator NEMO connects IKK complexes with IKK epsilon and TBK1 kinases. J Biol Chem 277:37029–37036

Cheong R, Bergmann A, Werner SL, Regal J, Hoffmann A et al (2006) Transient IkappaB kinase activity mediates temporal NF-kappaB dynamics in response to a wide range of tumor necrosis factor-alpha doses. J Biol Chem 281:2945–2950
Chiu Y, Macmillan JB, Chen ZJ (2009) RNA polymerase III detects cytosolic DNA and induces type I interferons through the RIG-I pathway. Cell 138:576–591
Creagh EM, O'Neill LAJ (2006) TLRs, NLRs and RLRs: a trinity of pathogen sensors that co-operate in innate immunity. Trends Immunol 27:352–357
Dennis A, Kudo T, Kruidenier L, Girard F, Crepin VF et al (2008) The p50 subunit of NF-kappaB is critical for in vivo clearance of the noninvasive enteric pathogen Citrobacter rodentium. Infect Immun 76:4978–4988
Dobrovolskaia MA, Vogel SN (2002) Toll receptors, CD14, and macrophage activation and deactivation by LPS. Microbes Infect 4:903–914
Doi TS, Takahashi T, Taguchi O, Azuma T, Obata Y (1997) NF-kappa B RelA-deficient lymphocytes: normal development of T cells and B cells, impaired production of IgA and IgG1 and reduced proliferative responses. J Exp Med 185:953–961
Du Z, Wei L, Murti A, Pfeffer SR, Fan M et al (2007) Non-conventional signal transduction by type 1 interferons: the NF-kappaB pathway. J Cell Biochem 102:1087–1094
El Gazzar M, Yoza BK, Hu JY, Cousart SL, McCall CE (2007) Epigenetic silencing of tumor necrosis factor alpha during endotoxin tolerance. J Biol Chem 282:26857–26864
Ellwood K, Chi T, Huang W, Mitsouras K, Carey M (1998) Cooperative assembly of RNA polymerase II transcription complexes. Cold Spring Harb Symp Quant Biol 63:253–261
Escalante CR, Shen L, Thanos D, Aggarwal AK (2002) Structure of NF-kappaB p50/p65 heterodimer bound to the PRDII DNA element from the interferon-beta promoter. Structure 10:383–391
Fitzgerald KA, Palsson-McDermott EM, Bowie AG, Jefferies CA, Mansell AS et al (2001) Mal (MyD88-adapter-like) is required for Toll-like receptor-4 signal transduction. Nature 413:78–83
Fitzgerald KA, McWhirter SM, Faia KL, Rowe DC, Latz E et al (2003a) IKKepsilon and TBK1 are essential components of the IRF3 signaling pathway. Nat Immunol 4:491–496
Fitzgerald KA, Rowe DC, Barnes BJ, Caffrey DR, Visintin A et al (2003b) LPS-TLR4 signaling to IRF-3/7 and NF-kappaB involves the toll adapters TRAM and TRIF. J Exp Med 198:1043–1055
Franchi L, Warner N, Viani K, Nuñez G (2009) Function of Nod-like receptors in microbial recognition and host defense. Immunol Rev 227:106–128
Franzoso G, Carlson L, Poljak L, Shores EW, Epstein S et al (1998) Mice deficient in nuclear factor (NF)-kappa B/p52 present with defects in humoral responses, germinal center reactions, and splenic microarchitecture. J Exp Med 187:147–159
Ghosh S, Hayden MS (2008) New regulators of NF-kappaB in inflammation. Nat Rev Immunol 8:837–848
Ghosh G, van Duyne G, Ghosh S, Sigler PB (1995) Structure of NF-kappa B p50 homodimer bound to a kappa B site. Nature 373:303–310
Grigoriadis G, Zhan Y, Grumont RJ, Metcalf D, Handman E et al (1996) The Rel subunit of NF-kappaB-like transcription factors is a positive and negative regulator of macrophage gene expression: distinct roles for Rel in different macrophage populations. EMBO J 15:7099–7107
Guo B, Cheng G (2007) Modulation of the interferon antiviral response by the TBK1/IKKi adaptor protein TANK. J Biol Chem 282:11817–11826
Häcker H, Karin M (2006) Regulation and function of IKK and IKK-related kinases. Sci STKE 2006:re13
Häcker H, Redecke V, Blagoev B, Kratchmarova I, Hsu L et al (2006) Specificity in Toll-like receptor signalling through distinct effector functions of TRAF3 and TRAF6. Nature 439:204–207
Harling-McNabb L, Deliyannis G, Jackson DC, Gerondakis S, Grigoriadis G et al (1999) Mice lacking the transcription factor subunit Rel can clear an influenza infection and have functional anti-viral cytotoxic T cells but do not develop an optimal antibody response. Int Immunol 11:1431–1439

Hasegawa M, Fujimoto Y, Lucas PC, Nakano H, Fukase K et al (2008) A critical role of RICK/RIP2 polyubiquitination in Nod-induced NF-kappaB activation. EMBO J 27:373–383

Hayden MS, West AP, Ghosh S (2006) NF-kappaB and the immune response. Oncogene 25:6758–6780

Hebbes TR, Clayton AL, Thorne AW, Crane-Robinson C (1994) Core histone hyperacetylation co-maps with generalized DNase I sensitivity in the chicken beta-globin chromosomal domain. EMBO J 13:1823–1830

Hemmi H, Takeuchi O, Sato S, Yamamoto M, Kaisho T et al (2004) The roles of two IkappaB kinase-related kinases in lipopolysaccharide and double stranded RNA signaling and viral infection. J Exp Med 199:1641–1650

Henricson BE, Neta R, Vogel SN (1991) An interleukin-1 receptor antagonist blocks lipopolysaccharide-induced colony-stimulating factor production and early endotoxin tolerance. Infect Immun 59:1188–1191

Hiscott J, Kwon H, Génin P (2001) Hostile takeovers: viral appropriation of the NF-kappaB pathway. J Clin Invest 107:143–151

Hiscott J, Nguyen TA, Arguello M, Nakhaei P, Paz S (2006) Manipulation of the nuclear factor-kappaB pathway and the innate immune response by viruses. Oncogene 25:6844–6867

Hitotsumatsu O, Ahmad R, Tavares R, Wang M, Philpott D et al (2008) The ubiquitin-editing enzyme A20 restricts nucleotide-binding oligomerization domain containing 2-triggered signals. Immunity 28:381–390

Hoffmann A, Baltimore D (2006) Circuitry of nuclear factor kappaB signaling. Immunol Rev 210:171–186

Hoffmann A, Leung TH, Baltimore D (2003) Genetic analysis of NF-kappaB/Rel transcription factors defines functional specificities. EMBO J 22:5530–5539

Horng T, Barton GM, Flavell RA, Medzhitov R (2002) The adaptor molecule TIRAP provides signalling specificity for Toll-like receptors. Nature 420:329–333

Hornung V, Ellegast J, Kim S, Brzózka K, Jung A et al (2006) 5′-Triphosphate RNA is the ligand for RIG-I. Science 314:994–997

Hoshino K, Sugiyama T, Matsumoto M, Tanaka T, Saito M et al (2006) IkappaB kinase-alpha is critical for interferon-alpha production induced by Toll-like receptors 7 and 9. Nature 440:949–953

Inohara N, Koseki T, Lin J, del Peso L, Lucas PC et al (2000) An induced proximity model for NF-kappa B activation in the Nod1/RICK and RIP signaling pathways. J Biol Chem 275:27823–27831

Ishii KJ, Coban C, Kato H, Takahashi K, Torii Y et al (2006) A Toll-like receptor-independent antiviral response induced by double-stranded B-form DNA. Nat Immunol 7:40–48

Ishii KJ, Kawagoe T, Koyama S, Matsui K, Kumar H et al (2008) TANK-binding kinase-1 delineates innate and adaptive immune responses to DNA vaccines. Nature 451:725–729

Ishikawa H, Claudio E, Dambach D, Raventos-Suarez C, Ryan C et al (1998) chronic inflammation and susceptibility to bacterial infections in mice lacking the polypeptide (p)105 precursor (NF-{kappa}B1) but expressing p50. J Exp Med 187:985–996

Kaiser WJ, Upton JW, Mocarski ES (2008) Receptor-interacting protein homotypic interaction motif-dependent control of NF-kappa B activation via the DNA-dependent activator of IFN regulatory factors. J Immunol 181:6427–6434

Kato H, Sato S, Yoneyama M, Yamamoto M, Uematsu S et al (2005) Cell type-specific involvement of RIG-I in antiviral response. Immunity 23:19–28

Kawai T, Akira S (2007) Signaling to NF-kappaB by Toll-like receptors. Trends Mol Med 13:460–469

Kawai T, Takahashi K, Sato S, Coban C, Kumar H et al (2005) IPS-1, an adaptor triggering RIG-I- and Mda5-mediated type I interferon induction. Nat Immunol 6:981–988

Kelly BL, Locksley RM (2000) Coordinate regulation of the IL-4, IL-13, and IL-5 cytokine cluster in Th2 clones revealed by allelic expression patterns. J Immunol 165:2982–2986

Kim TK, Maniatis T (1997) The mechanism of transcriptional synergy of an in vitro assembled interferon-beta enhanceosome. Mol Cell 1:119–129

Kim JI, Ho IC, Grusby MJ, Glimcher LH (1999) The transcription factor c-Maf controls the production of interleukin-4 but not other Th2 cytokines. Immunity 10:745–751

Kim SG, Kim JS, Kim JM, Chae Jung H, Sung Song I (2005) Inhibition of proinflammatory cytokine expression by NF-kappaB (p65) antisense oligonucleotide in *Helicobacter pylori*-infected mice. Helicobacter 10:559–566

Kishimoto T (2006) Interleukin-6: discovery of a pleiotropic cytokine. Arthritis Res Ther 8(Suppl 2):S2

Konno H, Yamamoto T, Yamazaki K, Gohda J, Akiyama T et al (2009) TRAF6 establishes innate immune responses by activating NF-kappaB and IRF7 upon sensing cytosolic viral RNA and DNA. PLoS ONE 4:e5674

Kubo M, Ransom J, Webb D, Hashimoto Y, Tada T et al (1997) T-cell subset-specific expression of the IL-4 gene is regulated by a silencer element and STAT6. EMBO J 16:4007–4020

Kwon H, Pelletier N, DeLuca C, Genin P, Cisternas S et al (1998) Inducible expression of IkappaBalpha repressor mutants interferes with NF-kappaB activity and HIV-1 replication in Jurkat T cells. J Biol Chem 273:7431–7440

Lavon I, Goldberg I, Amit S, Landsman L, Jung S et al (2000) High susceptibility to bacterial infection, but no liver dysfunction, in mice compromised for hepatocyte NF-kappaB activation. Nat Med 6:573–577

Lawrence T, Bebien M, Liu GY, Nizet V, Karin M (2005) IKK[alpha] limits macrophage NF-[kappa]B activation and contributes to the resolution of inflammation. Nature 434:1138–1143

Lee EG, Boone DL, Chai S, Libby SL, Chien M et al (2000) Failure to regulate TNF-induced NF-kappaB and cell death responses in A20-deficient mice. Science 289:2350–2354

Lin R, Yang L, Nakhaei P, Sun Q, Sharif-Askari E et al (2006) Negative regulation of the retinoic acid-inducible gene I-induced antiviral state by the ubiquitin-editing protein A20. J Biol Chem 281:2095–2103

Liou HC, Sha WC, Scott ML, Baltimore D (1994) Sequential induction of NF-kappa B/Rel family proteins during B-cell terminal differentiation. Mol Cell Biol 14:5349–5359

Mansell A, Smith R, Doyle SL, Gray P, Fenner JE et al (2006) Suppressor of cytokine signaling 1 negatively regulates Toll-like receptor signaling by mediating Mal degradation. Nat Immunol 7:148–155

Mason N, Aliberti J, Caamano JC, Liou H, Hunter CA (2002) Cutting edge: identification of c-Rel-dependent and -independent pathways of IL-12 production during infectious and inflammatory stimuli. J Immunol 168:2590–2594

McWhirter SM, Fitzgerald KA, Rosains J, Rowe DC, Golenbock DT et al (2004) IFN-regulatory factor 3-dependent gene expression is defective in Tbk1-deficient mouse embryonic fibroblasts. Proc Natl Acad Sci USA 101:233–238

Merika M, Thanos D (2001) Enhanceosomes. Curr Opin Genet Dev 11: 205–208

Meylan E, Burns K, Hofmann K, Blancheteau V, Martinon F et al (2004) RIP1 is an essential mediator of Toll-like receptor 3-induced NF-kappa B activation. Nat Immunol 5:503–507

Meylan E, Curran J, Hofmann K, Moradpour D, Binder M et al (2005) Cardif is an adaptor protein in the RIG-I antiviral pathway and is targeted by hepatitis C virus. Nature 437:1167–1172

Mise-Omata S, Kuroda E, Sugiura T, Yamashita U, Obata Y et al (2009) The NF-kappaB RelA subunit confers resistance to Leishmania major by inducing nitric oxide synthase 2 and Fas expression but not Th1 differentiation. J Immunol 182:4910–4916

Mogensen TH (2009) Pathogen recognition and inflammatory signaling in innate immune defenses. Clin Microbiol Rev 22:240–273 (Table of Contents)

Munshi N, Yie Y, Merika M, Senger K, Lomvardas S et al (1999) The IFN-beta enhancer: a paradigm for understanding activation and repression of inducible gene expression. Cold Spring Harb Symp Quant Biol 64:149–159

Nabel G, Baltimore D (1987) An inducible transcription factor activates expression of human immunodeficiency virus in T cells. Nature 326:711–713

Nenci A, Becker C, Wullaert A, Gareus R, van Loo G et al (2007) Epithelial NEMO links innate immunity to chronic intestinal inflammation. Nature 446:557–561

O'Donnell SM, Hansberger MW, Connolly JL, Chappell JD, Watson MJ et al (2005) Organ-specific roles for transcription factor NF-kappaB in reovirus-induced apoptosis and disease. J Clin Invest 115:2341–2350
Oganesyan G, Saha SK, Guo B, He JQ, Shahangian A et al (2006) Critical role of TRAF3 in the Toll-like receptor-dependent and -independent antiviral response. Nature 439:208–211
Ogura Y, Inohara N, Benito A, Chen FF, Yamaoka S et al (2001) Nod2, a Nod1/Apaf-1 family member that is restricted to monocytes and activates NF-kappaB. J Biol Chem 276:4812–4818
Panne D, Maniatis T, Harrison SC (2004) Crystal structure of ATF-2/c-Jun and IRF-3 bound to the interferon-beta enhancer. EMBO J 23:4384–4393
Panne D, Maniatis T, Harrison SC (2007) An atomic model of the interferon-beta enhanceosome. Cell 129:1111–1123
Patel A, Hanson J, McLean TI, Olgiate J, Hilton M et al (1998) Herpes simplex type 1 induction of persistent NF-kappa B nuclear translocation increases the efficiency of virus replication. Virology 247:212–222
Perry AK, Chow EK, Goodnough JB, Yeh W, Cheng G (2004) Differential requirement for TANK-binding kinase-1 in type I interferon responses to toll-like receptor activation and viral infection. J Exp Med 199:1651–1658
Peters RT, Maniatis T (2001) A new family of IKK-related kinases may function as I kappa B kinase kinases. Biochim Biophys Acta 1471:M57–M62
Ramirez-Carrozzi VR, Nazarian AA, Li CC, Gore SL, Sridharan R et al (2006) Selective and antagonistic functions of SWI/SNF and Mi-2beta nucleosome remodeling complexes during an inflammatory response. Genes Dev 20:282–296
Ramirez-Carrozzi VR, Braas D, Bhatt DM, Cheng CS, Hong C et al (2009) A unifying model for the selective regulation of inducible transcription by CpG islands and nucleosome remodeling. Cell 138:114–128
Rebsamen M, Heinz LX, Meylan E, Michallet M, Schroder K et al (2009) DAI/ZBP1 recruits RIP1 and RIP3 through RIP homotypic interaction motifs to activate NF-kappaB. EMBO Rep 10:916–922
Riggs AD, Pfeifer GP (1992) X-chromosome inactivation and cell memory. Trends Genet 8:169–174
Rodríguez CI, Nogal ML, Carrascosa AL, Salas ML, Fresno M et al (2002) African swine fever virus IAP-like protein induces the activation of nuclear factor kappa B. J Virol 76:3936–3942
Rong BL, Libermann TA, Kogawa K, Ghosh S, Cao LX et al (1992) HSV-1-inducible proteins bind to NF-kappa B-like sites in the HSV-1 genome. Virology 189:750–756
Roulston A, Marcellus RC, Branton PE (1999) Viruses and apoptosis. Annu Rev Microbiol 53:577–628
Saccani S, Pantano S, Natoli G (2003) Modulation of NF-kappaB activity by exchange of dimers. Mol Cell 11:1563–1574
Sadikot RT, Zeng H, Joo M, Everhart MB, Sherrill TP et al (2006) Targeted immunomodulation of the NF-kappaB pathway in airway epithelium impacts host defense against Pseudomonas aeruginosa. J Immunol 176:4923–4930
Saha SK, Pietras EM, He JQ, Kang JR, Liu S et al (2006) Regulation of antiviral responses by a direct and specific interaction between TRAF3 and Cardif. EMBO J 25:3257–3263
Sanjabi S, Hoffmann A, Liou HC, Baltimore D, Smale ST (2000) Selective requirement for c-Rel during IL-12 P40 gene induction in macrophages. Proc Natl Acad Sci USA 97:12705–12710
Sato S, Sugiyama M, Yamamoto M, Watanabe Y, Kawai T et al (2003) Toll/IL-1 receptor domain-containing adaptor inducing IFN-beta (TRIF) associates with TNF receptor-associated factor 6 and TANK-binding kinase 1, and activates two distinct transcription factors, NF-kappa B and IFN-regulatory factor-3, in the Toll-like receptor signaling. J Immunol 171:4304–4310
Scheidereit C (2006) IkappaB kinase complexes: gateways to NF-kappaB activation and transcription. Oncogene 25:6685–6705

Schübeler D, Francastel C, Cimbora DM, Reik A, Martin DI et al (2000) Nuclear localization and histone acetylation: a pathway for chromatin opening and transcriptional activation of the human beta-globin locus. Genes Dev 14:940–950.

Schwarz EM, Badorff C, Hiura TS, Wessely R, Badorff A et al (1998) NF-kappaB-mediated inhibition of apoptosis is required for encephalomyocarditis virus virulence: a mechanism of resistance in p50 knockout mice. J Virol 72:5654–5660

Seth RB, Sun L, Ea C, Chen ZJ (2005) Identification and characterization of MAVS, a mitochondrial antiviral signaling protein that activates NF-kappaB and IRF 3. Cell 122:669–682

Sha WC, Liou HC, Tuomanen EI, Baltimore D (1995) Targeted disruption of the p50 subunit of NF-kappa B leads to multifocal defects in immune responses. Cell 80:321–330

Sharma S, TenOever BR, Grandvaux N, Zhou G, Lin R et al (2003) Triggering the interferon antiviral response through an IKK-related pathway. Science 300:1148–1151

Speirs K, Caamano J, Goldschmidt MH, Hunter CA, Scott P (2002) NF-{kappa}B2 is required for optimal CD40-induced IL-12 production but dispensable for Th1 cell differentiation. J Immunol 168:4406–4413

Stetson DB, Medzhitov R (2006) Recognition of cytosolic DNA activates an IRF3-dependent innate immune response. Immunity 24:93–103

Tait SW, Reid EB, Greaves DR, Wileman TE, Powell PP (2000) Mechanism of inactivation of NF-kappa B by a viral homologue of I kappa b alpha. Signal-induced release of I kappa b alpha results in binding of the viral homologue to NF-kappa B. J Biol Chem 275:34656–34664

Takaoka A, Wang Z, Choi MK, Yanai H, Negishi H et al (2007) DAI (DLM-1/ZBP1) is a cytosolic DNA sensor and an activator of innate immune response. Nature 448:501–505

Takemoto N, Koyano-Nakagawa N, Yokota T, Arai N, Miyatake S et al (1998) Th2-specific DNase I-hypersensitive sites in the murine IL-13 and IL-4 intergenic region. Int Immunol 10:1981–1985

Thanos D, Maniatis T (1995) Virus induction of human IFN beta gene expression requires the assembly of an enhanceosome. Cell 83:1091–1100

Verstak B, Nagpal K, Bottomley SP, Golenbock DT, Hertzog PJ et al (2009) MyD88 adapter-like (Mal)/TIRAP interaction with TRAF6 is critical for TLR2- and TLR4-mediated NF-kappaB proinflammatory responses. J Biol Chem 284:24192–24203

Wang Y, Rickman BH, Poutahidis T, Schlieper K, Jackson EA et al (2008) c-Rel is essential for the development of innate and T cell-induced colitis. J Immunol 180:8118–8125

Weih F, Carrasco D, Durham SK, Barton DS, Rizzo CA et al (1995) Multiorgan inflammation and hematopoietic abnormalities in mice with a targeted disruption of RelB, a member of the NF-kappa B/Rel family. Cell 80:331–340

Weih F, Warr G, Yang H, Bravo R (1997) Multifocal defects in immune responses in RelB-deficient mice. J Immunol 158:5211–5218

Weinmann AS, Mitchell DM, Sanjabi S, Bradley MN, Hoffmann A et al (2001) Nucleosome remodeling at the IL-12 p40 promoter is a TLR-dependent, Rel-independent event. Nat Immunol 2:51–57

Weintraub H, Groudine M (1976) Chromosomal subunits in active genes have an altered conformation. Science 193:848–856

Werner SL, Barken D, Hoffmann A (2005) Stimulus specificity of gene expression programs determined by temporal control of IKK activity. Science 309:1857–1861

Wertz IE, O'Rourke KM, Zhou H, Eby M, Aravind L et al (2004) De-ubiquitination and ubiquitin ligase domains of A20 downregulate NF-kappaB signalling. Nature 430:694–699

Wessells J, Baer M, Young HA, Claudio E, Brown K et al (2004) BCL-3 and NF-kappaB p50 attenuate lipopolysaccharide-induced inflammatory responses in macrophages. J Biol Chem 279:49995–50003

Williams SA, Kwon H, Chen L, Greene WC (2007) Sustained induction of NF-kappa B is required for efficient expression of latent human immunodeficiency virus type 1. J Virol 81:6043–6056

Wu C, Wong YC, Elgin SC (1979) The chromatin structure of specific genes: II. Disruption of chromatin structure during gene activity. Cell 16:807–814

Xu L, Wang Y, Han K, Li L, Zhai Z et al (2005) VISA is an adapter protein required for virus-triggered IFN-beta signaling. Mol Cell 19:727–740

Yamamoto M, Sato S, Hemmi H, Sanjo H, Uematsu S et al (2002a) Essential role for TIRAP in activation of the signalling cascade shared by TLR2 and TLR4. Nature 420:324–329

Yamamoto M, Sato S, Mori K, Hoshino K, Takeuchi O et al (2002b) Cutting edge: a novel Toll/IL-1 receptor domain-containing adapter that preferentially activates the IFN-beta promoter in the Toll-like receptor signaling. J Immunol 169:6668–6672

Yamamoto M, Sato S, Hemmi H, Hoshino K, Kaisho T et al (2003) Role of adaptor TRIF in the MyD88-independent toll-like receptor signaling pathway. Science 301:640–643

Yamamoto M, Yamazaki S, Uematsu S, Sato S, Hemmi H et al (2004) Regulation of Toll/IL-1-receptor-mediated gene expression by the inducible nuclear protein IkappaBzeta. Nature 430:218–222

Yamaoka S, Courtois G, Bessia C, Whiteside ST, Weil R et al (1998) Complementation cloning of NEMO, a component of the IkappaB kinase complex essential for NF-kappaB activation. Cell 93:1231–1240

Yoneyama M, Kikuchi M, Matsumoto K, Imaizumi T, Miyagishi M et al (2005) Shared and unique functions of the DExD/H-box helicases RIG-I, MDA5, and LGP2 in antiviral innate immunity. J Immunol 175:2851–2858

Zaph C, Troy AE, Taylor BC, Berman-Booty LD, Guild KJ et al (2007) Epithelial-cell-intrinsic IKK-beta expression regulates intestinal immune homeostasis. Nature 446:552–556

Zaragoza C, Saura M, Padalko EY, Lopez-Rivera E, Lizarbe TR et al (2006) Viral protease cleavage of inhibitor of kappaBalpha triggers host cell apoptosis. Proc Natl Acad Sci USA 103:19051–19056

Zhang G, Ghosh S (2002) Negative regulation of toll-like receptor-mediated signaling by Tollip. J Biol Chem 277:7059–7065

Zhao T, Yang L, Sun Q, Arguello M, Ballard DW et al (2007) The NEMO adaptor bridges the nuclear factor-kappaB and interferon regulatory factor signaling pathways. Nat Immunol 8:592–600

NF-κB and Mucosal Homeostasis

Lars Eckmann and Andrew S. Neish

Abstract NF-κB is well characterized as a primary mediator of inflammatory responses during infection and immune reactions, but it has recently become evident that NF-κB also mediates a potent cytoprotective, homeostatic function under basal conditions. This role is especially evident in the mammalian intestine, which is challenged not only with a range of microbial pathogens, but is also in constant contact with potent proinflammatory commensal bacteria and their products. Present data lead to the overall conclusion that antiapoptotic actions of NF-κB in intestinal epithelial cells dominate tissue responses to many acute inflammatory and injurious challenges, whereas proinflammatory and cell survival functions of NF-κB in macrophages and T cells govern chronic intestinal inflammation. This review focuses on the protective and homeostatic functions of NF-κB, and the importance of NF-κB in determining host–microbe interactions in the intestinal tract.

Abbreviations

DSS	Dextran sulfate sodium
IKK	IκB kinase
IBD	Inflammatory bowel disease
JNK	Jun N-terminal kinase
MAMP	Microbial-associated molecular pattern

L. Eckmann (✉)
Department of Medicine, University of California,
9500 Gilman Drive, La Jolla, San Diego CA, 92093-0063, USA
e-mail: leckmann@ucsd.edu

A. S. Neish (✉)
Department of Pathology and Laboratory Medicine, Emory University,
615 Michaels St, Atlanta GA, 30322, USA
e-mail: aneish@emory.edu

Current Topics Microbiology (2011) 349: 145-158
DOI: 10.1007/82_2010_103

Published Online: 14 September 2010

NF-κB	Nuclear factor-κB
NLR	NOD-like receptor
PRR	Pattern recognition receptors
TLR	Toll-like receptor

Contents

1 Introduction

The gastrointestinal tract is a focal point of host–environment interaction in mammals. It has a large surface area, covering 300–400 m^2 comparable to that of a tennis court, to facilitate effective nutrient uptake under a wide range of physiological conditions. At the same time, it is colonized by $>10^{13}$ microbial organisms, which exceeds the number of cells in the human body by tenfold or more. Many of these microbes have the potential to elicit destructive host responses in other organs, yet normal function persists in the intestinal tract in the face of, and is even promoted by, the intestinal microbiota. This largely peaceful co-existence of the host and its intestinal microbiota is the result of a finely tuned system of checks and balances on both sides. Although we are far from understanding all the key elements and processes in this balancing act, it has become increasingly clear that the transcription factor, nuclear factor (NF)-κB, is a central player in maintaining homeostasis in the intestinal tract.

NF-κB, as described in greater detail in the other chapters of the current CTMI issue, comprises a family of proteins consisting of five members in mammals, c-Rel, RelA (p65), RelB, NF-κB1, and NF-κB2 (p100), which all share a conserved Rel-homology domain responsible for DNA-binding activity, protein dimerization, and nuclear translocation. These subunits form homodimers or heterodimers, which constitute the transcriptionally active or suppressive forms of NF-κB. Inactive NF-κB is located in the cytosol complexed with an inhibitory protein, IκB. Ligand binding to particular membrane or cytosolic receptors leads to activation of the key enzyme, IκB kinase (IKK), a complex composed of the regulatory IKKγ (also termed NEMO) subunit and two enzymatically active subunits, IKKα and IKKβ. Canonical IKK activation involves IKKβ and results in phosphorylation of IκB, ubiquitination, and ultimate proteasomal degradation of the inhibitor. Most commonly, this pathway leads to activation of the prototypic heterodimer, p50:RelA. In the alternative IKK-signaling pathway, IKKα is activated and causes phosphorylation and processing of p100, leading to formation of p52:RelB dimers. Upon activation, NF-κB dimers are translocated into the nucleus where they bind to selective target gene promoters and mediate the transcriptional activation or, in some cases, suppression of numerous (>200) genes involved in innate and adaptive immune responses.

NF-κB was initially discovered as a regulator of inflammatory responses. Consequently, it plays a role in the pathophysiology of clinically important inflammatory diseases in many organs. For example, mucosal inflammation in patients with inflammatory bowel disease (IBD) and in experimental models of intestinal inflammation is accompanied by elevated levels of activated NF-κB, particularly p65, p50, and c-Rel, as determined by electrophoretic mobility shift assays and immunostaining (Rogler et al. 1998; Schreiber et al. 1998). In parallel, expression of prototypic NF-κB target genes, including IL-1β, IL-6, TNFα, and IL-12 p40 is increased (Costello et al. 2005). Given that many of these gene products promote inflammation, it has been reasoned that inflammation in IBD and other conditions can be attenuated through inhibition of NF-κB activity. Initial data on murine inflammation models supported this contention (Neurath et al. 1996). However, findings in gene-targeted mice indicate that NF-κB has more diverse functions than initially anticipated, governing both protective and destructive responses, which depend on the cell types involved and the specific pathophysiological conditions. This review focuses on the protective and homeostatic functions of NF-κB, and the importance of NF-κB in determining host–microbe interactions in the intestinal tract.

2 NF-κB in Intestinal Homeostasis

Total ablation of several of the key components of the NF-κB signaling pathway is embryonically lethal in mice, precluding analysis of their physiological functions in the fully developed intestinal tract. However, studies in conditional gene-targeted mice have revealed important functions of NF-κB in maintaining normal intestinal homeostasis. Deletion of IKKγ, the common regulatory subunit of the IKK complex, in intestinal epithelial cells caused severe spontaneous colitis in mice at a young age (Nenci et al. 2007). Intestinal epithelial apoptosis was extensive in these mice, leading to loss of epithelial barrier and translocation of commensal bacteria into the mucosa (Nenci et al. 2007). In addition, expression of the antimicrobial peptide, β-defensin 3, was attenuated in the absence of epithelial

IKKγ, suggesting that a weakened constitutive epithelial defense may also contribute to increased bacterial influx into the mucosa. Recognition of translocated bacteria appeared to be important for sustaining inflammation, as additional deletion of the central Toll-like receptor (TLR) signal adaptor, MyD88, abolished colitis in the epithelial IKKγ-deficient mice (Nenci et al. 2007). A similar inflammation phenotype was observed in mice lacking both IKKα and IKKβ, whereas mice lacking either one of the two enzymatically active IKK subunits exhibit no spontaneous colitis (Egan et al. 2004; Nenci et al. 2007). These data suggest that complete loss of epithelial IKK signaling compromises normal intestinal homeostasis, whereas IKKα and IKKβ exhibit functional redundancy in this context.

In contrast to epithelial cells, much less is known about the importance of NF-κB signaling in other cell types for maintaining mucosal homeostasis. Loss of IKKβ in macrophages and neutrophils has no apparent impact on homeostasis (Greten et al. 2007), whereas mice lacking IKKγ, or both IKKα and IKKβ, in these cells have not been reported to date. Similarly, NF-κB is activated under certain conditions in structural cells of the intestinal tract, such as endothelial cells and myofibroblasts (Andoh et al. 2005; Rafiee et al. 2010), but little is known about the physiological functions of NF-κB in these cells in the intestinal mucosa. Such studies are in part hampered by the current lack of knowledge about genes that are uniquely expressed in these intestinal cell types, and could thus be exploited to generate mice with cell type-specific expression of Cre recombinase. Since the Cre-LoxP technology of somatic recombination has proven to be very powerful in the physiological analysis of signaling events in the intestinal tract (as it is for other organs), the development of suitable Cre-expressing mouse lines for other unique intestinal cell types will be of great importance in the future.

3 NF-κB in Protection Against Acute Intestinal Injury

In addition to a homeostatic function under resting conditions, NF-κB signaling has a role in protection against acute inflammatory injuries. For example, oral or rectal challenge of mice with a number of injurious agents, including dextran sulfate sodium (DSS) or acetic acid, causes acute but transient inflammation in the intestine. Despite the predominance of inflammation-associated cytokines, many of which are NF-κB targets, NF-κB has protective functions under these conditions. Selective loss of RelA in intestinal epithelial cells enhanced acute colitis and increased mortality induced by DSS feeding (Steinbrecher et al. 2008). The epithelial RelA-deficient mice exhibited increased epithelial apoptosis and ulcerations after DSS challenge, which was probably related to attenuated expression of key antiapoptotic gene products, such as Bcl-xL, that are known targets of NF-κB (Steinbrecher et al. 2008). In another study, a similar phenotype was observed in mice lacking intestinal epithelial IKKβ (Eckmann et al. 2008). These mice experienced more pronounced acute inflammation upon DSS administration, and showed delayed recovery after DSS discontinuation (Eckmann et al. 2008).

Importantly, pharmacologic inhibition of IKKβ in wild-type mice also exacerbated inflammation in the DSS-induced colitis model, indicating that the protective functions of NF-κB were dominant under these conditions, even if the functional loss was not confined to the epithelium (Eckmann et al. 2008).

A further example for the protective functions of NF-κB is provided in a model of intestinal damage caused by ischemia/reperfusion. Transient ischemia of the intestine followed by reperfusion leads to activation of NF-κB and rapid induction of inflammatory cytokines, most importantly TNFα (Chen et al. 2003). Upon entering the blood stream, this cytokine activates chemokine expression and massive leukocyte influx in the lungs, which is a major cause of mortality in this condition. Genetic ablation of IKKβ in the intestinal epithelium (Chen et al. 2003) or pharmacological inhibition of NF-κB (Suzuki et al. 2008) prevents TNFα induction and the ensuing lung inflammation, and significantly improves mortality in murine models. However, these interventions also exacerbated damage in the intestine (Chen et al. 2003; Zou et al. 2003), which was paralleled and probably caused by enhanced epithelial apoptosis (Chen et al. 2003). Thus, under conditions of intestinal ischemia/reperfusion, attenuation of systemic disease by NF-κB inhibition is obtained at the expense of increased local destruction, underlining that NF-κB has local protective functions. Interestingly, brief intentional exposure of tissues to ischemia protects against deleterious effects of prolonged/ischemia reperfusion (Moore-Olufemi et al. 2005). This "ischemic preconditioning", when applied to the small intestine, is accompanied by enhanced intestinal NF-κB activation (Ferencz et al. 2006), suggesting that controlled NF-κB activation may provide a strategy for intestinal protection during intestinal transplantation surgery.

4 NF-κB in Mucosa–Microbe Interactions

As mentioned, the intestinal mucosa is in constant contact with a quantitatively vast and qualitatively diverse normal microbiota composed of about 500 genera of bacteria, broadly grouped into two large taxa, the Bacteroidetes and Firmicutes (Eckburg et al. 2005). This host–microbe interaction in the human intestine has co-evolved over millennia resulting in a dynamic and symbiotic relationship (Ley et al. 2006). The microbiota thrives in a thermostable, nutrient-rich environment while providing beneficial functions to the host including caloric extraction of otherwise indigestible complex carbohydrates, vitamin and micronutrient syntheses, stimulation of immune development/function, and competitive exclusion of pathogens (Neish 2009). While NF-κB clearly plays a role in protecting the intestine against acute injuries from infection with pathogenic bacteria, recent evidence strongly suggests that this signaling system is also involved in basal monitoring of the normal microbiota and thereby contributes to mucosal homeostasis. In this context, the most important activators of NF-κB are TLRs and other innate immune receptors. These receptors, often broadly referred to as pattern recognition receptors (PRR), have key functions in the sensing of commensal and pathogenic microbes and thus provide a critical regulatory link between the intestinal microbiota and the host (Abreu et al. 2005; Akira et al. 2006). The PRRs collectively comprise a battery of transmembrane or intracytoplasmic receptors that are defined by their ability to specifically recognize and bind distinctive microbial macromolecular ligands designated microbial-associated molecular patterns (MAMPs), such as LPS, flagellin, peptidoglycans, and microbial nucleic acids. PRRs include TLRs, which have their ligand recognition motifs exposed to the extracellular space, and NOD-like receptors (NLRs) that are active in the intracellular cytoplasmic compartment. The well-known association of mutant forms of the NLR, NOD2, with the chronic intestinal inflammatory condition, Crohn's disease, clearly underscores the importance of PRR monitoring in intestinal health (Sartor 2008). As currently understood, binding of an appropriate MAMP ligand to a TLR results in dimerization and the formation of a cytoplasmic interface domain competent to bind a class of adaptor proteins (Ishii et al. 2008). The original member of this family is MyD88, and additional family members have been described in recent years, including MAL/TIRAP and TRIF/TICAM. Evidence is emerging that these different adaptor proteins (or combinations of them) may preferentially interact with specific TLRs or groups of TLRs and likely have a role in specifying the most appropriate signaling pathways for a given MAMP–TLR interaction. All MyD88 family adaptors interact with a second adaptor molecule, IRAK, of which several family members are known. IRAK, a serine kinase, then activates the cytoplasmic signaling intermediate TRAF6, possibly by phosphorylation. Activated TRAF6 is thought to activate the IKK complex and set in motion the downstream NF-κB pathways (Karin and Ben-Neriah 2000).

5 Basal Activation of Mucosal NF-κB

Microbial activation of NF-κB pathways can have effects in the mucosa beyond the classical activation of innate immunity and acute inflammation. Studies with germ-free mice have revealed that epithelial cells in the small intestinal crypts exhibit a reduced proliferation rate, with the crypt-to-villus transit time doubled in these animals (Hooper and Gordon 2001). Studies in axenic *Drosophila* also show strikingly reduced gut epithelial proliferation, indicating that gut–microbe interactions influencing epithelial physiology is a highly conserved, perhaps primordial phenomenon (Buchon et al. 2009). Gene expression elicited by PRR-stimulated NF-κB signaling likely mediates microbe-stimulated homeostatic effects in the gut. Mice with intestinal microbiota suppressed with antibiotics, thus rendering them highly deficient in luminal bacteria and MAMPs, were markedly more sensitive to experimentally induced colitis, and the mucosal injury could be ameliorated by oral administration of isolated MAMPS such as LPS and LTA (Rakoff-Nahoum et al. 2004). Additionally, this study demonstrated that the observed cytoprotective effects were lost in TLR2 and TLR4 null mice, implicating TLR signaling in the protective mechanism. Another investigation showed that regenerative responses to colonic injury were markedly attenuated in germ-free animals, indicating a necessary role of the flora in induction of epithelial proliferation and response to injury, and furthermore, restitution was shown to be similarly reduced in MyD88 null mice, reinforcing the notion that PRR-mediated signaling is necessary for trophic/wound healing effects (Pull et al. 2005). TLR2/MyD88-dependent signaling has also been demonstrated to enhance physiological epithelial barrier integrity (Cario et al. 2007). These and related observations with mice null in epithelial NF-κB pathway components (Chen et al. 2003; Nenci et al. 2007; Zaph et al. 2007) have suggested that some degree of PRR signaling is necessary for gut homeostasis, presumably because of the basal upregulation of cytoprotective genes (i.e., gene products with anti-apoptotic and antioxidant functions, and those reflecting chaperone/stress responses). In vivo, symbiotic bacteria have been shown to induce expression of cytoprotective genes such as heat shock proteins (Rakoff-Nahoum et al. 2004) and RELMβ (McVay et al. 2006), as well as anti-microbial peptides and lectins (Cash et al. 2006), which may contribute to mucosal homeostasis.

Microbial stimulation of NF-κB activation may be capable of mediating a "graded response" that permits differentiation between beneficial symbionts and harmful pathogens. Potentially, the same circuitry that when activated at "high gain" elicits acute cellular (neutrophilic) inflammation, can at "low gain" elicit a more limited (and possibly distinct) transcriptional response, that is mucosa-protective and does not provoke histopathologically evident inflammation (Fig. 1). This notion of "basal inflammatory tone" or "physiological inflammation" may

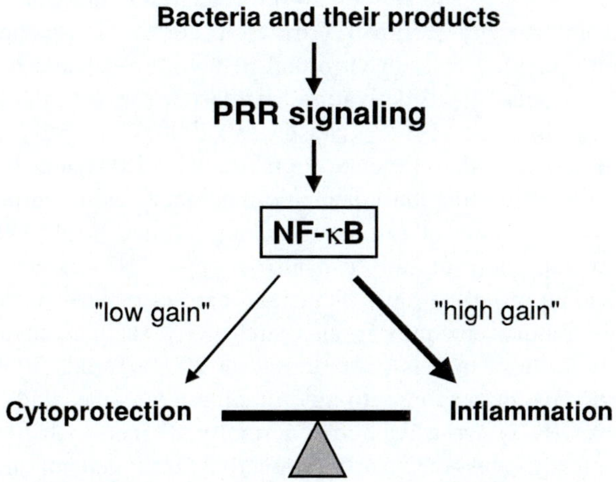

Fig. 1 Model of the balancing functions of NF-κB in intestinal homeostasis. Low-level constitutive ("low gain") activation of NF-κB by commensal bacteria and their products has basal homeostatic effects, while high-level ("high gain") activation in response to bacterial pathogens elicits acute inflammation. Blockade of NF-κB prevents both effects and renders the gut hypersensitive to physical, chemical, and immunological insults and pathogen challenges

explain at a molecular level why a bacterial presence, contained within the proper boundaries and of the proper constitution and intensity, may make a positive contribution to intestinal homeostasis and thus overall health.

6 Microbial Modulation of NF-κB Signaling: Commensals and Pathogens

6.1 Commensals

Strong evidence now exists to suggest that members of the microbial gut community are able to influence inflammatory signaling pathways including NF-κB (Iyer et al. 2008; Kelly et al. 2005). Multiple laboratories have observed that distinct bacterial strains represented in the normal microbiota, many with proposed probiotic function, are able to suppress NF-κB activation and inflammatory effector functions (Madsen et al. 1999; Menard et al. 2004; Pena and Versalovic 2003; Yan et al. 2007). Several mechanisms have been elucidated. For example, the intestinal symbiont *Bacteroides thetaiotaomicron* has been shown to inhibit NF-κB pathways by regulating cytoplasmic to nuclear translocation of the p65 subunit by means of the transcription factor PPAR-γ selectively binding to nuclear p65 (Kelly et al. 2004). Other investigators have demonstrated that symbiotic bacteria are able to influence inflammatory pathways, and very likely other cellular regulatory processes, by manipulating the ubiquitin system (Angot et al. 2007; Kim et al. 2005; Rytkonen and Holden 2007). Bacterial contact has been shown to repress proteasome activity in vitro (Petrof et al. 2004). Non-pathogenic bacteria interacting with epithelial cells in vitro and in vivo are capable of blocking IκB ubiquitination and thus NF-κB activation by interference with the function of the IκB ubiquitination ligase, $SCF^{\beta TrCP}$ (Neish et al. 2000; Collier-Hyams et al. 2005; Lee 2008). Furthermore, these events are mediated by transient oxidant-induced inactivation of the ubiquitination enzymatic machinery as a consequence of prokaryotic-elicited production of reactive oxidants (Kumar et al. 2007; Lee 2008). The bacterial metabolite, butyrate, can also suppress NF-κB activation via this mechanism (Kumar et al. 2009). Transient oxidative inactivation of a wide spectrum of regulatory enzymes is an increasingly recognized mechanism for influencing cellular homeostasis (Chiarugi et al. 2003; Terada 2006). Generation of reactive oxidants in response to microbial interactions, and specifically in response to MAMPs, is pervasive across virtually all metazoan life (Ogier-Denis et al. 2008), making this mechanism attractive as a general and non-species selective means by which a complex floral community could influence a wide range of host signaling and homeostatic processes (Lee 2008). Regardless of the mechanism, attenuation (not total blockade) of inflammatory signaling by the microbiota (or distinct members of the microbiota) may allow the gut to establish as "rheostat" governing the appropriate level of NF-κB signaling.

Such effects may have therapeutic value. Numerous investigators have shown probiotic bacteria can suppress inflammation and enhance epithelial barrier function (Neish et al. 2000; Petrof et al. 2004; Tien et al. 2006; Iyer et al. 2008). *Lactobacillus rhamnosus* GG can suppress gut inflammation in an in vivo model of necrotizing enterocolitis (Lin et al. 2009). Other researchers have found that anti-inflammatory/pro-restitution effects of probiotics can be mediated by isolated MAMPs. For example, purified unmethylated probiotic DNA has been shown to ameliorate DSS colitis. Furthermore, the protective effects were lost in TLR9 null mice, directly implicating TLR signaling in intestinal cytoprotection (Katakura et al. 2005). The flagellin/TLR5 ligand receptor pair has also been shown to mediate homeostatic effects in the gut. As a MAMP, flagellin is recognized by plants, invertebrates, and mammals (Vijay-Kumar et al. 2006; Zeng et al. 2003). Solely among TLR null murine phenotypes, TLR5 knock-out animals are known to develop spontaneous colitis (Vijay-Kumar et al. 2007). Flagellin seems to be particularly adept at eliciting cytoprotective responses in the gut (Vijay-Kumar et al. 2006; Zeng et al. 2003), and as TLR5 is not expressed widely outside the intestinal tract, systemic shock apparently does not occur if flagellin enters the vascular space. Several recent articles have illustrated the potential of exploiting flagellin as a systemic agent for prophylaxis against potentially detrimental stimuli to the gut and perhaps other tissues (Burdelya et al. 2008; Vijay-Kumar et al. 2008).

6.2 Pathogens

Inhibition of NF-κB can occur during enteric bacterial pathogenesis (Sansonetti 2004), and is obviously a feature of a parasitic (rather than commensal) relationship. Inhibiting NF-κB would attenuate the upregulation of the inflammatory response, thus blocking the influx of phagocytic leukocytes, and/or activate or augment apoptotic pathways that otherwise would be aborted by NF-κB activation, events permissive for bacterial proliferation and dissemination. One means of how bacteria influence host cell signaling pathways is through soluble effector proteins. Such proteins are often translocated into the host cells or the environment via a "type III secretion apparatus" (Galan 2009). The effector proteins are generally assumed to usurp host cellular functions, including inflammatory signaling, for the benefit of the invading organism. For example, the *Salmonella* secreted factor L (SseL), suppresses NF-κB activation in cells infected with *Salmonella* by removing ubiquitin monomers from phosphorylated IκB, thereby preventing its proteasomal degradation. Infection of mice with an *SseL* mutant of *Salmonella* caused greater liver inflammation, presumably as a consequence of derepressed NF-κB activation and higher expression of NF-κB dependent inflammatory cytokines (Le Negrate et al. 2008). Another family of secreted effector proteins with NF-κB inhibitory effects is the YopJ family. These proteins are acetyltransferases that variably modify and inactivate MAPKK including IKKβ, and are found in a variety of bacteria that associate intimately with enteric epithelia

(Mukherjee et al. 2007). YopJ of *Yersina enterocolitica* inhibits the NF-κB (and other MAPKK) pathway in infected macrophages and induces rapid apoptotic death (Orth et al. 1999). Other examples are found in *Aeromonas salmonicida* (AopP) and *Vibro parahemalyticus* (VopP), both of which cause inflammatory gastroenteritis with strong induction of apoptosis in infected cells. Similarly, the potently proapoptotic effects of enteric *Shigella* infection are mediated by the type III effectors, OspG, which blocks E2 function upstream of IκB ubiquitination (Kim et al. 2005), and OspF, which suppresses NF-κB at the epigenetic level by altering the chromatin structure of promoters of several genes encoding proinflammatory products (Arbibe et al. 2007). In these situations, the proapoptotic effects of NF-κB blockade outweigh the suppression of cellular inflammation. Interestingly, another member of the YopJ family found in *Salmonella*, AvrA, was also shown to inhibit NF-κB activation, as well as the Jun N-terminal kinase (JNK) signaling pathway, resulting in inflammatory suppression without the attendant activation of apoptosis (Collier-Hyams et al. 2002; Jones et al. 2008). These results may indicate a role of JNK in NF-κB induced apoptosis and illustrates how pathogens can circumvent the proapoptotic effects of NF-κB blockade. Future study will undoubtedly uncover additional mechanisms by which microbial pathogens can affect the NF-κB pathway.

7 Summary

In summary, NF-κB, while maintaining a well studied and key role in the cellular response to overt physical and chemical threats and pathogen infection, also is required for basal homeostasis of the mucosa, predominantly by sensing the normal microbiota. This notion is perhaps not surprising given the ancient lineage of the pathway, the long co-evolution of animal host and intestinal prokaryote, and the overwhelming relative abundance of intestinal commensal bacteria over enteric pathogens. The growing appreciation that the NF-κB pathway can affect more than purely inflammatory responses may indicate that we need to rethink strategies aimed at manipulating the pathway in a therapeutic fashion. Additionally, the front line role of NF-κB in monitoring the microbiota, and the diverse roles by which the microbiota can influence the NF-κB pathway, may suggest that manipulation of the microbiota and/or its products may be a means of enhancing mucosal health.

References

Abreu MT, Fukata M, Arditi M (2005) TLR signaling in the gut in health and disease. J Immunol 174:4453–4460

Akira S, Uematsu S, Takeuchi O (2006) Pathogen recognition and innate immunity. Cell 124:783–801

Andoh A, Zhang Z, Inatomi O, et al (2005) Interleukin-22, a member of the IL-10 subfamily, induces inflammatory responses in colonic subepithelial myofibroblasts. Gastroenterology 129:969–984

Angot A, Vergunst A, Genin S, Peeters N (2007) Exploitation of eukaryotic ubiquitin signaling pathways by effectors translocated by bacterial type III and type IV secretion systems. PLoS Pathog 3:e3

Arbibe L, Kim DW, Batsche E, Pedron T, Mateescu B, Muchardt C, Parsot C, Sansonetti PJ (2007) An injected bacterial effector targets chromatin access for transcription factor NF-kappaB to alter transcription of host genes involved in immune responses. Nat Immunol 8:47–56

Buchon N, Broderick NA, Chakrabarti S, Lemaitre B (2009) Invasive and indigenous microbiota impact intestinal stem cell activity through multiple pathways in Drosophila. Genes Dev 23:2333–2344

Burdelya LG, Krivokrysenko VI, Tallant TC et al (2008) An agonist of toll-like receptor 5 has radioprotective activity in mouse and primate models. Science 320:226–230

Cario E, Gerken G, Podolsky DK (2007) Toll-like receptor 2 controls mucosal inflammation by regulating epithelial barrier function. Gastroenterology 132:1359–1374

Cash HL, Whitham CV, Behrendt CL, Hooper LV (2006) Symbiotic bacteria direct expression of an intestinal bactericidal lectin. Science 313:1126–1130

Chen LW, Egan L, Li ZW, Greten FR, Kagnoff MF, Karin M (2003) The two faces of IKK and NF-kappaB inhibition: prevention of systemic inflammation but increased local injury following intestinal ischemia-reperfusion. Nat Med 9:575–581

Chiarugi P, Pani G, Giannoni E et al (2003) Reactive oxygen species as essential mediators of cell adhesion: the oxidative inhibition of a FAK tyrosine phosphatase is required for cell adhesion. J Cell Biol 161:933–944

Collier-Hyams LS, Sloane V, Batten BC, Neish AS (2005) Cutting edge: bacterial modulation of epithelial signaling via changes in neddylation of cullin-1. J Immunol 175:4194–4198

Collier-Hyams LS, Zeng H, Sun J, Tomlinson AD, Bao ZQ, Chen H, Madara JL, Orth K, Neish AS (2002) Cutting edge: Salmonella AvrA effector inhibits the key proinflammatory, anti-apoptotic NF-kappa B pathway. J Immunol 169:2846–2850

Costello CM, Mah N, Hasler R et al (2005) Dissection of the inflammatory bowel disease transcriptome using genome-wide cDNA microarrays. PLoS Med 2:e199

Eckburg PB, Bik EM, Bernstein CN, Purdom E, Dethlefsen L, Sargent M, Gill SR, Nelson KE, Relman DA (2005) Diversity of the human intestinal microbial flora. Science 308:1635–1638

Eckmann L, Nebelsiek T, Fingerle AA et al (2008) Opposing functions of IKKbeta during acute and chronic intestinal inflammation. Proc Natl Acad Sci USA 105:15058–15063

Egan LJ, Eckmann L, Greten FR, Chae S, Li ZW, Myhre GM, Robine S, Karin M, Kagnoff MF (2004) IkappaB-kinasebeta-dependent NF-kappaB activation provides radioprotection to the intestinal epithelium. Proc Natl Acad Sci USA 101:2452–2457

Ferencz A, Racz B, Gasz B, Kalmar-Nagy K, Horvath OP, Roth E (2006) Threshold level of NF-kB activation in small bowel ischemic preconditioning procedure. Transplant Proc 38:1800–1802

Galan JE (2009) Common themes in the design and function of bacterial effectors. Cell Host Microbe 5:571–579

Greten FR, Arkan MC, Bollrath J et al (2007) NF-kappaB is a negative regulator of IL-1beta secretion as revealed by genetic and pharmacological inhibition of IKKbeta. Cell 130:918–931

Hooper LV, Gordon JI (2001) Commensal host-bacterial relationships in the gut. Science 292:1115–1118

Ishii KJ, Koyama S, Nakagawa A, Coban C, Akira S (2008) Host innate immune receptors and beyond: making sense of microbial infections. Cell Host Microbe 3:352–363

Iyer C, Kosters A, Sethi G, Kunnumakkara AB, Aggarwal BB, Versalovic J (2008) Probiotic *Lactobacillus reuteri* promotes TNF-induced apoptosis in human myeloid leukemia-derived cells by modulation of NF-kappaB and MAPK signalling. Cell Microbiol 10:1442–1452

Jones RM, Wu H, Wentworth C, Luo L, Collier-Hyams L, Neish AS (2008) Salmonella AvrA coordinates suppression of host immune and apoptotic defenses via JNK pathway blockade. Cell Host Microbe 3:233–244

Karin M, Ben-Neriah Y (2000) Phosphorylation meets ubiquitination: the control of NF-[kappa]B activity. Annu Rev Immunol 18:621–663

Katakura K, Lee J, Rachmilewitz D, Li G, Eckmann L, Raz E (2005) Toll-like receptor 9-induced type I IFN protects mice from experimental colitis. J Clin Invest 115:695–702

Kelly D, Campbell JI, King TP, Grant G, Jansson EA, Coutts AG, Pettersson S, Conway S (2004) Commensal anaerobic gut bacteria attenuate inflammation by regulating nuclear-cytoplasmic shuttling of PPAR-gamma and RelA. Nat Immunol 5:104–112

Kelly D, Conway S, Aminov R (2005) Commensal gut bacteria: mechanisms of immune modulation. Trends Immunol 26:326–333

Kim DW, Lenzen G, Page AL, Legrain P, Sansonetti PJ, Parsot C (2005) The Shigella flexneri effector OspG interferes with innate immune responses by targeting ubiquitin-conjugating enzymes. Proc Natl Acad Sci USA 102:14046–14051

Kumar A, Wu H, Collier-Hyams LS, Hansen JM, Li T, Yamoah K, Pan ZQ, Jones DP, Neish AS (2007) Commensal bacteria modulate cullin-dependent signaling via generation of reactive oxygen species. Embo J 26:4457–4466

Kumar A, Wu H, Collier-Hyams LS, Kwon YM, Hanson JM, Neish AS (2009) The bacterial fermentation product butyrate influences epithelial signaling via reactive oxygen species-mediated changes in cullin-1 neddylation. J Immunol 182:538–546

Le Negrate G, Faustin B, Welsh K et al (2008) Salmonella secreted factor L deubiquitinase of Salmonella typhimurium inhibits NF-kappaB, suppresses IkappaBalpha ubiquitination and modulates innate immune responses. J Immunol 180:5045–5056

Lee WJ (2008) Bacterial-modulated signaling pathways in gut homeostasis. Sci Signal 1:pe24

Ley RE, Peterson DA, Gordon JI (2006) Ecological and evolutionary forces shaping microbial diversity in the human intestine. Cell 124:837–848

Lin PW, Myers LE, Ray L et al (2009) *Lactobacillus rhamnosus* blocks inflammatory signaling in vivo via reactive oxygen species generation. Free Radic Biol Med 47:1205–1211

Madsen KL, Doyle JS, Jewell LD, Tavernini MM, Fedorak RN (1999) Lactobacillus species prevents colitis in interleukin 10 gene-deficient mice. Gastroenterology 116:1107–1114

McVay LD, Keilbaugh SA, Wong TM et al (2006) Absence of bacterially induced RELMbeta reduces injury in the dextran sodium sulfate model of colitis. J Clin Invest 116:2914–2923

Menard S, Candalh C, Bambou JC, Terpend K, Cerf-Bensussan N, Heyman M (2004) Lactic acid bacteria secrete metabolites retaining anti-inflammatory properties after intestinal transport. Gut 53:821–828

Moore-Olufemi SD, Kozar RA, Moore FA, Sato N, Hassoun HT, Cox CS Jr, Kone BC (2005) Ischemic preconditioning protects against gut dysfunction and mucosal injury after ischemia/reperfusion injury. Shock 23:258–263

Mukherjee S, Hao YH, Orth K (2007) A newly discovered post-translational modification—the acetylation of serine and threonine residues. Trends Biochem Sci 32:210–216

Neish AS (2009) Microbes in gastrointestinal health and disease. Gastroenterology 136:65–80

Neish AS, Gewirtz AT, Zeng H, Young AN, Hobert ME, Karmali V, Rao AS, Madara JL (2000) Prokaryotic regulation of epithelial responses by inhibition of IkappaB-alpha ubiquitination. Science 289:1560–1563

Nenci A, Becker C, Wullaert A et al (2007) Epithelial NEMO links innate immunity to chronic intestinal inflammation. Nature 446:557–561

Neurath MF, Pettersson S, Meyer zum Buschenfelde KH, Strober W (1996) Local administration of antisense phosphorothioate oligonucleotides to the p65 subunit of NF-kappa B abrogates established experimental colitis in mice. Nat Med 2:998–1004

Ogier-Denis E, Mkaddem SB, Vandewalle A (2008) NOX enzymes and toll-like receptor signaling. Semin Immunopathol 30:291–300

Orth K, Palmer LE, Bao ZQ, Stewart S, Rudolph AE, Bliska JB, Dixon JE (1999) Inhibition of the mitogen-activated protein kinase kinase superfamily by a Yersinia effector. Science 285:1920–1923

Pena JA, Versalovic J (2003) *Lactobacillus rhamnosus* GG decreases TNF-alpha production in lipopolysaccharide-activated murine macrophages by a contact-independent mechanism. Cell Microbiol 5:277–285

Petrof EO, Kojima K, Ropeleski MJ, Musch MW, Tao Y, De Simone C, Chang EB (2004) Probiotics inhibit nuclear factor-kappaB and induce heat shock proteins in colonic epithelial cells through proteasome inhibition. Gastroenterology 127:1474–1487

Pull SL, Doherty JM, Mills JC, Gordon JI, Stappenbeck TS (2005) Activated macrophages are an adaptive element of the colonic epithelial progenitor niche necessary for regenerative responses to injury. Proc Natl Acad Sci USA 102:99–104

Rafiee P, Stein DJ, Nelson VM, Otterson MF, Shaker R, Binion DG (2010) Thalidomide inhibits inflammatory and angiogenic activation of human intestinal microvascular endothelial cells (HIMEC). Am J Physiol Gastrointest Liver Physiol 298:G167–G176

Rakoff-Nahoum S, Paglino J, Eslami-Varzaneh F, Edberg S, Medzhitov R (2004) Recognition of commensal microflora by toll-like receptors is required for intestinal homeostasis. Cell 118:229–241

Rogler G, Brand K, Vogl D et al (1998) Nuclear factor kappaB is activated in macrophages and epithelial cells of inflamed intestinal mucosa. Gastroenterology 115:357–369

Rytkonen A, Holden DW (2007) Bacterial interference of ubiquitination and deubiquitination. Cell Host Microbe 1:13–22

Sansonetti PJ (2004) War and peace at mucosal surfaces. Nat Rev Immunol 4:953–964

Sartor RB (2008) Microbial influences in inflammatory bowel diseases. Gastroenterology 134:577–594

Schreiber S, Nikolaus S, Hampe J (1998) Activation of nuclear factor kappa B inflammatory bowel disease. Gut 42:477–484

Steinbrecher KA, Harmel-Laws E, Sitcheran R, Baldwin AS (2008) Loss of epithelial RelA results in deregulated intestinal proliferative/apoptotic homeostasis and susceptibility to inflammation. J Immunol 180:2588–2599

Suzuki T, Yamashita K, Jomen W et al (2008) The novel NF-kappaB inhibitor, dehydroxymethylepoxyquinomicin, prevents local and remote organ injury following intestinal ischemia/reperfusion in rats. J Surg Res 149:69–75

Terada LS (2006) Specificity in reactive oxidant signaling: think globally, act locally. J Cell Biol 174:615–623

Tien MT, Girardin SE, Regnault B, Le Bourhis L, Dillies MA, Coppee JY, Bourdet-Sicard R, Sansonetti PJ, Pedron T (2006) Anti-inflammatory effect of *Lactobacillus casei* on Shigella-infected human intestinal epithelial cells. J Immunol 176:1228–1237

Vijay-Kumar M, Aitken JD, Sanders CJ, Frias A, Sloane VM, Xu J, Neish AS, Rojas M, Gewirtz AT (2008) Flagellin treatment protects against chemicals, bacteria, viruses, and radiation. J Immunol 180:8280–8285

Vijay-Kumar M, Sanders CJ, Taylor RT et al (2007) Deletion of TLR5 results in spontaneous colitis in mice. J Clin Invest 117:3909–3921

Vijay-Kumar M, Wu H, Jones R, Grant G, Babbin B, King TP, Kelly D, Gewirtz AT, Neish AS (2006) Flagellin suppresses epithelial apoptosis and limits disease during enteric infection. Am J Pathol 169:1686–1700

Yan F, Cao H, Cover TL, Whitehead R, Washington MK, Polk DB (2007) Soluble proteins produced by probiotic bacteria regulate intestinal epithelial cell survival and growth. Gastroenterology 132:562–575

Zaph C, Troy AE, Taylor BC et al (2007) Epithelial-cell-intrinsic IKK-beta expression regulates intestinal immune homeostasis. Nature 446:552–556

Zeng H, Carlson AQ, Guo Y, Yu Y, Collier-Hyams LS, Madara JL, Gewirtz AT, Neish AS (2003) Flagellin is the major proinflammatory determinant of enteropathogenic Salmonella. J Immunol 171:3668–3674

Zeng H, Wu H, Sloane V, Jones R, Yu Y, Lin P, Gewirtz AT, Neish AS (2006) Flagellin/TLR5 responses in epithelia reveal intertwined activation of inflammatory and apoptotic pathways. Am J Physiol Gastrointest Liver Physiol 290:G96–G108

Zou L, Attuwaybi B, Kone BC (2003) Effects of NF-kappa B inhibition on mesenteric ischemia-reperfusion injury. Am J Physiol Gastrointest Liver Physiol 284:G713–G721

IKK- and NF-κB-Mediated Functions in Carcinogenesis

Melek C. Arkan and Florian R. Greten

Abstract Since the initial cloning of RelA and its close relationship to c-Rel, the cellular homolog of the viral oncoprotein v-Rel, the nuclear factor κB (NF-κB) signaling pathway and its upstream activating kinase complex (IκB-kinase) have been suspected to play a major role in tumorigenesis. This was further corroborated by the discovery of oncogenic mutations in NF-κB proteins in certain lymphoid malignancies and the notion that NF-κB is persistently activated in a large variety of solid tumors. With the advent of conditional knockout mice allowing tissue-specific targeting of the various components of the NF-κB signaling pathway, it was possible to genetically test the cell autonomous and non-autonomous functions of NF-κB in inflammation-associated cancer as well as sporadic cancers. Here, we review molecular evidence that demonstrates the various functions of NF-κB during different tumor stages and that supports the rationale to target NF-κB in cancer prevention and therapy.

Contents

M. C. Arkan and F. R. Greten (✉)
2nd Department of Medicine, Klinikum rechts der Isar, Technical University Munich, Ismaningerstr. 22, 81675, Munich Germany
e-mail: florian.greten@lrz.tum.de

Current Topics Microbiology (2011) 349: 159-169
DOI: 10.1007/82_2010_97

Published Online: 16 September 2010

1 Nuclear Factor κB (NF-κB) Signaling Pathway

NF-κB consists of a number of closely associated Rel family proteins that bind a common sequence motif known as the κB site (Greten and Karin 2004). The Rel protein family members comprises two classes: proteins that are synthesized in their mature forms such as RelA (p65), RelB and c-Rel, which contain an N-terminal Rel homology domain (RHD) that is responsible for dimerization and DNA binding, and transcription modulating domains at their C-terminus. The second class consists of NF-κB1 (p105/p50) and NF-κB2 (p100/p52), which are synthesized as large precursors (p105 and p100) with an N-terminal RHD and a C-terminal transactivating domain containing ankyrin-like repeats (Ghosh and Karin 2002). Ubiquitin-dependent proteolysis removes the C-terminal domains, resulting in production of the mature DNA binding proteins p50 and p52 that contain the RHD but lack the transcription modulating domains. These proteins can form different NF-κB homo- and heterodimers, whose activation depends on two major pathways, the canonical or the alternative. The canonical NF-κB activation pathway, which is triggered upon binding of a large variety of stimuli including pathogen-associated molecular patterns (PAMP) and pro-inflammatory cytokines (TNF-α, IL-1β), applies to dimers composed of RelA, c-Rel and p50, which are held in the cytoplasm by their specific inhibitors, the IκB proteins. Upon phosphorylation by the IκB-kinase β (IKKβ) and subsequent polyubiquitination and proteasomal degradation of IκBs, NF-κB heterodimers (in most cases RelA/p50 dimers) shuttle into the nucleus and stimulate transcription of genes that are mainly involved in inflammatory responses. The IKK complex consists of two catalytic subunits IKKα and IKKβ, and IKKγ that serves as the regulatory subunit. The alternative NF-κB pathway, which is independent of IKKβ and IKKγ, leads to processing of NF-κB2/p100 and primarily to the nuclear localization of p52/RelB dimers. This pathway is activated by TNF family members (lymphotoxin α, β), BAFF, and CD40L (Vallabhapurapu and Karin 2009). Although different NF-κB dimers appear to have distinct regulatory and partially opposing functions, however, how these two IKK catalytic subunits lead to distinct functions harbors great interest as NF-κB signaling takes its spin in both health and disease.

2 Different Ways to Activate NF-κB in Hematological and Solid Malignancies

In several malignant diseases including solid tumors as well as lymphoid malignancies, persistent NF-κB activity can be found and causes prevention of apoptosis, increases in proliferation or enhanced invasive growth (Gilmore et al. 2002; Karin et al. 2002). While in solid tumors no activating mutations in any members of the IKK, IκBα, or NF-κB proteins have yet been described, various chromosomal translocations, amplifications, deletions and mutations effecting genes encoding for the NF-κB and IκB proteins can result in constitutive NF-κB activity during lymphomagenesis. In non-Hodgkin's B-cell lymphoma amplifications of c-Rel are found and B- and T-cell lymphomas, including chronic lymphocytic leukemia (CLL), multiple myeloma and cutaneous B- and T-cell lymphomas exhibit chromosomal rearrangements affecting the NFKB2 locus (Gilmore 1999). The exact contribution of these mutations to the pathogenesis of the disease is still not completely elucidated. However, also mutations in upstream signaling components of the NF-κB pathway are also frequently found in certain lymphomas. For example, translocations leading to Bcl-10 overexpression or chromosomal translocations in MALT1 itself were identified in MALT lymphomas (Willis et al. 1999). MALT1 interacts with Bcl-10 and Carma-1 to induce IKKβ-dependent NF-κB activation, thus providing B cells with the necessary survival advantage through the upregulation of several anti-apoptotic genes. Moreover, in diffuse large B-cell lymphoma (DLBCL), activation of NF-κB has been reported to be required for survival of activated B-cell-like DBLCL (ABC-DLBCL), but not germinal center B-cell-like DLBCL (GCB-DLBCL) (Davis et al. 2001). Similar to MALT lymphomas, it is CARD11 a constituent of the CARD11:MALT1:Bcl-10 complex that is responsible for the observed constitutive NF-κB activity in ABC-DLBCL (Ngo et al. 2006) and accordingly CARD11 mutations can be found in 10% of patients suffering from such lymphoma type (Lenz et al. 2008). In addition to these genetic causes, constitutive NF-κB activity can be induced either by viral oncoproteins, such as the TAX oncoprotein of human T-cell leukemia virus (HTLV)-1, or by EBV nuclear antigen (EBNA)-2 and latent membrane protein-1 (LMP-1) that can directly interact with the IKK complex through interaction with IKKγ/NEMO or that can lead to IKKβ-independent activation of RelB/p52 heterodimers (Luftig et al. 2004; Mosialos 1997; Xiao et al. 2001). Furthermore, activated Ras, Bcr-Abl as well as members of the Rho GTPases and the DBL family lead to NF-κB activation (Aznar and Lacal 2001; Finco et al. 1997; Montaner et al. 1998; Perona et al. 1997; Reuther et al. 1998).

3 Cell Autonomous and Non-Autonomous Functions of NF-κB During Tumorigenesis

The first genetic in vivo evidence for a role of NF-κB in solid malignancies came from a mouse model recapitulating colitis-associated carcinogenesis (CAC) and demonstrated that NF-κB can promote tumor development in a direct as well as an indirect manner (Greten et al. 2004). Inflammatory bowel disease (IBD) and in particular ulcerative colitis is a major risk factor for the development of colon cancer and although only 1% of all colon cares are associated with IBD, patients with longstanding ulcerative colitis that do not respond well to anti-inflammatory therapy have an increased risk that can increase up to 20% after 30 years of disease (Eaden et al. 2001). To induce colonic tumor development in the CAC model, mice were injected with the pro-carcinogen azoxymethane (AOM), which induces G:A transitions and the formation of DNA adducts. One of the most frequently induced mutations comprises bases in exon3 of *Ctnnb* that encode for serine and threonine residues that are required for phosphorylation by GSK3β. Lack of these phosphorylation sites leads to constitutive Wnt-activation thereby recapitulating the situation in human cancers, although in humans Wnt signaling is induced by a loss of APC function in the majority of cases (Markowitz and Bertagnolli 2009). Following the initiation stage, mice were administered repetitive cycles of dextran sulfate sodium salt (DSS) in their drinking water, which acts as a tumor promoter in this model. DSS induces apoptosis of intestinal epithelial cells (IEC) that leads to the loss of the intestinal barrier and consecutively to intestinal inflammation. A tumor-promoting role of NF-κB in this model could be demonstrated by conditional deletion of *Ikkβ* in either IEC or in myeloid cells which both decreased colonic adenoma formation. In IEC, this cell autonomous effect was caused by a NF-κB-dependent suppression of apoptosis mainly through transcriptional induction of Bcl-x_L, which prevented the elimination of premalignant-mutated IEC during the DSS-triggered promotion stage. In contrast, in myeloid cells, NF-κB regulated the transcription of various pro-inflammatory cytokines, which act in a paracrine manner to stimulate IEC proliferation during the acute inflammatory response. While IEC-restricted ablation of NF-κB signaling affected tumor incidence but not tumor size, the lack of transcription of pro-proliferative cytokines in myeloid cells decreased both the average size of colonic adenomas as well as their numbers. This suggested that NF-κB in IEC was responsible for apoptosis control but not proliferation, while in myeloid cells it induced transcription of pro-proliferative cytokines.

In an attempt to examine which of the cytokines secreted by myeloid cells was responsible for the observed paracrine-mediated proliferation control, the IL-6 signaling pathway, which had been shown to have pro-proliferative properties in various cell culture models, as well as the AOM/DSS model, was examined. Using either mice with an IEC-restricted deletion of Stat3 or mice with a mutant form of gp130, the receptor subunit responsible for binding of IL-6 family cytokines, that leads to Stat3 hyperactivation, it could be demonstrated that it was indeed IL-6- and IL-11-triggered activation of Stat3 in IEC that controlled proliferation in the AOM/DSS model of CAC (Bollrath et al. 2009). Several downstream targets that are known to be involved in cell cycle progression (c-myc, cyclin D1, cyclin B1 and RegIIIγ) were controlled by Stat3 activation. In addition, Stat3 affected the expression of various genes coding for anti-apoptotic proteins, demonstrating the importance of this particular signaling pathway for the pathogenesis of CAC. Both NF-κB and Stat3 represent central signaling nodes that control a plethora of downstream mediators involved in cell survival, cell cycle and inflammation (Bollrath and Greten 2009).

Additional examples demonstrating the cell autonomous and non-autonomous functions of NF-κB in other malignancies have recently been described using mouse models of lung and stomach cancer (Meylan et al. 2009; Shibata et al. 2009). When NF-κB signaling was inhibited through the expression of an IκBα-superrepressor in p53-deficient, K-ras-mutated lung tumor cells, apoptosis was induced and tumor growth in vivo inhibited (Meylan et al. 2009). Moreover, loss of IKKβ in gastric epithelial cells also induced apoptosis, which, however, led to an increased inflammatory response and ultimately to a more rapid progression of gastric pre-neoplasia (Shibata et al. 2009), similar to the increased tumor incidence found in mice with a hepatocyte-restricted deletion of IKKβ in the diethylnitrosamine (DEN) model (Maeda et al. 2005; discussed in more detail in Chaps. 100, 104). In contrast, loss of IKKβ in myeloid cells delayed gastric tumor progression. Further indirect effects of NF-κB in myeloid cells were recently reported in an elegant study addressing the role of tobacco smoke during K-ras lung tumor promotion (Takahashi et al. 2010). Tobacco smoke induces a low-grade pulmonary inflammation (increased levels of TNF-α and IL-6), hyperproliferation of epithelial cells and ultimately acceleration of tumor development in the context of oncogenic K-ras expression. Thus, similar to the situation during acute colitis in the CAC-model, also when an environmental irritant induces only a low-grade inflammation, myeloid-specific deletion of IKKβ reduces expression of pro-inflammatory cytokines and subsequently proliferation of tumor cells.

Another function of NF-κB specifically found in tumor associated macrophages (TAM) was demonstrated by Fran Balkwill's group using a model of metastasized ovarian cancer (Hagemann et al. 2008). Conditional loss of IKKβ or adoptive transfer of macrophages adenovirally infected with a dominant-negative form of IKKβ blocked intraperitoneal growth of ovarian cancer cells through the induction of IL-12 and inducible NO synthase (iNOS) and the inhibition of arginase, IL-10 and TNF-α in macrophages. These "re-educated" macrophages conferred a direct tumoricidal activity as well as an IL-12-dependent recruitment of NK cells, which further supported the anti-tumor response. Thus, in addition to secreting pro-proliferative cytokines in lung, stomach, liver and colon cancer, NF-κB in macrophages could also be responsible for maintaining an immunosuppressive profile. Because this particular mode of action has been described only in the ovarian cancer model, it remains to be examined whether this function is limited to specific tumor stages (progression rather than promotion) or whether it is restricted to certain tumor entities.

4 NF-κB and Pancreatic Cancer

Another fatal tumor entity with a very poor prognosis that suggests an important role for NF-κB activation during tumorigenesis comprises pancreatic ductal adenocarcinoma (PDAC). Although molecular deregulations such as constitutive NF-κB activation in PDAC are more thoroughly defined than in other cancer types, neither the exact mechanism that leads to its hyperactivation in pancreatic tumors nor its function during the different stages of tumor development has yet been genetically defined. Since inflammation has recently been proposed as an additional hallmark of cancer (Mantovani 2009), NF-κB's role in chronic inflammation and pancreatic tumorigenesis has regained attention. However, NF-κB is responsible for the activation of a wide range of gene sets involved in various functions all of which together constitute the essential and the sequential steps of the carcinogenic process in PDAC. NF-κB-regulated genes such as Bcl-2, Bcl-x_L coordinate anti-apoptotic responses, proteolytic enzymes such as matrix metalloproteases and cell adhesion molecules such as ICAM-1 regulate invasion and metastasis, and VEGF that regulates angiogenesis (Farrow et al. 2004; Karin et al. 2002; Sclabas et al. 2003). Furthermore, in a mouse model of PDAC based on oncogenic K-ras activation (Tuveson et al. 2004), inflammation or tissue damage proved to be essential for tumor promotion and progression (Guerra et al. 2007). Oncogenic activation of K-ras during embryonic stages resulted in a full range of pancreatic epithelial neoplasia (PanIN), the tumor precursor lesions, and eventually PDAC. However, post-natal activation of the oncogene, which resembles the situation in humans more closely, failed to induce any of the phenotypes observed when activated embryonically unless cerulein-induced chronic pancreatitis was induced. Intriguingly, chronic pancreatitis led to NF-κB activation (Guerra et al. 2007). Although this study did not provide any direct evidence demonstrating that pancreatitis-induced NF-κB activation was causally involved in enhanced tumor progression, it is likely to be the case considering the results from other autochthonous tumor models. Further proof for a crucial role for inflammation and thus presumably NF-κB activation in PanIN progression came from a study using high-fat diet-induced obesity in the context of oncogenic K-ras activation in the pancreas (Khasawneh et al. 2009). Diet-induced chronic low-grade inflammation in addition to the pre-existing inflammatory stroma accelerated PanIN progression in mice, clearly suggesting that diet-induced pro-inflammatory cytokine expression played a crucial role in disease development/progression (Khasawneh et al. 2009). Previously, it was shown in a mouse model of dietary or genetic obesity that NF-κB plays a major role linking inflammation and obesity (Arkan et al. 2005). One important mechanism underlying this link involves NF-κB-dependent expression of pro-inflammatory cytokines that lead to local and systemic effects. This study provided substantial evidence that NF-κB-mediated inflammatory responses during an obese state could potentiate many of the increased disease incidences that obesity is proposed to be associated with, especially that of diabetes and cancer. As IL-1β and TNF-α activate myeloid cells and lead to production of further pro-inflammatory cytokines through regulation of the IKKβ-NF-κB axis, it is highly likely that myeloid cells may play a crucial role in propagating an initial inflammatory signal generated by the excessive uptake of lipids in insulin-responsive tissues, thereby providing obesity a possible direct role in tumorigenesis. In agreement with this hypothesis, abrogation of TNFR-1 signaling protected mice from obesity-enhanced PanIN progression, thereby bringing NF-κB-mediated inflammatory responses back again into track in pancreatic cancer. However, since TNFR deletion was global in this model, tissue-specific role of TNF-α/NF-κB axis during pancreatic tumorigenesis needs further insight.

Recently, cancer-associated fibroblasts (CAFs) were shown to have a pro-inflammatory NF-κB-dependent signature in tumor models of skin, mammary and pancreatic cancer as well as their cognate human counterparts (Erez et al. 2010). Recruitment of macrophages, neovascularization and tumor cell proliferation was dependent on NF-κB signaling in CAF. Thus, the inflammatory infiltrates and proliferating mesenchymal cells in the pancreatic tumor microenvironment presumably provide essential growth factors and signaling molecules in a NF-κB-dependent manner that could further support proliferation and invasion of transformed cells. Although RelA/NF-κB was consistently shown to be activated in human pancreatic cancer, the field faces a new challenge to adequately define the cell source of this activation and furthermore the function in terms of innate and adaptive immune responses in order to be able to come up with therapeutic interventions using IKK inhibitors. In this context, it is interesting albeit counterintuitive to note that chronic high-dose aspirin administration is associated with an increased risk of pancreatic cancer (Langman et al. 2000; Schernhammer et al. 2004). Although aspirin is only a non-specific inhibitor of NF-κB (Yin et al. 1998), the specific role of NF-κB on macrophage function and regulation of innate immunity in response to tissue damage, healing, and resolution of inflammation in pancreatic cancers needs to be clarified before inhibition of the canonical NF-κB pathway can be considered as a novel treatment strategy to fight against this deadly disease.

5 NF-κB is Involved in Expansion of Tumor Stem Cells During Tumor Initiation

The so far described cell autonomous functions of NF-κB addressed mostly the promotion stage of tumorigenesis in the various inflammation-associated tumor models. We could recently highlight now a novel function of NF-κB affecting the expansion of tumor stem cells during the initiation of primarily inflammation-independent sporadic intestinal tumorigenesis. In a genetic model of constitutive Wnt activation, which was achieved by the inducible and IEC-restricted deletion of exon3 of *Ctnnb*, loss of NF-κB in IEC prolonged the median survival of *Ctnnb* mutant mice up to 60%, while hyperactivation of the pathway shortened the survival by almost 30% (Schwitalla and Greten unpublished results). Comparative gene expression analysis revealed that NF-κB could modulate the expression Wnt-regulated stem cell genes in IEC. This was caused by an interaction between NF-κB and β-catenin at the Tcf/Lef binding sites of promoters of these stem cell genes through recruitment of NF-κB by the co-activator CBP. Furthermore, enhanced NF-κB activity could cooperate with β-catenin to de-differentiate post-mitotic IEC to induce re-expression of stem cell markers (such as Lgr-5, Ascl-2, Sox9) in differentiated enterocytes, thus enabling them to initiate tumorigenesis.

Thus, independent of NF-κB's well-described functions in control of inflammation, cell survival and proliferation, the classical IKKβ-dependent NF-κB pathway has also the capacity to modulate the formation of intestinal tumor stem cells.

6 Distinct Functions of IKKα During Tumorigenesis

The role IKKβ and NF-κB in cancer development is undisputed by now; however, the functional importance of IKKα in tumorigenesis, the other catalytic subunit of the IKK complex, is less well defined. While in keratinocytes IKKα can prevent skin cancer through repression of an EGFR-driven autocrine loop (Liu et al. 2008), in mammary epithelial cells it is in contrast required for cell proliferation (Cao et al. 2001) and is an important player in models of ErbB2-driven or carcinogen-induced mammary tumorigenesis (Cao et al. 2007). Furthermore, in two animal models of prostate cancer, IKKα regulated metastasis and growth of androgen-independent tumors after castration: in TRAMP transgenic mice, nuclear IKKα repressed the transcription of the metastasis inhibitor maspin and therefore controlled metastatic progression (Luo et al. 2007). Interestingly, this was independent of classical or alternative NF-κB activation. In contrast, in androgen-independent cancer after castration a particular crosstalk between IKKα and IKKβ could be exploited (Ammirante et al. 2010). Upon castration, androgen-dependent tumor cells underwent apoptosis or necrosis and released inflammatory mediators that led to the recruitment of B cells. These B cells secreted in an IKKβ-dependent manner lymphotoxin α and β as well as other cytokines, which in turn activated IKKα and Stat3 in remaining cancer cells thus leading to the re-emergence of androgen-independent tumors. Pharmacological blockade or genetic ablation of Stat3, IKKα or IKKβ could block tumor growth of androgen-independent tumor cells highlighting the complex interaction between the different signaling cascades.

7 Therapeutic Implications

A vast amount of genetic data obtained during the last decade has by now proven the long anticipated importance of the IKKβ-dependent NF-κB activation for a variety of malignancies. It is undisputable that classical NF-κB activation through cell autonomous as well as non-autonomous functions represents a major molecular link between inflammation and cancer. However, apart from controlling cell survival and transcription of inflammatory mediators, emerging evidence points to additional functions of this central regulator in tumor stem cell biology. Furthermore, cell type-specific inactivation of NF-κB signaling revealed very complex cell–cell interactions that ultimately lead not only to activation of additional pathways, such as Stat3 signaling, but also to crosstalk with IKKα. Collectively, these data strongly support the rationale to pharmacologically target

IKKβ/NF-κB in cancer. Although it is unlikely that such inhibitors will be successful as mono-therapeutics of solid tumors, they might be very beneficial in combination with cytotoxic regimens such as chemotherapy or irradiation. Inhibition of NF-κB can increase the sensitivity of tumor cells to such approaches that would allow the application of lower amounts of cytotoxic drugs, which consequently could decrease side effects that are associated with these therapies. One major disadvantage one has to consider in the context of long-term IKKβ inhibition is the development of immunodeficiency and neutrophilia, which can dramatically enhance pro-inflammatory response to bacterial infections through increased processing of IL-1β (Greten et al. 2007). However, the genetic mouse studies have revealed that targeting Stat3 or the upstream activating cytokines, such as TNF-α or IL-6, might represent promising alternatives as well. It remains to be evaluated which of these strategies will be most efficient for the treatment of inflammation-associated as well as primarily inflammation-independent cancers. Maybe, even cell type-specific inhibition will become feasible in the near future, as this would eliminate many of the unwarranted detrimental side effects associated with NF-κB inhibition. Thus, although we now understand many of the molecular underpinnings of NF-κB's function in cancer development, there is still a long road ahead of us in order to translate this knowledge safely into the clinic for the benefit of millions of cancer patients.

References

Ammirante M, Luo JL, Grivennikov S, Nedospasov S, Karin M (2010) B-cell-derived lymphotoxin promotes castration-resistant prostate cancer. Nature 464:302–305

Arkan MC, Hevener AL, Greten FR, Maeda S, Li ZW, Long JM, Wynshaw-Boris A, Poli G, Olefsky J, Karin M (2005) IKK-beta links inflammation to obesity-induced insulin resistance. Nat Med 11:191–198

Aznar S, Lacal JC (2001) Rho signals to cell growth and apoptosis. Cancer Lett 165:1–10

Bollrath J, Greten FR (2009) IKK/NF-kappaB and STAT3 pathways: central signalling hubs in inflammation-mediated tumour promotion and metastasis. EMBO Rep 10:1314–1319

Bollrath J, Phesse TJ, von Burstin VA, Putoczki T, Bennecke M, Bateman T, Nebelsiek T, Lundgren-May T, Canli O, Schwitalla S, Matthews V, Schmid RM, Kirchner T, Arkan MC, Ernst M, Greten FR (2009) gp130-mediated Stat3 activation in enterocytes regulates cell survival and cell-cycle progression during colitis-associated tumorigenesis. Cancer Cell 15: 91–102

Cao Y, Bonizzi G, Seagroves TN, Greten FR, Johnson R, Schmidt EV, Karin M (2001) IKKalpha provides an essential link between RANK signaling and cyclin D1 expression during mammary gland development. Cell 107:763–775

Cao Y, Luo JL, Karin M (2007) IkappaB kinase alpha kinase activity is required for self-renewal of ErbB2/Her2-transformed mammary tumor-initiating cells. Proc Natl Acad Sci USA 104: 15852–15857

Davis RE, Brown KD, Siebenlist U, Staudt LM (2001) Constitutive nuclear factor kappaB activity is required for survival of activated B cell-like diffuse large B cell lymphoma cells. J Exp Med 194:1861–1874

Eaden JA, Abrams KR, Mayberry JF (2001) The risk of colorectal cancer in ulcerative colitis: a meta-analysis. Gut 48:526–535

Erez N, Truitt M, Olson P, Hanahan D (2010) Cancer-associated fibroblasts are activated in incipient neoplasia to orchestrate tumor-promoting inflammation in an NF-kappaB-dependent manner. Cancer Cell 17(2):135–144

Farrow B, Sugiyama Y, Chen A, Uffort E, Nealon W, Mark Evers B (2004) Inflammatory mechanisms contributing to pancreatic cancer development. Ann Surg 239: 763–769; discussion 769–771

Finco TS, Westwick JK, Norris JL, Beg AA, Der CJ, Baldwin AS Jr (1997) Oncogenic Ha-Ras-induced signaling activates NF-kappaB transcriptional activity, which is required for cellular transformation. J Biol Chem 272:24113–24116

Ghosh S, Karin M (2002) Missing pieces in the NF-kappaB puzzle. Cell 109(Suppl):S81–S96

Gilmore T, Gapuzan ME, Kalaitzidis D, Starczynowski D (2002) Rel/NF-kappa B/I kappa B signal transduction in the generation and treatment of human cancer. Cancer Lett 181:1–9

Gilmore TD (1999) Multiple mutations contribute to the oncogenicity of the retroviral oncoprotein v-Rel. Oncogene 18:6925–6937

Greten FR, Arkan MC, Bollrath J, Hsu LC, Goode J, Miething C, Goktuna SI, Neuenhahn M, Fierer J, Paxian S, Van Rooijen N, Xu Y, O'Cain T, Jaffee BB, Busch DH, Duyster J, Schmid RM, Eckmann L, Karin M (2007) NF-kappaB is a negative regulator of IL-1beta secretion as revealed by genetic and pharmacological inhibition of IKKbeta. Cell 130:918–931

Greten FR, Eckmann L, Greten TF, Park JM, Li ZW, Egan LJ, Kagnoff MF, Karin M (2004) IKKbeta links inflammation and tumorigenesis in a mouse model of colitis-associated cancer. Cell 118:285–296

Greten FR, Karin M (2004) The IKK/NF-kappaB activation pathway-a target for prevention and treatment of cancer. Cancer Lett 206:193–199

Guerra C, Schuhmacher AJ, Canamero M, Grippo PJ, Verdaguer L, Perez-Gallego L, Dubus P, Sandgren EP, Barbacid M (2007) Chronic pancreatitis is essential for induction of pancreatic ductal adenocarcinoma by K-Ras oncogenes in adult mice. Cancer Cell 11:291–302

Hagemann T, Lawrence T, McNeish I, Charles KA, Kulbe H, Thompson RG, Robinson SC, Balkwill FR (2008) "Re-educating" tumor-associated macrophages by targeting NF-kappaB. J Exp Med 205:1261–1268

Karin M, Cao Y, Greten FR, Li ZW (2002) NF-kappaB in cancer: from innocent bystander to major culprit. Nat Rev Cancer 2:301–310

Khasawneh J, Schulz MD, Walch A, Rozman J, Hrabe de Angelis M, Klingenspor M, Buck A, Schwaiger M, Saur D, Schmid RM, Kloppel G, Sipos B, Greten FR, Arkan MC (2009) Inflammation and mitochondrial fatty acid beta-oxidation link obesity to early tumor promotion. Proc Natl Acad Sci USA 106:3354–3359

Langman MJ, Cheng KK, Gilman EA, Lancashire RJ (2000) Effect of anti-inflammatory drugs on overall risk of common cancer: case–control study in general practice research database. BMJ 320:1642–1646

Lenz G, Davis RE, Ngo VN, Lam L, George TC, Wright GW, Dave SS, Zhao H, Xu W, Rosenwald A, Ott G, Muller-Hermelink HK, Gascoyne RD, Connors JM, Rimsza LM, Campo E, Jaffe ES, Delabie J, Smeland EB, Fisher RI, Chan WC, Staudt LM (2008) Oncogenic CARD11 mutations in human diffuse large B cell lymphoma. Science 319:1676–1679

Liu B, Xia X, Zhu F, Park E, Carbajal S, Kiguchi K, DiGiovanni J, Fischer SM, Hu Y (2008) IKKalpha is required to maintain skin homeostasis and prevent skin cancer. Cancer Cell 14:212–225

Luftig M, Yasui T, Soni V, Kang MS, Jacobson N, Cahir-McFarland E, Seed B, Kieff E (2004) Epstein-Barr virus latent infection membrane protein 1 TRAF-binding site induces NIK/IKK alpha-dependent noncanonical NF-kappaB activation. Proc Natl Acad Sci USA 101:141–146

Luo JL, Tan W, Ricono JM, Korchynskyi O, Zhang M, Gonias SL, Cheresh DA, Karin M (2007) Nuclear cytokine-activated IKKalpha controls prostate cancer metastasis by repressing Maspin. Nature 446:690–694

Maeda S, Kamata H, Luo JL, Leffert H, Karin M (2005) IKKbeta couples hepatocyte death to cytokine-driven compensatory proliferation that promotes chemical hepatocarcinogenesis. Cell 121:977–990

Mantovani A (2009) Cancer: Inflaming metastasis. Nature 457:36–37

Markowitz SD, Bertagnolli MM (2009) Molecular origins of cancer: molecular basis of colorectal cancer. N Engl J Med 361:2449–2460

Meylan E, Dooley AL, Feldser DM, Shen L, Turk E, Ouyang C, Jacks T (2009) Requirement for NF-kappaB signalling in a mouse model of lung adenocarcinoma. Nature 462:104–107

Montaner S, Perona R, Saniger L, Lacal JC (1998) Multiple signalling pathways lead to the activation of the nuclear factor kappaB by the Rho family of GTPases. J Biol Chem 273:12779–12785

Mosialos G (1997) The role of Rel/NF-kappa B proteins in viral oncogenesis and the regulation of viral transcription. Semin Cancer Biol 8:121–129

Ngo VN, Davis RE, Lamy L, Yu X, Zhao H, Lenz G, Lam LT, Dave S, Yang L, Powell J, Staudt LM (2006) A loss-of-function RNA interference screen for molecular targets in cancer. Nature 441:106–110

Perona R, Montaner S, Saniger L, Sanchez-Perez I, Bravo R, Lacal JC (1997) Activation of the nuclear factor-kappaB by Rho, CDC42, and Rac-1 proteins. Genes Dev 11:463–475

Reuther JY, Reuther GW, Cortez D, Pendergast AM, Baldwin AS Jr (1998) A requirement for NF-kappaB activation in Bcr-Abl-mediated transformation. Genes Dev 12:968–981

Schernhammer ES, Kang JH, Chan AT, Michaud DS, Skinner HG, Giovannucci E, Colditz GA, Fuchs CS (2004) A prospective study of aspirin use and the risk of pancreatic cancer in women. J Natl Cancer Inst 96:22–28

Sclabas GM, Fujioka S, Schmidt C, Evans DB, Chiao PJ (2003) NF-kappaB in pancreatic cancer. Int J Gastrointest Cancer 33:15–26

Shibata W, Takaishi S, Muthupalani S, Pritchard DM, Whary MT, Rogers AB, Fox JG, Betz KS, Kaestner KH, Karin M, Wang TC (2009) Conditional deletion of IkappaB-Kinase-beta accelerates helicobacter-dependent gastric apoptosis, proliferation, and preneoplasia. Gastroenterology 138(3):1022–1034

Takahashi H, Ogata H, Nishigaki R, Broide DH, Karin M (2010) Tobacco smoke promotes lung tumorigenesis by triggering IKKbeta- and JNK1-dependent inflammation. Cancer Cell 17: 89–97

Tuveson DA, Shaw AT, Willis NA, Silver DP, Jackson EL, Chang S, Mercer KL, Grochow R, Hock H, Crowley D, Hingorani SR, Zaks T, King C, Jacobetz MA, Wang L, Bronson RT, Orkin SH, DePinho RA, Jacks T (2004) Endogenous oncogenic K-ras(G12D) stimulates proliferation and widespread neoplastic and developmental defects. Cancer Cell 5:375–387

Vallabhapurapu S, Karin M (2009) Regulation and function of NF-kappaB transcription factors in the immune system. Annu Rev Immunol 27:693–733

Willis TG, Jadayel DM, Du MQ, Peng H, Perry AR, Abdul-Rauf M, Price H, Karran L, Majekodunmi O, Wlodarska I, Pan L, Crook T, Hamoudi R, Isaacson PG, Dyer MJ (1999) Bcl10 is involved in t(1;14)(p22;q32) of MALT B cell lymphoma and mutated in multiple tumor types. Cell 96:35–45

Xiao G, Cvijic ME, Fong A, Harhaj EW, Uhlik MT, Waterfield M, Sun SC (2001) Retroviral oncoprotein Tax induces processing of NF-kappaB2/p100 in T cells: evidence for the involvement of IKKalpha. EMBO J 20:6805–6815

Yin MJ, Yamamoto Y, Gaynor RB (1998) The anti-inflammatory agents aspirin and salicylate inhibit the activity of I(kappa)B kinase-beta. Nature 396:77–80

Macrophages and NF-κB in Cancer

Toby Lawrence

Abstract Macrophages are tissue resident phagocytes with important roles in development, wound healing, and inflammation. There is enormous heterogeneity in macrophage phenotype, from 'classically' activated macrophages that have important roles in inflammation and innate immunity, to 'alternative' macrophage activation that is associated with wound healing, angiogenesis, and immune-suppression. Most, if not all, solid tumors have a significant macrophage population, clinical and experimental evidence suggests tumor-associated macrophages (TAM) are linked with tumor progression. The trophic functions of TAM are associated with increased angiogenesis, malignant cell invasion, and metastasis. NF-κB is s central regulator of inflammation and NF-κB activation particularly in TAM is linked with promotion of carcinogenesis in various experimental models of inflammation-associated cancer. NF-κB activation in TAM has, therefore, been suggested to represent a molecular link between inflammation and cancer. However, TAM frequently display an anti-inflammatory phenotype linked with immune-suppression that is not easily reconciled with a pro-inflammatory function for NF-κB in TAM. Here, I review the form and function of TAM and discuss the role of NF-κB activation in TAM in carcinogenesis.

Contents

T. Lawrence (✉)
Inflammation Biology Group, Centre d'Immunologie Marseille-Luminy,
Parc Scientifique de Luminy, Case 906, 13288 Marseille, France
e-mail: lawrence@ciml.univ-mrs.fr
URL: http://www.ciml.univ-mrs.fr/Lab/Lawrence.htm

Current Topics Microbiology (2011) 349: 171–184
DOI: 10.1007/82_2010_100

Published Online: 16 November 2010

1 Tumor-Associated Macrophages

Macrophages are tissue resident phagocytes derived from blood monocytes, they have diverse functions in development and immunity and display enormous phenotypic heterogeneity in vivo (Gordon and Taylor 2005). Macrophages in different organs have specialized and specific functions, for example, kupffer cells in the liver have an important role in the clearance of debris from the blood and liver regeneration after injury, Langerhan's cells in the skin mediate immune-surveillance, osteoclasts are critical for bone morphogenesis, and microglia in the brain support neuron survival and repair after injury (Fig. 1). These resident macrophage populations have important functions in organ development and physiology (Pollard 2009). In addition, in response to inflammation or injury, monocytes are recruited into tissue and differentiate locally into macrophages, depending on the nature of the insult or injury these macrophages may acquire distinct phenotypes (Gordon and Taylor 2005). In the context of inflammation, two particular macrophage phenotypes have been described: 'classically' activated or M1 macrophages are characterized by production of pro-inflammatory cytokines and increased microbicidal or tumoricidal activity. The second, 'alternatively' activated or M2 macrophages, in contrast produce anti-inflammatory cytokines and are linked to angiogenesis, tissue repair, and remodeling (Martinez et al. 2009) (Fig. 2). These polarized phenotypes have been described based on in vitro stimulation of macrophages with either interferon (IFN) γ, in the case of M1 macrophages, or interleukin (IL)-4 for M2 macrophages. It is still not clear what correlates these populations have in vivo and their physiological relevance remains ambiguous.

Most, if not all, experimental and human solid tumors have a significant macrophage infiltrate (Pollard 2004). Although M1 macrophages have intrinsic anti-tumor potential, through the increased production of cytotoxic reactive oxygen (ROS) and nitrogen (RNS) species and as innate immune cells with the ability to activate anti-tumor immunity, TAM are thought to contribute to tumor progression by promoting malignant cell invasion, metastasis, and angiogenesis (Pollard 2004) (Fig. 2). Clinical studies have shown that increased numbers of TAM frequently correlates with poor prognosis in various types of cancer (Lewis and Pollard 2006). Furthermore, increased expression of macrophage colony-stimulating factor (M-CSF; CSF-1) and other macrophage chemokines is associated with poor prognosis in many types of cancer. In experimental models of carcinogenesis, macrophage depletion inhibits tumor progression, angiogenesis,

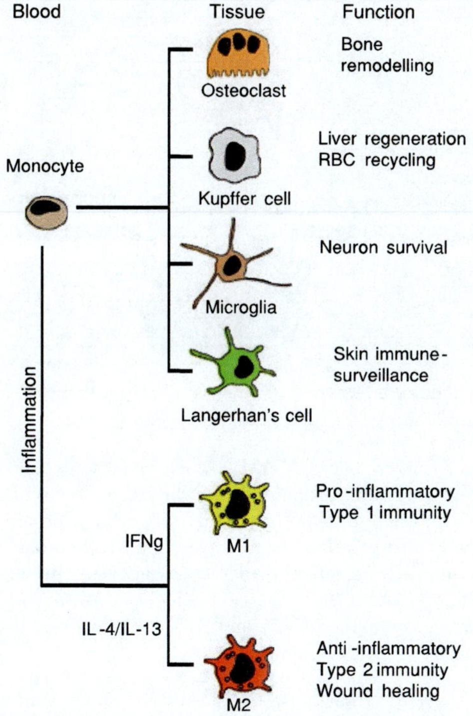

Fig. 1 Macrophage heterogeneity. Blood monocytes are recruited into various tissues during development where they differentiate into specific macrophage populations with specialized functions. Osteoclasts have an important role in bone homeostasis. Kupffer cells in the liver have a role in liver regeneration after injury and the recycling of spent red blood cells (RBC). Microglia in the brain promote neuron survival. Langerhan's cells in the skin mediate immune-surveillance. In response to inflammation blood monocytes are recruited to the inflammatory site, depending on the nature of the insult or injury monocytes may differentiate into functionally distinct macrophage populations. In the presence of interferon (IFN) γ, macrophages acquire a M1 phenotype characterized by increased production of pro-inflammatory mediators, antimicrobial functions, and activation of type 1 immune responses. In the presence of IL-4 or IL-13, macrophages acquire an alternative activation phenotype, also called M2, these cells are associated with anti-inflammatory functions, type 2 immune responses and wound healing

and metastases (Lin et al. 2001, 2006; Qian et al. 2009). This has been most convincingly demonstrated in a genetic mouse model of mammary carcinogenesis, the polyoma middle T (pyMT) model, these mice show significantly reduced tumor progression and metastasis in the absence of CSF-1, but this could be rescued by the transgenic expression of CSF-1 in mammary epithelial cells (Lin et al. 2001). Similar studies in a genetic model of colorectal carcinoma and several transplantable models have shown that the absence of macrophages caused by deletion of CSF-1 significantly reduces tumor progression (Pollard 2004).

The specific phenotype of TAM has been a topic of great interest, several studies have shown that TAM in experimental and human cancers have a M2-like

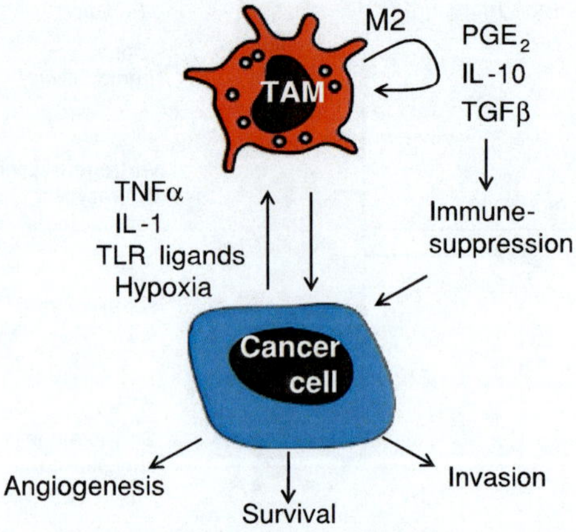

Fig. 2 Tumor-associated macrophages (TAM). Macrophages in solid tumors support tumor progression and suppress anti-tumor immunity. The tumor microenvironment activates macrophages to produce cytokines and growth factors that support cancer cell survival, angiogenesis, and invasion. Cancer cells also polarize macrophages to a M2-like phenotype that is associated with increased expression of anti-inflammatory cytokines and immune-suppression. Several factors in the tumor microenvironment have been suggested to be important in the pro-tumor function of TAM including; cytokines TNFα and IL-1, endogenous TLR ligands, and hypoxia

phenotype (Mantovani et al. 2002), that is they express anti-inflammatory cytokines and genes associated with tissue repair and angiogenesis (Biswas et al. 2006; Sica et al. 2008). However, TAM also express some pro-inflammatory cytokines, such as TNFα and IL-6, and have been shown to express IFN-regulated genes including CXCL10, CXCL9 that are not usually associated with M2 macrophages (Biswas et al. 2006). While the M2 phenotype of TAM is somewhat ambiguous, markers of M1 macrophage activation; MHC II, IL-12 and NOS2, are generally not expressed by TAM. The most useful characterization of TAM, however, is functional; they are associated with trophic functions and immune-suppression that is clearly linked to tumor progression.

1.1 Angiogenesis

Studies in mouse models of carcinogenesis have shown an important role for macrophages in tumor angiogenesis. In particular, Pollard and colleagues have shown that macrophage infiltration of primary tumors in a mouse model of mammary carcinogenesis coincides with an 'angiogenic switch' and malignant progression (Lin et al. 2006). These studies have used macrophage-deficient mice through targeting of CSF-1 or its receptor, Csf1r (CD115). Other studies have clearly shown an association between hypoxia in tumors and macrophage recruitment (Murdoch et al. 2004; Murdoch and Lewis 2005), the critical role for hypoxia in angiogenesis suggesting that TAM may cooperate with tumor cells to promote new blood vessel growth. Hypoxia triggers expression of angiogenic factors in macrophages including vascular endothelial growth factor (VEGF), matrix metalloproteases (MMPs), urokinase (uPA), prostaglandin E2 (PGE2), and the chemokine IL-8, although these factors have all been shown to be important regulators of angiogenesis it is not clear what contribution TAM-mediated production has in tumor-progression (Crowther et al. 2001). In fact, recent studies have shown that the specific deletion of VEGF-A in macrophages increased tumor growth (Stockmann et al. 2008), this was associated with increased efficacy of chemotherapy. It seems that macrophage-derived VEGF-A promoted the abnormal vasculature associated with tumor growth, deletion of VEGF-A in macrophages normalized tumor-associated vasculature, although this was associated with enhanced tumor growth the more efficient vascular network increased delivery of chemotherapeutic agents—usually inhibited by abnormal tumor vasculature.

The pro-angiogenic activity of TAM mirrors many characteristics of M2 macrophages; trophic functions associated with 'alternative' macrophage activation include matrix remodeling, wound healing, and angiogenesis (Martinez et al. 2009), which could be considered parallel to the activities of TAM.

1.2 Invasion and Metastasis

Some of the experiments described above also suggested a role for TAM in metastasis (Pollard 2004), although it was difficult to separate the role of TAM in angiogenesis from a specific role in metastasis. Many studies have shown that macrophages are able to increase the invasive and migratory behavior of malignant cells (Condeelis and Pollard 2006), this coupled with the ability to promote angiogenesis may contribute to metastatic spread. However, direct roles for TAM in metastatic growth had not been demonstrated until recently. Again, the Pollard group used several methods of macrophage depletion to show an important role in establishment and growth of metastatic tumors (Qian et al. 2009). Importantly, in the metastatic niche, it was the recruited macrophages that were required for persistent growth rather than the resident macrophage population. This population was distinct from the angiogenic macrophages involved in progression of primary tumors in the same model.

1.3 Immune-Suppression

There is increasing evidence that TAM also contribute to suppression of antitumor immune responses (Sica and Bronte 2007); the TAM phenotype is associated with increased expression of arginase 1 (Arg1), a prototypical marker of M2 macrophages (Mantovani et al. 2002; Martinez et al. 2009). Increased arginase activity depletes arginine; in addition, the substrate for NOS and elevated Arg1 expression is invariably associated with down-regulation of NOS activity linked to inhibition macrophage tumoricidal function. Arginine depletion through up-regulation of arginase also inhibits antigen-specific T cell activation through down-regulation of T cell receptor signaling (Bronte and Zanovello 2005). The M2-like phenotype of TAM is also associated with increased expression of immunosuppressive cytokines such as IL-10 and TGFβ (Biswas et al. 2006). The immuno-suppressive function of TAM should not be confused with so called 'myeloid-derived suppressor cells' or MDSC (Marigo et al. 2008). These represent a heterogeneous population of myeloid cells that accumulate, mainly in the spleen, in several transplantable mouse tumor models. MDSC include mononuclear and polymorphonuclear cells and are characterized by expression of both Ly6G (Gr1) and CD11b (Mac1), usually characteristic of neutrophils, the mononuclear fraction of these cells also express IL-4 receptor α chain (CD124) (Gallina et al. 2006). These cells display potent immuno-suppressive activity attributed to variety of different mechanisms (Marigo et al. 2008). MDSC expansion also appears to be specific only to certain tumor models, mostly transplantable tumors, and is by no means as conserved as the accumulation of TAM in both experimental and human cancers. Although MDSC are not TAM, since they usually accumulate in the periphery, the monocytic fraction of this population may represent precursors of M2-like TAM given the high expression of CD124 that has been shown to be required for M2 macrophage development several disease models (Martinez et al. 2009). Interestingly, a recent study using a spontaneous mouse model of mammary carcinoma showed IL-4 production by CD4+ T cells promotes carcinogenesis through activation of an M2 phenotype in TAM (DeNardo et al. 2009). However, this was not attributed to immuno-suppressive activity that is a characteristic of MDSC, in fact T cell-derived IL-4 promoted the trophic functions of TAM linked with angiogenesis, invasion, and metastasis.

It is clear the M2-like phenotype of TAM has the potential to suppress anti-tumor immunity, this can be demonstrated in transplantable tumor models that are easily recognized by the immune system, however, there is not yet clear evidence for this mechanism in more clinically relevant models of spontaneous carcinogenesis.

2 NF-κB Activation and TAM

Nuclear Factor (NF)-κB is a generic term for a family of transcription factors with important roles in inflammation and immunity. NF-κB activation is triggered in response to pro-inflammatory cytokines, cell stress, and infection. Studies in mouse models of cancer, specifically colitis-associated colorectal cancer (CAC) and hepatocellular carcinoma (HCC), suggest a tumor-promoting role for NF-κB activation in TAM (Greten et al. 2004; Maeda et al. 2005). Maeda et al. (2005) showed that targeted deletion of IKKβ, an essential activator of NF-κB, in myeloid cells resulted in a marked reduction in tumor burden in a model of DEN-induced HCC. It was also shown in another genetic model of HCC that inhibition of NF-κB activation through over-expression of the endogenous inhibitory protein IκBα reduced tumor formation by blocking the tumor-promoting function for TNFα (Pikarsky et al. 2004). Naugler et al. (2007) demonstrated the TLR adaptor protein MyD88, is required upstream of NF-κB activation in DEN-HCC for IL-6 expression by TAM, and IL-6 production was linked to tumor growth. These studies also suggested that hepatocyte necrosis stimulated pro-inflammatory cytokine production by liver macrophages (Kupffer cells) during tumor development. Maeda et al. (2005) and Luedde et al. (2007) have demonstrated that inhibition of NF-κB by targeted deletion of IKKβ or NEMO (IKKγ) in hepatocytes triggered apoptosis that was linked to increased TNFα and IL-6 production by Kupffer cells. Hepatocyte apoptosis was shown to increase tumor-growth through compensatory proliferation, possibly driven by Kupffer cell-derived TNFα and IL-6. IKKβ deletion in myeloid cells has also been shown to reduce growth of tumors in colitis-associated colorectal cancer (CAC) (Greten et al. 2004). Significantly, mutation of the tumor-suppressor β-catenin in intestinal epithelial cells and the initiation of carcinogenesis and was not affected, but tumor burden was significantly reduced, indicating a specific role for NF-κB activation in myeloid cells in tumor-promotion and not initiation this model (Greten et al. 2004). However, these studies did demonstrate the anti-apoptotic role of NF-κB in malignant epithelial cells was linked to initiation of carcinogenesis. Recently, NF-κB activation in myeloid cells was also shown to contribute to the acceleration of lung tumorigenesis by tobacco smoke, again in these studies, NF-κB activation in lung macrophages was shown to increase production of pro-inflammatory cytokines including TNFα and IL-6 (Takahashi et al. 2010).

3 Pro- or Anti-Inflammatory Roles for NF-κB in TAM?

The studies described above in mouse models of HCC, CAC, and lung carcinogenesis suggest NF-κB activation in TAM has a pro-inflammatory role through the production of cytokines, such as TNFα and IL-6, would reflect a M1 activation phenotype; this is in contrast to the anti-inflammatory M2-like phenotype of TAM described in other mouse models and human cancers (Biswas et al. 2006; Sica et al. 2008). Although NF-κB is considered a major pro-inflammatory transcription factor, recent studies have shown that NF-κB activation also regulates anti-inflammatory pathways, particularly in macrophages (Lawrence and Fong 2009). We demonstrated both pro- and anti-inflammatory roles of NF-κB in acute inflammation and bacterial infection by tissue specific deletion of IKKβ (Fong et al. 2008; Lawrence et al. 2001); these studies showed inflammation was inhibited in mice lacking IKKβ in epithelial cells but deletion of IKKβ in myeloid cells increased inflammation. Greten et al. (2007) also recently showed an anti-inflammatory role for IKKβ in myeloid cells in a model of systemic inflammation. Several other studies have also described anti-inflammatory roles for NF-κB in inflammation and infection (Erdman et al. 2001; Tomczak et al. 2006), interesting this was also attributed to NF-κB activation in myeloid cells. The anti-inflammatory functions for NF-κB activation in macrophages somehow conflict with the proposed pro-inflammatory role for NF-κB in TAM.

It is clear that NF-κB activation in TAM has a role in tumor promotion (Hagemann et al. 2009), but is this due to pro- or anti-inflammatory roles for NF-κB in macrophages? For example, defective NF-κB function has been demonstrated in TAM from chemically induced murine fibrosarcomas associated with a M2-like phenotype (Biswas et al. 2006; Saccani et al. 2006). This defect was attributed to the over-expression of nuclear p50 that acts as a dominant-negative inhibitor of pro-inflammatory NF-κB-dependent genes, including TNFα and IL-12p40. TAM from p50 deficient mice re-gained a pro-inflammatory (M1) phenotype associated with reduced tumor growth; thought to be due to restored canonical NF-κB activity. NF-κB activation has also been associated with tumor regression in a mouse mammary carcinoma model (Guiducci et al. 2005), the TLR9 agonist CpG was used to activate NF-κB in combination with an IL-10 receptor blocking antibody and the chemokine CCL16 to promote T cell infiltration and activation, TAM were redirected toward anti-tumor functions by CpG with the acquisition of a M1 phenotype. In contrast, we recently showed that blocking NF-κB activation in TAM isolated from established ovarian cancers increased their tumoricidal activity and switched their tumor-promoting M2-like phenotype toward M1 activation (Hagemann et al. 2008). These studies suggest that NF-κB activation maintains the M2-like phenotype of TAM in this model. Targeted deletion of IKKβ in TAM (Hagemann et al. 2008), or macrophages during infection (Lawrence et al. 2001), was associated with increased activation of the transcription factor STAT-1 which is critical for IL-12, NOS2, and MHC II expression, hallmarks of M1 macrophage activation. In contrast to the studies using spontaneous HCC and CAC models described above (Greten et al. 2004; Luedde et al. 2007; Maeda et al. 2005; Naugler et al. 2007; Pikarsky et al. 2004), these observations were obtained in TAM isolated from tumors in advanced stages, it is possible, the role of NF-κB activation in TAM may differ depending on the stage of tumor development and the tumor microenvironment. One could envisage that M1 macrophage activation would be associated with necrosis and the breakdown of epithelial barrier function during the initiation of carcinogenesis in mouse models of HCC and CAC, respectively. However, in proliferative and vascularised areas of solid tumors, M2-like macrophages may dominate (Lewis and Pollard 2006; Sica et al. 2008), NF-κB activation may have differential roles in these distinct populations of TAM. The balance between these different macrophage phenotypes can clearly affect tumor progression and the molecular mechanisms involved may represent important therapeutic targets.

4 What Drives NF-κB Activation in TAM?

There is a complicated network of factors released by both malignant cells and TAM that drive tumor progression (Mantovani et al. 2008; Pollard 2004) (Fig. 2). Notably this network includes pro-inflammatory signals for recruitment and activation of myeloid cells but also factors that promote the M2 phenotype of TAM. TNFα, IL-1, and TLR signaling are important triggers for NF-κB activation in macrophages in the context of infection and inflammation, and several tumor-derived signals have also been shown to activate these pathways in TAM, described above (Hagemann et al. 2009; Karin et al. 2006) (Fig. 3). Voronov et al. (2003) showed IL-1β was involved in the production of pro-tumor factors, including VEGF, IL-6 and TNFα, in co-cultures of macrophages and B16 melanoma cells. Our studies have also shown macrophages from IL-1R deficient mice failed to promote tumor growth in a model of ovarian cancer, and IL-1-signaling appeared to be important to maintain the M2 phenotype in this model (Hagemann et al. 2008). As described above, MyD88 signaling (a critical adaptor for TLR/IL-1R) is also linked with IL-6 and TNFα production in HCC and CAC (Naugler et al. 2007; Rakoff-Nahoum and Medzhitov 2007). Moreover, a recent study has showed the extracellular matrix (ECM) proteoglycan versican increased metastatic growth of Lewis lung carcinoma (LLC), by inducing TNFα production in TAM through TLR2 (Kim et al. 2009). Activation of TLRs on TAM by other ligands, including hyaluronan (HA) fragments (Kuang et al. 2007) or heat shock proteins (HSP) (Tsan and Gao 2004), can render them immunosuppressive which may also contribute to tumor progression.

Another facet of the tumor microenvironment linked to NF-κB activation in TAM is hypoxia. It has been shown that TAM are abundant in poorly vascularised

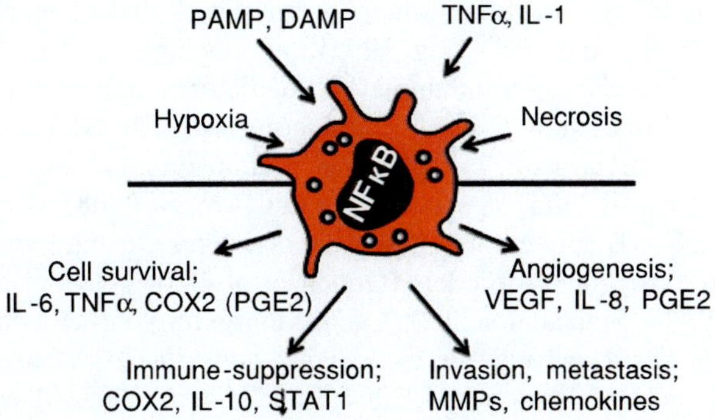

Fig. 3 NF-κB activation in TAM. Several factors in the tumor microenvironment have been linked with NF-κB activation in TAM including; pro-inflammatory cytokines, TNFα and IL-1, endogenous TLR ligands and hypoxia. NF-κB target genes in TAM include regulators of cell survival (IL-6, TNFα, COX2), angiogenesis (VEGF, IL-8, COX2), invasion and metastasis (MMPs, chemokines). NF-κB also mediates immune-suppression in tumors through increased production of IL-10, COX2 and inhibition STAT1-dependent genes; NOS2, MHC II, and IL-12

regions of tumors (Leek et al. 2002; Lewis and Pollard 2006) and high TAM density in these area correlates with increased angiogenesis and poor prognosis (Leek et al. 2002). Hypoxia induces a profound change in the phenotype of TAM through the activation of hypoxia-inducible factor (HIF) (Schioppa et al. 2003; Talks et al. 2000), hypoxic conditions increase expression of genes in macrophages that promote proliferation, invasion, and metastasis of malignant cells and increase angiogenesis (Siveen and Kuttan 2009). Hypoxia also activates NF-κB (Scortegagna et al. 2008; Walmsley et al. 2005) and recently it was shown NF-κB-mediated HIF-1α mRNA expression, in response to hypoxia, was blocked in IKKβ deficient macrophages (Rius et al. 2008). Activation of NF-κB by pro-inflammatory stimuli has also been shown to induce HIF activation; Frede et al. (2006) showed the TLR4-agonist LPS induced HIF-1α in human monocytes and macrophages under normoxic conditions, involving p44/42 MAPK signaling and NF-κB activation. Moreover, a synergistic induction of HIF-1α protein and transcriptional activity by hypoxia and LPS has been described in macrophages (Mi et al. 2008).

Many factors have been suggested to be important in maintaining the pro-tumor phenotype of TAM and several of these can also be linked to NF-κB activation, including TNFα, IL-1, hypoxia, HMGB1, and TLR ligands (Hagemann et al. 2009) (Fig. 3). But further studies are required to determine a hierarchy for these factors and what the critical mediators or pathways are that can be targeted to block the tumor-promoting functions of these cells and possibly restore anti-tumor activity.

5 'Re-educating' TAM by Targeting NF-κB

Several existing anti-cancer agents, such as paclitaxel, have been proposed to act at least in part to inhibit TAM recruitment or function (Allavena et al. 2005; Ghosh and Maiti 2007; Hwang and Ding 1995). Interestingly, most of these agents activate TAM to produce pro-inflammatory mediators, such as TNFα, IL-1β, and NOS2-derived nitric oxide (NO), by activating NF-κB. However, as with all current anti-cancer treatments, because of lack of specificity, there are serious side effects associated with these agents (Swain and Arezzo 2008). Conversely, strategies to target NF-κB activation in TAM are also likely to show success based on evidence from experimental models (Greten et al. 2004; Hagemann et al. 2008; Luedde et al. 2007; Maeda et al. 2005), indeed targeting NF-κB activation in both malignant cells and TAM may be of added benefit due to the role of NF-κB in malignant cell survival (Greten et al. 2004; Luedde et al. 2007; Maeda et al. 2005). However, studies in mouse HCC also showed increased hepatocyte apoptosis was linked to tumor-promotion through activation of NF-κB in liver macrophages (Luedde et al. 2007; Naugler et al. 2007), suggesting at least in this model that specific targeting of NF-κB in TAM may be more beneficial. Systemically targeting NF-κB may also have adverse effects given its fundamental role in innate immunity (Bonizzi and Karin 2004), however, our studies have shown specific targeting of NF-κB in macrophages actually increased immunity to infection associated with activation of M1 macrophages (Fong et al. 2008), again suggesting the specific targeting of NF-κB in TAM may avoid these potential adverse effects.

Targeting NF-κB to block the tumor-promoting roles of TAM in cancer and possibly increasing anti-tumor immunity maybe an attractive therapeutic approach. However, it is highly unlikely such a strategy will have a significant impact on advanced cancer alone, but in combination with conventional therapeutic approaches ‘re-educating’ TAM by targeting NF-κB could have an impact in the clinic.

References

Allavena P, Signorelli M, Chieppa M, Erba E, Bianchi G, Marchesi F, Olimpio CO, Bonardi C, Garbi A, Lissoni A, de Braud F, Jimeno J, D’Incalci M (2005) Anti-inflammatory properties of the novel antitumor agent yondelis (trabectedin): inhibition of macrophage differentiation and cytokine production. Cancer Res 65:2964–2971

Biswas SK, Gangi L, Paul S, Schioppa T, Saccani A, Sironi M, Bottazzi B, Doni A, Vincenzo B, Pasqualini F, Vago L, Nebuloni M, Mantovani A, Sica A (2006) A distinct and unique transcriptional program expressed by tumor-associated macrophages (defective NF-kappaB and enhanced IRF-3/STAT1 activation). Blood 107:2112–2122

Bonizzi G, Karin M (2004) The two NF-kappaB activation pathways and their role in innate and adaptive immunity. Trends Immunol 25:280–288

Bronte V, Zanovello P (2005) Regulation of immune responses by L-arginine metabolism. Nat Rev Immunol 5:641–654

Condeelis J, Pollard JW (2006) Macrophages: obligate partners for tumor cell migration, invasion, and metastasis. Cell 124:263–266

Crowther M, Brown NJ, Bishop ET, Lewis CE (2001) Microenvironmental influence on macrophage regulation of angiogenesis in wounds and malignant tumors. J Leukoc Biol 70:478–490

DeNardo DG, Barreto JB, Andreu P, Vasquez L, Tawfik D, Kolhatkar N, Coussens LM (2009) CD4(+) T cells regulate pulmonary metastasis of mammary carcinomas by enhancing protumor properties of macrophages. Cancer Cell 16:91–102

Erdman S, Fox JG, Dangler CA, Feldman D, Horwitz BH (2001) Typhlocolitis in NF-kappa B-deficient mice. J Immunol 166:1443–1447

Fong CH, Bebien M, Didierlaurent A, Nebauer R, Hussell T, Broide D, Karin M, Lawrence T (2008) An antiinflammatory role for IKKbeta through the inhibition of “classical” macrophage activation. J Exp Med 205:1269–1276

Frede S, Stockmann C, Freitag P, Fandrey J (2006) Bacterial lipopolysaccharide induces HIF-1 activation in human monocytes via p44/42 MAPK and NF-kappaB. Biochem J 396:517–527

Gallina G, Dolcetti L, Serafini P, De Santo C, Marigo I, Colombo MP, Basso G, Brombacher F, Borrello I, Zanovello P, Bicciato S, Bronte V (2006) Tumors induce a subset of inflammatory monocytes with immunosuppressive activity on CD8+ T cells. J Clin Invest 116:2777–2790

Ghosh D, Maiti TK (2007) Effects of native and heat-denatured Abrus agglutinin on tumor-associated macrophages in Dalton’s lymphoma mice. Immunobiology 212:667–673

Gordon S, Taylor PR (2005) Monocyte and macrophage heterogeneity. Nat Rev Immunol 5:953–964

Greten FR, Eckmann L, Greten TF, Park JM, Li ZW, Egan LJ, Kagnoff MF, Karin M (2004) IKKbeta links inflammation and tumorigenesis in a mouse model of colitis-associated cancer. Cell 118:285–296

Greten FR, Arkan MC, Bollrath J, Hsu LC, Goode J, Miething C, Goktuna SI, Neuenhahn M, Fierer J, Paxian S, Van Rooijen N, Xu Y, O'Cain T, Jaffee BB, Busch DH, Duyster J, Schmid RM, Eckmann L, Karin M (2007) NF-kappaB is a negative regulator of IL-1beta secretion as revealed by genetic and pharmacological inhibition of IKKbeta. Cell 130:918–931

Guiducci C, Vicari AP, Sangaletti S, Trinchieri G, Colombo MP (2005) Redirecting in vivo elicited tumor infiltrating macrophages and dendritic cells towards tumor rejection. Cancer Res 65:3437–3446

Hagemann T, Lawrence T, McNeish I, Charles KA, Kulbe H, Thompson RG, Robinson SC, Balkwill FR (2008) "Re-educating" tumor-associated macrophages by targeting NF-kappaB. J Exp Med 205:1261–1268

Hagemann T, Biswas SK, Lawrence T, Sica A, Lewis CE (2009) Regulation of macrophage function in tumors: the multifaceted role of NF-kappaB. Blood 113:3139–3146

Hwang S, Ding A (1995) Activation of NF-kappa B in murine macrophages by taxol. Cancer Biochem Biophys 14:265–272

Karin M, Lawrence T, Nizet V (2006) Innate immunity gone awry: linking microbial infections to chronic inflammation and cancer. Cell 124:823–835

Kim S, Takahashi H, Lin WW, Descargues P, Grivennikov S, Kim Y, Luo JL, Karin M (2009) Carcinoma-produced factors activate myeloid cells through TLR2 to stimulate metastasis. Nature 457:102–106

Kuang DM, Wu Y, Chen N, Cheng J, Zhuang SM, Zheng L (2007) Tumor-derived hyaluronan induces formation of immunosuppressive macrophages through transient early activation of monocytes. Blood 110:587–595

Lawrence T, Fong C (2009) The resolution of inflammation: anti-inflammatory roles for NF-kappaB. Int J Biochem Cell Biol 42:519–523

Lawrence T, Gilroy DW, Colville-Nash PR, Willoughby DA (2001) Possible new role for NF-kappaB in the resolution of inflammation. Nat Med 7:1291–1297

Leek RD, Talks KL, Pezzella F, Turley H, Campo L, Brown NS, Bicknell R, Taylor M, Gatter KC, Harris AL (2002) Relation of hypoxia-inducible factor-2 alpha (HIF-2 alpha) expression in tumor-infiltrative macrophages to tumor angiogenesis and the oxidative thymidine phosphorylase pathway in Human breast cancer. Cancer Res 62:1326–1329

Lewis CE, Pollard JW (2006) Distinct role of macrophages in different tumor microenvironments. Cancer Res 66:605–612

Lin EY, Nguyen AV, Russell RG, Pollard JW (2001) Colony-stimulating factor 1 promotes progression of mammary tumors to malignancy. J Exp Med 193:727–740

Lin EY, Li JF, Gnatovskiy L, Deng Y, Zhu L, Grzesik DA, Qian H, Xue XN, Pollard JW (2006) Macrophages regulate the angiogenic switch in a mouse model of breast cancer. Cancer Res 66:11238–11246

Luedde T, Beraza N, Kotsikoris V, van Loo G, Nenci A, De Vos R, Roskams T, Trautwein C, Pasparakis M (2007) Deletion of NEMO/IKKgamma in liver parenchymal cells causes steatohepatitis and hepatocellular carcinoma. Cancer Cell 11:119–132

Maeda S, Kamata H, Luo JL, Leffert H, Karin M (2005) IKKbeta couples hepatocyte death to cytokine-driven compensatory proliferation that promotes chemical hepatocarcinogenesis. Cell 121:977–990

Mantovani A, Sozzani S, Locati M, Allavena P, Sica A (2002) Macrophage polarization: tumor-associated macrophages as a paradigm for polarized M2 mononuclear phagocytes. Trends Immunol 23:549–555

Mantovani A, Allavena P, Sica A, Balkwill F (2008) Cancer-related inflammation. Nature 454:436–444

Marigo I, Dolcetti L, Serafini P, Zanovello P, Bronte V (2008) Tumor-induced tolerance and immune suppression by myeloid derived suppressor cells. Immunol Rev 222:162–179

Martinez FO, Helming L, Gordon S (2009) Alternative activation of macrophages: an immunologic functional perspective. Annu Rev Immunol 27:451–483

Mi Z, Rapisarda A, Taylor L, Brooks A, Creighton-Gutteridge M, Melillo G, Varesio L (2008) Synergystic induction of HIF-1alpha transcriptional activity by hypoxia and lipopolysaccharide in macrophages. Cell Cycle 7:232–241

Murdoch C, Lewis CE (2005) Macrophage migration and gene expression in response to tumor hypoxia. Int J Cancer 117:701–708

Murdoch C, Giannoudis A, Lewis CE (2004) Mechanisms regulating the recruitment of macrophages into hypoxic areas of tumors and other ischemic tissues. Blood 104:2224–2234

Naugler WE, Sakurai T, Kim S, Maeda S, Kim K, Elsharkawy AM, Karin M (2007) Gender disparity in liver cancer due to sex differences in MyD88-dependent IL-6 production. Science 317:121–124

Pikarsky E, Porat RM, Stein I, Abramovitch R, Amit S, Kasem S, Gutkovich-Pyest E, Urieli-Shoval S, Galun E, Ben-Neriah Y (2004) NF-kappaB functions as a tumour promoter in inflammation-associated cancer. Nature 431:461–466

Pollard JW (2004) Tumour-educated macrophages promote tumour progression and metastasis. Nat Rev Cancer 4:71–78

Pollard JW (2009) Trophic macrophages in development and disease. Nat Rev Immunol 9:259–270

Qian B, Deng Y, Im JH, Muschel RJ, Zou Y, Li J, Lang RA, Pollard JW (2009) A distinct macrophage population mediates metastatic breast cancer cell extravasation, establishment and growth. PLoS One 4:e6562

Rakoff-Nahoum S, Medzhitov R (2007) Regulation of spontaneous intestinal tumorigenesis through the adaptor protein MyD88. Science 317:124–127

Rius J, Guma M, Schachtrup C, Akassoglou K, Zinkernagel AS, Nizet V, Johnson RS, Haddad GG, Karin M (2008) NF-kappaB links innate immunity to the hypoxic response through transcriptional regulation of HIF-1alpha. Nature 453:807–811

Saccani A, Schioppa T, Porta C, Biswas SK, Nebuloni M, Vago L, Bottazzi B, Colombo MP, Mantovani A, Sica A (2006) p50 nuclear factor-kappaB overexpression in tumor-associated macrophages inhibits M1 inflammatory responses and antitumor resistance. Cancer Res 66:11432–11440

Schioppa T, Uranchimeg B, Saccani A, Biswas SK, Doni A, Rapisarda A, Bernasconi S, Saccani S, Nebuloni M, Vago L, Mantovani A, Melillo G, Sica A (2003) Regulation of the chemokine receptor CXCR4 by hypoxia. J Exp Med 198:1391–1402

Scortegagna M, Cataisson C, Martin RJ, Hicklin DJ, Schreiber RD, Yuspa SH, Arbeit JM (2008) HIF-1alpha regulates epithelial inflammation by cell autonomous NFkappaB activation and paracrine stromal remodeling. Blood 111:3343–3354

Sica A, Bronte V (2007) Altered macrophage differentiation and immune dysfunction in tumor development. J Clin Invest 117:1155–1166

Sica A, Larghi P, Mancino A, Rubino L, Porta C, Totaro MG, Rimoldi M, Biswas SK, Allavena P, Mantovani A (2008) Macrophage polarization in tumour progression. Semin Cancer Biol 18:349–355

Siveen KS, Kuttan G (2009) Role of macrophages in tumour progression. Immunol Lett 123:97–102

Stockmann C, Doedens A, Weidemann A, Zhang N, Takeda N, Greenberg JI, Cheresh DA, Johnson RS (2008) Deletion of vascular endothelial growth factor in myeloid cells accelerates tumorigenesis. Nature 456:814–818

Swain SM, Arezzo JC (2008) Neuropathy associated with microtubule inhibitors: diagnosis, incidence, and management. Clin Adv Hematol Oncol 6:455–467

Takahashi H, Ogata H, Nishigaki R, Broide DH, Karin M (2010) Tobacco smoke promotes lung tumorigenesis by triggering IKKbeta- and JNK1-dependent inflammation. Cancer Cell 17:89–97

Talks KL, Turley H, Gatter KC, Maxwell PH, Pugh CW, Ratcliffe PJ, Harris AL (2000) The expression and distribution of the hypoxia-inducible factors HIF-1alpha and HIF-2alpha in normal human tissues, cancers, and tumor-associated macrophages. Am J Pathol 157:411–421

Tomczak MF, Erdman SE, Davidson A, Wang YY, Nambiar PR, Rogers AB, Rickman B, Luchetti D, Fox JG, Horwitz BH (2006) Inhibition of Helicobacter hepaticus-induced colitis by IL-10 requires the p50/p105 subunit of NF-kappa B. J Immunol 177:7332–7339
Tsan MF, Gao B (2004) Endogenous ligands of Toll-like receptors. J Leukoc Biol 76:514–519
Voronov E, Shouval DS, Krelin Y, Cagnano E, Benharroch D, Iwakura Y, Dinarello CA, Apte RN (2003) IL-1 is required for tumor invasiveness and angiogenesis. Proc Natl Acad Sci USA 100:2645–2650
Walmsley SR, Print C, Farahi N, Peyssonnaux C, Johnson RS, Cramer T, Sobolewski A, Condliffe AM, Cowburn AS, Johnson N, Chilvers ER (2005) Hypoxia-induced neutrophil survival is mediated by HIF-1alpha-dependent NF-kappaB activity. J Exp Med 201:105–115

NF-κB in Liver Cancer: The Plot Thickens

Shlomi Finkin and Eli Pikarsky

Abstract The role of the NF-κB signaling pathway in liver cancer is complex. While some evidence suggests that in the liver, like in many other organ systems, NF-κB is oncogenic, there is strong evidence showing that in certain liver cancer models NF-κB suppresses tumorigenesis. These contrasting findings cannot be dismissed on technicalities and are likely due to the complex nature of the NF-κB response. Similar contrasting findings regarding NF-κB activity are revealed in skin cancer models. Thus, it is possible that the contradictory role of NF-κB in tumorigenesis is a general phenomenon and not an oddity related solely to the liver. Further studies are indicated to decipher the underlying molecular mechanisms. Revealing these mechanisms may facilitate the identification of patient subgroups and specific situations in which NF-κB inhibition will be a preferred therapeutic option. Moreover, it is possible that specific interventions could boost the tumor suppressor functions of NF-κB in tumors that harbor mutations that render this pathway constitutively active.

Contents

S. Finkin and E. Pikarsky (✉)
Department of Immunology and Cancer Research and Department of Pathology, IMRIC, Hebrew University Hadassah Medical School, Ein Kerem, 91120 Jerusalem, Israel
e-mail: peli@hadassah.org.il

Current Topics Microbiology (2011) 349: 185–196
DOI: 10.1007/82_2010_104

Published Online: 21 September 2010

NF-κB activation is strongly associated with cancer. NF-κB is abnormally activated in many types of human cancer, including breast cancer (Ahmed et al. 2006), Hodgkin's and non-Hodgkin's lymphomas (Sasaki et al. 2007) multiple myeloma (Annunziata et al. 2007; Keats et al. 2007) and HCC (Arsura and Cavin 2005). Many mechanisms have been suggested to explain the contribution of NF-κB to different phases of neoplastic transformation. NF-κB plays a protective role against apoptosis through transcriptional up regulation of anti-apoptotic target genes, including BCL-X_L (Tsukahara et al. 1999), FLICE-like inhibitory proteins (Kreuz et al. 2001; Micheau et al. 2001) and members of the inhibitor of apoptosis family (Stehlik et al. 1998; Wang et al. 1998). Another important mechanism by which NF-κB contributes to tumorigenesis may be by directly stimulating cell cycle progression through transcriptional activation of cell cycle regulatory genes, particularly, Cyclin D1 (Joyce et al. 2001). This dual function of NF-κB, as an activator of anti-apoptotic genes on the one hand and as a potent cell cycle regulator on the other, makes it clear why NF-κB might confer growth survival benefits on transforming cells. Moreover, NF-κB family members have been shown to be involved in chromosomal amplifications, translocation breakpoints, and other genetic aberrations that are considered to play a causative role in carcinogenesis (Rayet and Gelinas 1999).

The first clue for the importance of NF-κB signaling in hepatocytes came from the observation that knocking out the p65/RelA gene resulted in mid-gestation in utero death due to TNF-induced degeneration of the fetal liver (Beg et al. 1995).

Backcrossing the p65 knockout (KO) mice with TNF or TNF receptor deficient mice reversed the lethal phenotype (Beg et al. 1995; Doi et al. 1999; Rosenfeld et al. 2000). Mice deficient in IKKβ (Li et al. 1999a, b) or IKKγ/Nemo (Makris et al. 2000; Rudolph et al. 2000) also die in utero due to massive liver apoptosis; thus, it is clear that the canonical NF-κB pathway has a major anti-apoptotic role in the liver in vivo.

A protumorigenic role for NF-κB was established in multiple studies that used hepatocellular carcinoma (HCC) cell lines. There is evidence of constitutive activation of NF-κB in HCC cell lines (Tai et al. 2000; Arsura and Cavin 2005; Qiao et al. 2006).

The anti-apoptotic role of NF-κB in malignant hepatocytes is also well documented (Bellas et al. 1997; Plumpe et al. 2000; Chiao et al. 2002; Kim et al. 2002; Shigeno et al. 2003) and involves the blocking of TGFβ, activation of anti-apoptotic regulators (Arsura et al. 1997) and reducing the levels of reactive oxygen species (ROS) in the cells (Wang et al. 2008). Recently, the pro-inflammatory mediators S100A8 and S100A9 were identified as novel NF-κB target genes, suggesting that their co-expression during inflammation associated liver carcinogenesis can enhance ROS activity in HCC cells and may contribute to the malignant progression by induction of ROS-dependent anti-apoptotic defense (Nemeth et al. 2009). NF-κB can promote the cell cycle and lead to proliferation of HCC cells in culture directly through the transcriptional activation of G1 cyclins, or by activating the production of proliferation promoting proteins (Waris et al. 2001; Joo et al. 2003). In addition, NF-κB can stimulate the proliferation of cells by activating target genes such as, GM-CSF (Bunting et al. 2007) and IL-2 (Hoyos et al. 1989) which encode growth factors that stimulate the proliferation of myeloid cells, which in turn will activate hepatocyte proliferation in a paracrine manner. NF-κB can also promote angiogenesis and hepatocyte metastasis by induction of vascular endothelial growth factor and matrix metalloproteinases expression in hepatocyte cell lines (Liu et al. 2010).

1 NF-κB and Human HCC

HCC is the fifth most common cancer in the world and the most frequent type of liver cancer, accounting for almost 90% of primary malignant liver tumors in adults (El-Serag and Rudolph 2007). HCC constitutes a major health problem, being the third leading cause of cancer-related deaths worldwide, and its incidence is continually increasing in the USA (El-Serag and Mason 1999). Chronic inflammation plays a major role in most cases of human HCC and the most prominent etiologies linked to HCC development include chronic hepatitis B (HBV) and C (HCV) viral infection and chronic alcohol consumption, all of which cause liver injury, inflammation, and cirrhosis (Farazi and DePinho 2006). Abnormally, high nuclear localization and activity of NF-κB have been found in liver parenchymal cells derived from HCC patients (Tai et al. 2000; Arsura and Cavin 2005; Qiao et al. 2006). Many target gene of NF-κB have been implicated in the pathogenesis of HCC and inhibition of the NF-κB pathway or its downstream effectors have been associated with accelerated apoptosis of the tumor cells and improved prognosis of HCC patients (Garcia et al. 2002; Shi et al. 2008). Moreover, activation of NF-κB in the non-tumor tissue adjacent to the HCC correlates with poor prognosis and a high recurrence rate (Hoshida et al. 2008), suggesting that NF-κB activation may play a role early in disease progression. NF-κB activation in HCC tumor cells was found in 25% of human HCCs based on positive staining for phospho-p65/RelA (He et al. 2010). While most of the data point to the role of the canonical NF-κB pathway in HCC, in which the p65/RELA-p50 is the predominant heterodimer involved in gene regulation in the hepatocytes, there is some evidence pointing to involvement of the non-canonical pathway as well, mediated by the nuclear accumulation of p50 or p52 homodimers and regulated by the oncoprotein Bcl-3 (O'Neil et al. 2007).

2 Mouse Models of HCC

Mouse models of cancer offer a unique opportunity to delineate the outcome of different perturbations in specific cell types, at each stage of disease progression in various disease models, each with its unique advantages and disadvantages. This powerful tool can thus reveal the intricate network of interactions that operates at the tissue level. One should bear in mind that the final outcome of a specific intervention reflects the cumulative effects of many processes and counter regulatory and protective mechanisms that are activated as a result of the initial intervention. Indeed, it turns out that NF-κB plays contradicting roles in different mouse models of HCC: in certain models it plays a pro-oncogenic role, while in others it suppresses tumorigenesis.

3 Mouse Model-Based Evidence that NF-κB Plays a Pro-Oncogenic Role in HCC

In line with the known anti-apoptotic role of NF-κB in many cell types, we showed that NF-κB promotes inflammation-induced cancer in mouse liver carcinogenesis (Pikarsky et al. 2004), thus validating the perception that NF-κB inhibition can be used to inhibit cancer development in patients with chronic inflammation. Mdr2-KO mice, in which the absence of the Mdr2 transporter leads to accumulation of bile acids and phospholipids, develop chronic low-grade inflammation, followed with HCC at 10–12 months of age (Smit et al. 1993). By monitoring the hepatitis and cancer progression in the Mdr2-KO mice, we showed that the biliary originated inflammation triggers hepatocyte NF-κB activation and that this activation was induced by TNF originating from adjacent inflammatory cells and can be suppressed by anti inflammatory drugs or by TNF blocking antibodies. Using an inducible IκB-super repressor (IκB-SR) transgene which is expressed specifically in hepatocytes, we showed that while NF-κB is not required for the early neoplastic events, it is indeed an important factor in tumor promotion. These results are in agreement with the tumor promoting role of NF-κB in a chemical-induced model of colitis-associated cancer (CAC) studied by Greten and colleagues. Elimination of IKKβ specifically in the colonic epithelium, resulted in reduced tumor incidence in the distal colon (Greten et al. 2004).

Another recently published work by Haybaeck and colleagues demonstrated a protumorigenic role for NF-κB in HCC (Haybaeck et al. 2009). They found that the cytokines lymphotoxin-α (LTα) and lymphotoxin-β (LTβ) and their receptor LTβR are upregulated in HBV or HCV induced hepatitis as well as in HCC in humans. Using a cleverly designed transgenic mouse model, they found that concomitant over expression of LTα and LTβ in a liver-specific manner (tg1223 transgenic mice) (Heikenwalder et al. 2005) results in chronic progressive hepatitis which culminates in HCC. This sequence of events nicely recapitulates most cases of human HCC. In order to study the role of NF-κB in disease progression in this model they intercrossed the tg1223 mice with mice deficient in hepatocyte IKKβ ($IKK\beta^{\Delta hep}$) (Maeda et al. 2005). Remarkably, the development of chronic hepatitis as well as HCC in these mice was dramatically dependent on hepatocyte NF-κB, but was independent of TNF receptor 1. Inhibition of LTβR signaling in the tg1223 mice suppressed the development of chronic hepatitis and HCC, while engagement of LTβR resulted in the activation of NF-κB in normal hepatocytes, but not in the IKK$\beta^{\Delta hep}$ livers. Overall this study suggests that suppression of hepatic LTβR or NF-κB signaling in the liver of patients with elevated levels of LTα or LTβ could be of value.

The idea that chronic inflammation is linked to cancer through NF-κB received further support also in mouse models of cancer in other organ systems (Budunova et al. 1999; Greten et al. 2004; Meylan et al. 2009).

Two additional studies focused their attention on pro-oncogenic micro RNAs that are transcriptionally controlled by NF-κB. These studies show that miR 143 (Zhang et al. 2009) and miR155 (Wang et al. 2009) are bona fide NF-κB targets, that they are upregulated in HCC and that they play a protumorigenic role in mouse models of HCC. Yet, the direct contribution of NF-κB in these models was not assessed. The fact that NF-κB is activated in various chronic liver diseases, such as autoimmune liver diseases, cholestasis, and hepatitis B and C, which are associated with higher HCC risk further supports this notion and suggests that NF-κB inhibition may serve as an attractive target in the prevention of inflammation-induced liver cancer.

4 Mouse Model-Based Evidence that NF-κB Functions as a Tumor Suppressor in HCC

In stark contrast with the heretofore enumerated reports, it turns out that in some HCC mouse models inhibition of NF-κB in hepatocytes facilitates tumorigenesis (Luedde et al. 2007) or can even lead to spontaneous tumorigenesis (Maeda et al. 2005). These findings challenge the consideration of NF-κB inhibition as a means of cancer treatment or prophylaxis in predisposed patients.

Maeda and colleagues clearly demonstrated that in a carcinogen-induced model of HCC, NF-κB functions as a tumor suppressor (Maeda et al. 2005). The carcinogen used in this model was diethylnitrosamine (DEN). DEN is a pro-carcinogen which becomes activated in the liver following its metabolism by CYP enzymes and can function as a full carcinogen if injected to 2-week-old male mice. Hepatocyte-specific ablation of IKKβ (IKK$\beta^{\Delta hep}$) in DEN-injected mice resulted in a marked increase in hepatocarcinogenesis, in contrast to the Mdr2-KO and Lymphtoxin-driven HCC models. In order to begin to elucidate the mechanisms through which NF-κB suppresses DEN-induced HCC Maeda et al. tested the effect of IKKβ depletion on hepatocyte apoptosis. As expected, deletion of IKKβ increased hepatocyte apoptosis, but this also leads to enhanced compensatory proliferation of hepatocytes. They suggested that this proliferative response could facilitate the growth of mutated, thus cancer prone hepatocytes, eventually leading to an increased HCC incidence in the IKK$\beta^{\Delta hep}$ mice (Maeda et al. 2005). Furthermore, by deleting IKKβ both in hepatocytes together with non-parenchymal cells they demonstrated that the anti-tumorigenic role of NF-κB is unique to hepatocytes and showed that NF-κB signaling in non-parenchymal cells promotes tumor development. As much of the compensatory, proliferation is dependent on cytokines and growth factors, including TNF, IL-6, and hepatocyte growth factor (HGF), which are produced primarily by liver non-parenchymal cells, ablation of IKKβ in these cells diminished expression of these cytokines, explaining the reduced HCC load upon NF-κB inhibition in liver macrophages. In order to gain further insight into the direct mechanism through which IKKβ deletion in hepatocytes inhibits DEN-induced hepatocarcinogenesis, the same group generated IKK$\beta^{\Delta hep}$/JNK1$^{-/-}$ double KO mice (Sakurai et al. 2006). The reason for this was that they noted earlier that the IKKβ deficient hepatocytes demonstrated sustained JNK activation in response to TNF. Co-ablation of JNK1 in IKK$\beta^{\Delta hep}$ mice resulted in reduced compensatory proliferation after DEN and reduced tumor load. This proves that JNK1 is a critical mediator of DEN-induced hepatocarcinogenesis, yet the question whether NF-κB suppresses hepatocarcinogenesis by inhibiting JNK1 still remains. In another report, the same group investigated the role of IKKβ in hepatocyte proliferation (Koch et al. 2009). They found that IKKβ deleted hepatocytes displayed growth advantages over normal hepatocytes consisting of precocious PCNA and cyclin D1 expression during liver regeneration, and enhanced recovery efficiency, cyclin D1 expression and cell proliferation after plating. However, in a complementary study, Irene Ng and her colleagues could not detect any effect of constitutively active IKKβ on hepatocarcinogenesis in vivo, despite a documented increase in NF-κB activity (Yau et al. 2009).

Finally, Luedde et al. reported that mice with ablation of IKKγ/Nemo in hepatocytes (IKK$\gamma^{\Delta hep}$ mice) developed spontaneous chronic hepatitis, displayed enhanced hepatocyte apoptosis, liver inflammation, steatohepatitis, and chronic inflammation, which triggered compensatory proliferation and development of HCC by the age of 12 months (Luedde et al. 2007). Prevention of apoptosis in these mice by hepatocyte-specific ablation of FADD, an adaptor molecule for TNF receptor 1 required for the activation of caspase-8, or by feeding with the antioxidant BHA resulted in reduced inflammation, steatohepatitis, and hepatocyte proliferation, thus suggesting that the development of liver disease in these mice is secondary to hepatic cell death. As discussed earlier, hepatocyte inhibition of NF-κB by deletion of IKKβ or p65, or by the expression of IκB-SR did not cause hepatitis or HCC. Several explanations could reconcile the different outcomes of these distinct modes of NF-κB inhibition. First, it is possible that NEMO deletion results in stronger NF-κB inhibition compared with IKKβ deletion or IκB-SR overexpression. Alternatively, it is possible that the NEMO effect involves other targets besides the NF-κB pathway (Chariot 2009) which trigger the death of hepatocytes and the subsequent inflammatory disease, but the identity of such factors and the molecular mechanisms behind their effect on hepatocarcinogenesis remains unclear for now. Furthermore, the group of Manolis Pasparakis has shown that epithelial NF-κB is important for protection against pathogens and that NEMO deletion in the gut epithelium triggered a chronic inflammatory response in the colon (Nenci et al. 2007). Previously, Yinon Ben-Neriah's group has shown that inhibition of hepatocyte NF-κB (using the IκB-SR model) resulted in a similar increased sensitivity to pathogens (Lavon et al. 2000). Thus, it is theoretically possible that NEMO deletion in hepatocytes led to indolent infection explaining the steatohepatitis and finally cancer. Further complicating this story are the recent reports showing that while TAK1 deletion per se induces HCC (Bettermann et al. 2010; Inokuchi et al. 2010), deleting both TAK1 and NEMO inhibits HCC (Bettermann et al. 2010). Thus, the latter work now reveals a protumorigenic role for NEMO in the liver.

Similar results concerning the role of NF-κB in cancer were also documented in a mouse model of chemically induced skin cancer. Inhibition of NF-κB in keratinocytes significantly enhanced the development of squamous cell carcinoma (SCC) after exposure to DMBA plus TPA (van Hogerlinden et al. 1999, 2002).

It is possible that the opposing roles of NF-κB in the different models of HCC, stem from the nature of the inflammation in each of these models. In the chronic inflammation models (Mdr2-KO and lymphotoxin-driven models of HCC and IKK$\beta^{\Delta hep}$ model of CAC), the activation of NF-κB is prolonged and in turn, its effect in these models is on tumor promotion, while in the chemically induced model of HCC and SCC the activation of NF-κB is limited to the acute injury phase after carcinogen administration. It is possible that blocking NF-κB in this acute inflammation period, which is the initiation phase of carcinogenesis in these models, promotes the proliferation of mutated cells through compensatory proliferation. These issues have been discussed at length elsewhere (Vainer et al. 2008).

The mechanism by which NF-κB suppresses cancer is not fully elucidated. Compensatory proliferation could explain part of this effect (Maeda et al. 2005). However, if this was the only reason underlying the tumor suppressor role of NF-κB then deletion of any anti-apoptotic protein would induce compensatory proliferation and would turn into an oncogenes in situations were a strong proapoptotic stimulus, such as genotoxic stress prevails. It seems that other, cell autonomous effects also play a role in the tumor suppressive functions of IKKβ (Koch et al. 2009), and possibly NF-κB.

It is interesting to note that other molecules are also noted to act as either oncogenes or tumor suppressors, depending on the cellular context. For example, USP10 suppresses tumor cell growth in cells with wild type p53 but promotes cancer cell proliferation in tumors harboring mutant p53. Thus, USP10 expression is downregulated in a high percentage of renal cell carcinomas, known to have few p53 mutations; USP10 is upregulated in some breast cancer and glioblastoma samples which harbor p53 mutations (Yuan et al. 2010). This nice example provides direct mechanistic evidence explaining the Dr Jekyll and Mr Hyde oncomodulatory activity of USP10.

Another interesting example for the paradoxical and context-dependent suppressor activity of a classic pro-oncogenic signaling pathway can be found in mouse HCC models based on HGF and the c-Met pathway. Transgenic mice overexpressing HGF in the liver develop HCC (Sakata et al. 1996). However, when HGF was over-expressed in c-Myc transgenic mice in a liver-specific manner it resulted in the complete abolishment of HCC in HGF/c-Myc over-expressing mice, compared with 60% HCC in the c-Myc single transgenic mice (Santoni-Rugiu et al. 1996). Similarly, HGF inhibited tumor formation in TGF-α transgenic mice (Shiota et al. 1995). Moreover, while overexpression of wild type c-Met in the liver induces HCC development (Wang et al. 2001), it appears that loss of c-Met signaling leads to enhancement in the early stages of DEN-induced carcinogenesis (Takami et al. 2007), with increased oxidative stress, similar to the results of the DEN-induced HCC in NF-κB inhibited mice (Maeda et al. 2005).

Other examples for such paradoxical pro- and anti-oncogenic activity of the same molecule are noted in cases where protein cleavage can reverse the activity of the protein. Thus, for example, livin can act either as an oncogene or as a tumor suppressor depending on context (Lazar et al. 2010). Finally, the wildtype allele of *Kras2* was shown to inhibit the activity of a mutant *Kras* allele (Zhang et al. 2001). The same phenomenon was hypothesized to explain how genetic variants underlying a previously mapped lung cancer susceptibility locus can have opposing effects on cancer risk depending on context (To et al. 2006). Other similar phenomena that bear some similarity to these processes are oncogene-induced senescence (Mooi and Peeper 2006; Bartek et al. 2007) and oncogene-induced differentiation, which occur with some oncogenic transcription factors (Shah and Sukumar 2010).

Opposing effects of the same molecule on neoplasia can have far reaching implications. On the one hand, they can reduce the utility of targeting specific molecules in the clinical setting. This can be avoided if we gain specific insight into the molecular mechanisms that underlie the opposing effects of the same molecule, allowing us to avoid situations in which its inhibition could be detrimental. On the other hand, this knowledge could even allow one to devise specific treatment regimens that will be particularly harmful to tumor cells in which this molecule is constitutively active if we can make use of the Mr Hyde side of the molecule.

Acknowledgments We are grateful to members of our lab as well as Dr. Yinon Ben-Neriah and members of his lab for continuous fruitful discussions. Work in the laboratory of Eli Pikarsky is supported by grants from the Dr. Miriam and Sheldon G. Adelson Medical Research Foundation, the Israel Science Foundation, the Israel Cancer Research Fund, the DKFZ MOST collaboration, and the Ministry of Health.

References

Ahmed KM, Cao N, Li JJ (2006) HER-2 and NF-kappaB as the targets for therapy-resistant breast cancer. Anticancer Res 26:4235–4243

Annunziata CM, Davis RE, Demchenko Y, Bellamy W, Gabrea A, Zhan F, Lenz G, Hanamura I, Wright G, Xiao W, Dave S, Hurt EM, Tan B, Zhao H, Stephens O, Santra M, Williams DR, Dang L, Barlogie B, Shaughnessy JD Jr, Kuehl WM, Staudt LM (2007) Frequent engagement of the classical and alternative NF-kappaB pathways by diverse genetic abnormalities in multiple myeloma. Cancer Cell 12:115–130

Arsura M, Cavin LG (2005) Nuclear factor-kappaB and liver carcinogenesis. Cancer Lett 229:157–169

Arsura M, FitzGerald MJ, Fausto N, Sonenshein GE (1997) Nuclear factor-kappaB/Rel blocks transforming growth factor beta1-induced apoptosis of murine hepatocyte cell lines. Cell Growth Differ 8:1049–1059

Bartek J, Bartkova J, Lukas J (2007) DNA damage signalling guards against activated oncogenes and tumour progression. Oncogene 26:7773–7779

Beg AA, Sha WC, Bronson RT, Ghosh S, Baltimore D (1995) Embryonic lethality and liver degeneration in mice lacking the RelA component of NF-kappa B. Nature 376:167–170

Bellas RE, FitzGerald MJ, Fausto N, Sonenshein GE (1997) Inhibition of NF-kappa B activity induces apoptosis in murine hepatocytes. Am J Pathol 151:891–896

Bettermann K, Vucur M, Haybaeck J, Koppe C, Janssen J, Heymann F, Weber A, Weiskirchen R, Liedtke C, Gassler N, Muller M, de Vos R, Wolf MJ, Boege Y, Seleznik GM, Zeller N, Erny D, Fuchs T, Zoller S, Cairo S, Buendia MA, Prinz M, Akira S, Tacke F, Heikenwalder M, Trautwein C, Luedde T (2010) TAK1 suppresses a NEMO-dependent but NF-kappaB-independent pathway to liver cancer. Cancer Cell 17:481–496

Budunova IV, Perez P, Vaden VR, Spiegelman VS, Slaga TJ, Jorcano JL (1999) Increased expression of p50-NF-kappaB and constitutive activation of NF-kappaB transcription factors during mouse skin carcinogenesis. Oncogene 18:7423–7431

Bunting K, Rao S, Hardy K, Woltring D, Denyer GS, Wang J, Gerondakis S, Shannon MF (2007) Genome-wide analysis of gene expression in T cells to identify targets of the NF-kappa B transcription factor c-Rel. J Immunol 178:7097–7109

Chariot A (2009) The NF-kappaB-independent functions of IKK subunits in immunity and cancer. Trends Cell Biol 19:404–413

Chiao PJ, Na R, Niu J, Sclabas GM, Dong Q, Curley SA (2002) Role of Rel/NF-kappaB transcription factors in apoptosis of human hepatocellular carcinoma cells. Cancer 95:1696–1705

Doi TS, Marino MW, Takahashi T, Yoshida T, Sakakura T, Old LJ, Obata Y (1999) Absence of tumor necrosis factor rescues RelA-deficient mice from embryonic lethality. Proc Natl Acad Sci USA 96:2994–2999

El-Serag HB, Mason AC (1999) Rising incidence of hepatocellular carcinoma in the United States. N Engl J Med 340:745–750

El-Serag HB, Rudolph KL (2007) Hepatocellular carcinoma: epidemiology and molecular carcinogenesis. Gastroenterology 132:2557–2576

Farazi PA, DePinho RA (2006) Hepatocellular carcinoma pathogenesis: from genes to environment. Nat Rev Cancer 6:674–687

Garcia EJ, Lawson D, Cotsonis G, Cohen C (2002) Hepatocellular carcinoma and markers of apoptosis (bcl-2, bax, bcl-x): prognostic significance. Appl Immunohistochem Mol Morphol 10:210–217

Greten FR, Eckmann L, Greten TF, Park JM, Li ZW, Egan LJ, Kagnoff MF, Karin M (2004) IKKbeta links inflammation and tumorigenesis in a mouse model of colitis-associated cancer. Cell 118:285–296

Haybaeck J, Zeller N, Wolf MJ, Weber A, Wagner U, Kurrer MO, Bremer J, Iezzi G, Graf R, Clavien PA, Thimme R, Blum H, Nedospasov SA, Zatloukal K, Ramzan M, Ciesek S, Pietschmann T, Marche PN, Karin M, Kopf M, Browning JL, Aguzzi A, Heikenwalder M (2009) A lymphotoxin-driven pathway to hepatocellular carcinoma. Cancer Cell 16:295–308

He G, Yu GY, Temkin V, Ogata H, Kuntzen C, Sakurai T, Sieghart W, Peck-Radosavljevic M, Leffert HL, Karin M (2010) Hepatocyte IKKbeta/NF-kappaB inhibits tumor promotion and progression by preventing oxidative stress-driven STAT3 activation. Cancer Cell 17:286–297

Heikenwalder M, Zeller N, Seeger H, Prinz M, Klohn PC, Schwarz P, Ruddle NH, Weissmann C, Aguzzi A (2005) Chronic lymphocytic inflammation specifies the organ tropism of prions. Science 307:1107–1110

Hoshida Y, Villanueva A, Kobayashi M, Peix J, Chiang DY, Camargo A, Gupta S, Moore J, Wrobel MJ, Lerner J, Reich M, Chan JA, Glickman JN, Ikeda K, Hashimoto M, Watanabe G, Daidone MG, Roayaie S, Schwartz M, Thung S, Salvesen HB, Gabriel S, Mazzaferro V, Bruix J, Friedman SL, Kumada H, Llovet JM, Golub TR (2008) Gene expression in fixed tissues and outcome in hepatocellular carcinoma. N Engl J Med 359:1995–2004

Hoyos B, Ballard DW, Bohnlein E, Siekevitz M, Greene WC (1989) Kappa B-specific DNA binding proteins: role in the regulation of human interleukin-2 gene expression. Science 244:457–460

Inokuchi S, Aoyama T, Miura K, Osterreicher CH, Kodama Y, Miyai K, Akira S, Brenner DA, Seki E (2010) Disruption of TAK1 in hepatocytes causes hepatic injury, inflammation, fibrosis, and carcinogenesis. Proc Natl Acad Sci USA 107:844–849

Joo JH, Kim JW, Lee Y, Yoon SY, Kim JH, Paik SG, Choe IS (2003) Involvement of NF-kappaB in the regulation of S100A6 gene expression in human hepatoblastoma cell line HepG2. Biochem Biophys Res Commun 307:274–280

Joyce D, Albanese C, Steer J, Fu M, Bouzahzah B, Pestell RG (2001) NF-kappaB and cell-cycle regulation: the cyclin connection. Cytokine Growth Factor Rev 12:73–90

Keats JJ, Fonseca R, Chesi M, Schop R, Baker A, Chng WJ, Van Wier S, Tiedemann R, Shi CX, Sebag M, Braggio E, Henry T, Zhu YX, Fogle H, Price-Troska T, Ahmann G, Mancini C, Brents LA, Kumar S, Greipp P, Dispenzieri A, Bryant B, Mulligan G, Bruhn L, Barrett M, Valdez R, Trent J, Stewart AK, Carpten J, Bergsagel PL (2007) Promiscuous mutations activate the noncanonical NF-kappaB pathway in multiple myeloma. Cancer Cell 12:131–144

Kim YS, Schwabe RF, Qian T, Lemasters JJ, Brenner DA (2002) TRAIL-mediated apoptosis requires NF-kappaB inhibition and the mitochondrial permeability transition in human hepatoma cells. Hepatology 36:1498–1508

Koch KS, Maeda S, He G, Karin M, Leffert HL (2009) Targeted deletion of hepatocyte Ikkbeta confers growth advantages. Biochem Biophys Res Commun 380:349–354

Kreuz S, Siegmund D, Scheurich P, Wajant H (2001) NF-kappaB inducers upregulate cFLIP, a cycloheximide-sensitive inhibitor of death receptor signaling. Mol Cell Biol 21:3964–3973

Lavon I, Goldberg I, Amit S, Landsman L, Jung S, Tsuberi BZ, Barshack I, Kopolovic J, Galun E, Bujard H, Ben-Neriah Y (2000) High susceptibility to bacterial infection, but no liver dysfunction, in mice compromised for hepatocyte NF-kappaB activation. Nat Med 6:573–577

Lazar I, Yaacov B, Shiloach T, Eliahoo E, Kadouri L, Lotem M, Perlman R, Zakay-Rones Z, Panet A, Ben-Yehuda D (2010) The oncolytic activity of Newcastle disease virus NDV-HUJ on chemoresistant primary melanoma cells is dependent on the proapoptotic activity of the inhibitor of apoptosis protein Livin. J Virol 84:639–646

Li Q, Van Antwerp D, Mercurio F, Lee KF, Verma IM (1999a) Severe liver degeneration in mice lacking the IkappaB kinase 2 gene. Science 284:321–325

Li ZW, Chu W, Hu Y, Delhase M, Deerinck T, Ellisman M, Johnson R, Karin M (1999b) The IKKbeta subunit of IkappaB kinase (IKK) is essential for nuclear factor kappaB activation and prevention of apoptosis. J Exp Med 189:1839–1845

Liu LP, Liang HF, Chen XP, Zhang WG, Yang SL, Xu T, Ren L (2010) The role of NF-kappaB in hepatitis B virus X protein-mediated upregulation of VEGF and MMPs. Cancer Invest 28(5):443–451

Luedde T, Beraza N, Kotsikoris V, van Loo G, Nenci A, De Vos R, Roskams T, Trautwein C, Pasparakis M (2007) Deletion of NEMO/IKKgamma in liver parenchymal cells causes steatohepatitis and hepatocellular carcinoma. Cancer Cell 11:119–132

Maeda S, Kamata H, Luo JL, Leffert H, Karin M (2005) IKKbeta couples hepatocyte death to cytokine-driven compensatory proliferation that promotes chemical hepatocarcinogenesis. Cell 121:977–990

Makris C, Godfrey VL, Krahn-Senftleben G, Takahashi T, Roberts JL, Schwarz T, Feng L, Johnson RS, Karin M (2000) Female mice heterozygous for IKK gamma/NEMO deficiencies develop a dermatopathy similar to the human X-linked disorder incontinentia pigmenti. Mol Cell 5:969–979

Meylan E, Dooley AL, Feldser DM, Shen L, Turk E, Ouyang C, Jacks T (2009) Requirement for NF-kappaB signalling in a mouse model of lung adenocarcinoma. Nature 462:104–107

Micheau O, Lens S, Gaide O, Alevizopoulos K, Tschopp J (2001) NF-kappaB signals induce the expression of c-FLIP. Mol Cell Biol 21:5299–5305

Mooi WJ, Peeper DS (2006) Oncogene-induced cell senescence—halting on the road to cancer. N Engl J Med 355:1037–1046

Nemeth J, Stein I, Haag D, Riehl A, Longerich T, Horwitz E, Breuhahn K, Gebhardt C, Schirmacher P, Hahn M, Ben-Neriah Y, Pikarsky E, Angel P, Hess J (2009) S100A8 and

S100A9 are novel nuclear factor kappa B target genes during malignant progression of murine and human liver carcinogenesis. Hepatology 50:1251–1262

Nenci A, Becker C, Wullaert A, Gareus R, van Loo G, Danese S, Huth M, Nikolaev A, Neufert C, Madison B, Gumucio D, Neurath MF, Pasparakis M (2007) Epithelial NEMO links innate immunity to chronic intestinal inflammation. Nature 446:557–561

O'Neil BH, Buzkova P, Farrah H, Kashatus D, Sanoff H, Goldberg RM, Baldwin AS, Funkhouser WK (2007) Expression of nuclear factor-kappaB family proteins in hepatocellular carcinomas. Oncology 72:97–104

Pikarsky E, Porat RM, Stein I, Abramovitch R, Amit S, Kasem S, Gutkovich-Pyest E, Urieli-Shoval S, Galun E, Ben-Neriah Y (2004) NF-kappaB functions as a tumour promoter in inflammation-associated cancer. Nature 431:461–466

Plumpe J, Malek NP, Bock CT, Rakemann T, Manns MP, Trautwein C (2000) NF-kappaB determines between apoptosis and proliferation in hepatocytes during liver regeneration. Am J Physiol Gastrointest Liver Physiol 278:G173–G183

Qiao L, Zhang H, Yu J, Francisco R, Dent P, Ebert MP, Rocken C, Farrell G (2006) Constitutive activation of NF-kappaB in human hepatocellular carcinoma: evidence of a cytoprotective role. Hum Gene Ther 17:280–290

Rayet B, Gelinas C (1999) Aberrant rel/nfkb genes and activity in human cancer. Oncogene 18:6938–6947

Rosenfeld ME, Prichard L, Shiojiri N, Fausto N (2000) Prevention of hepatic apoptosis and embryonic lethality in RelA/TNFR-1 double knockout mice. Am J Pathol 156:997–1007

Rudolph D, Yeh WC, Wakeham A, Rudolph B, Nallainathan D, Potter J, Elia AJ, Mak TW (2000) Severe liver degeneration and lack of NF-kappaB activation in NEMO/IKKgamma-deficient mice. Genes Dev 14:854–862

Sakata H, Takayama H, Sharp R, Rubin JS, Merlino G, LaRochelle WJ (1996) Hepatocyte growth factor/scatter factor overexpression induces growth, abnormal development, and tumor formation in transgenic mouse livers. Cell Growth Differ 7:1513–1523

Sakurai T, Maeda S, Chang L, Karin M (2006) Loss of hepatic NF-kappa B activity enhances chemical hepatocarcinogenesis through sustained c-Jun N-terminal kinase 1 activation. Proc Natl Acad Sci USA 103:10544–10551

Santoni-Rugiu E, Preisegger KH, Kiss A, Audolfsson T, Shiota G, Schmidt EV, Thorgeirsson SS (1996) Inhibition of neoplastic development in the liver by hepatocyte growth factor in a transgenic mouse model. Proc Natl Acad Sci USA 93:9577–9582

Sasaki Y, Schmidt-Supprian M, Derudder E, Rajewsky K (2007) Role of NFkappaB signaling in normal and malignant B cell development. Adv Exp Med Biol 596:149–154

Shah N, Sukumar S (2010) The Hox genes and their roles in oncogenesis. Nat Rev Cancer 10:361–371

Shi YH, Ding WX, Zhou J, He JY, Xu Y, Gambotto AA, Rabinowich H, Fan J, Yin XM (2008) Expression of X-linked inhibitor-of-apoptosis protein in hepatocellular carcinoma promotes metastasis and tumor recurrence. Hepatology 48:497–507

Shigeno M, Nakao K, Ichikawa T, Suzuki K, Kawakami A, Abiru S, Miyazoe S, Nakagawa Y, Ishikawa H, Hamasaki K, Nakata K, Ishii N, Eguchi K (2003) Interferon-alpha sensitizes human hepatoma cells to TRAIL-induced apoptosis through DR5 upregulation and NF-kappa B inactivation. Oncogene 22:1653–1662

Shiota G, Kawasaki H, Nakamura T, Schmidt EV (1995) Characterization of double transgenic mice expressing hepatocye growth factor and transforming growth factor alpha. Res Commun Mol Pathol Pharmacol 90:17–24

Smit JJ, Schinkel AH, Oude Elferink RP, Groen AK, Wagenaar E, van Deemter L, Mol CA, Ottenhoff R, van der Lugt NM, van Roon MA et al (1993) Homozygous disruption of the murine mdr2 P-glycoprotein gene leads to a complete absence of phospholipid from bile and to liver disease. Cell 75:451–462

Stehlik C, de Martin R, Kumabashiri I, Schmid JA, Binder BR, Lipp J (1998) Nuclear factor (NF)-kappaB-regulated X-chromosome-linked iap gene expression protects endothelial cells from tumor necrosis factor alpha-induced apoptosis. J Exp Med 188:211–216

Tai DI, Tsai SL, Chen YM, Chuang YL, Peng CY, Sheen IS, Yeh CT, Chang KS, Huang SN, Kuo GC, Liaw YF (2000) Activation of nuclear factor kappaB in hepatitis C virus infection: implications for pathogenesis and hepatocarcinogenesis. Hepatology 31:656–664

Takami T, Kaposi-Novak P, Uchida K, Gomez-Quiroz LE, Conner EA, Factor VM, Thorgeirsson SS (2007) Loss of hepatocyte growth factor/c-Met signaling pathway accelerates early stages of N-nitrosodiethylamine induced hepatocarcinogenesis. Cancer Res 67:9844–9851

To MD, Perez-Losada J, Mao JH, Hsu J, Jacks T, Balmain A (2006) A functional switch from lung cancer resistance to susceptibility at the Pas1 locus in Kras2LA2 mice. Nat Genet 38:926–930

Tsukahara T, Kannagi M, Ohashi T, Kato H, Arai M, Nunez G, Iwanaga Y, Yamamoto N, Ohtani K, Nakamura M, Fujii M (1999) Induction of Bcl-x(L) expression by human T-cell leukemia virus type 1 Tax through NF-kappaB in apoptosis-resistant T-cell transfectants with Tax. J Virol 73:7981–7987

Vainer GW, Pikarsky E, Ben-Neriah Y (2008) Contradictory functions of NF-kappaB in liver physiology and cancer. Cancer Lett 267:182–188

van Hogerlinden M, Rozell BL, Ahrlund-Richter L, Toftgard R (1999) Squamous cell carcinomas and increased apoptosis in skin with inhibited Rel/nuclear factor-kappaB signaling. Cancer Res 59:3299–3303

van Hogerlinden M, Auer G, Toftgard R (2002) Inhibition of Rel/Nuclear Factor-kappaB signaling in skin results in defective DNA damage-induced cell cycle arrest and Ha-ras- and p53-independent tumor development. Oncogene 21:4969–4977

Wang CY, Mayo MW, Korneluk RG, Goeddel DV, Baldwin AS Jr (1998) NF-kappaB antiapoptosis: induction of TRAF1 and TRAF2 and c-IAP1 and c-IAP2 to suppress caspase-8 activation. Science 281:1680–1683

Wang R, Ferrell LD, Faouzi S, Maher JJ, Bishop JM (2001) Activation of the Met receptor by cell attachment induces and sustains hepatocellular carcinomas in transgenic mice. J Cell Biol 153:1023–1034

Wang F, Kaur S, Cavin LG, Arsura M (2008) Nuclear-factor-kappaB (NF-kappaB) and radical oxygen species play contrary roles in transforming growth factor-beta1 (TGF-beta1)-induced apoptosis in hepatocellular carcinoma (HCC) cells. Biochem Biophys Res Commun 377:1107–1112

Wang B, Majumder S, Nuovo G, Kutay H, Volinia S, Patel T, Schmittgen TD, Croce C, Ghoshal K, Jacob ST (2009) Role of microRNA-155 at early stages of hepatocarcinogenesis induced by choline-deficient and amino acid-defined diet in C57BL/6 mice. Hepatology 50:1152–1161

Waris G, Huh KW, Siddiqui A (2001) Mitochondrially associated hepatitis B virus X protein constitutively activates transcription factors STAT-3 and NF-kappa B via oxidative stress. Mol Cell Biol 21:7721–7730

Yau TO, Chan CF, Gee-San Lam S, Cheung OF, Ching YP, Jin DY, Sham MH, Ng IO (2009) Hepatocyte-specific activation of NF-kappaB does not aggravate chemical hepatocarcinogenesis in transgenic mice. J Pathol 217:353–361

Yuan J, Luo K, Zhang L, Cheville JC, Lou Z (2010) USP10 regulates p53 localization and stability by deubiquitinating p53. Cell 140:384–396

Zhang Z, Wang Y, Vikis HG, Johnson L, Liu G, Li J, Anderson MW, Sills RC, Hong HL, Devereux TR, Jacks T, Guan KL, You M (2001) Wildtype Kras2 can inhibit lung carcinogenesis in mice. Nat Genet 29:25–33

Zhang X, Liu S, Hu T, Liu S, He Y, Sun S (2009) Up-regulated microRNA-143 transcribed by nuclear factor kappa B enhances hepatocarcinoma metastasis by repressing fibronectin expression. Hepatology 50:490–499

NF-κB as a Target for Oncogenic Viruses

Shao-Cong Sun and Ethel Cesarman

Abstract NF-κB is a pivotal transcription factor that controls cell survival and proliferation in diverse physiological processes. The activity of NF-κB is tightly controlled through its cytoplasmic sequestration by specific inhibitors, IκBs. Various cellular stimuli induce the activation of an IκB kinase, which phosphorylates IκBs and triggers their proteasomal degradation, causing nuclear translocation of activated NF-κB. Under normal conditions, the activation of NF-κB occurs transiently, thus ensuring rapid but temporary induction of target genes. Deregulated NF-κB activation contributes to the development of various diseases, including cancers and immunological disorders. Accumulated studies demonstrate that the NF-κB signaling pathway is a target of several human oncogenic viruses, including the human T cell leukemia virus type 1, the Kaposi sarcoma-associated herpesvirus, and the Epstein–Bar virus. These viruses encode specific oncoproteins that target different signaling components of the NF-κB pathway, leading to persistent activation of NF-κB. This chapter will discuss the molecular mechanisms by which NF-κB is activated by the viral oncoproteins.

Abbreviations

IKK	IκB kinase
HTLV1	Human T cell leukemia virus type 1

S.-C. Sun (✉)
Department of Immunology, The University of Texas MD Anderson Cancer Center and The University of Texas Graduate School of Biomedical Sciences at Houston, Houston, TX 77030, USA
e-mail: ssun@mdanderson.org

E. Cesarman (✉)
Department of Pathology and Laboratory Medicine, Weill Cornell Medical College, 1300 York Ave, New York, NY 10065, USA
e-mail: ecesarm@med.cornell.edu

Current Topics Microbiology (2011) 349: 197-244
DOI: 10.1007/82_2010_108

Published Online: 16 September 2010

KSHV	Kaposi sarcoma-associated herpesvirus
EBV	Epstein–Bar virus
IκB	Inhibitory κB
ATL	Adult T cell leukemia
IL-2	Interleukin-2
LTR	Long-terminal repeat
TCR	T cell receptor
K63	Lysine 63
UBA	Ubiquitin association
TAB 2	Tak1-binding protein 2
LZ	Leucine zipper
NRP	NEMO-related protein
NIK	NF-κB inducing kinase
HBZ	HTLV1 basic leucine zipper
PI3K	PI3 kinase
MCD	Multicentric Castleman's disease
KS	Kaposi's sarcoma
HAART	Highly active antiretroviral treatment
LANA	Latency-associated nuclear antigen
PEL	Primary effusion lymphomas
vCYC	Viral cyclin
vFLIP	Viral FLICE inhibitor protein
GPCR	G-protein coupled receptor
TPA	Tetradecanoyl phorbol acetate
DED	Death effector domains
DISC	Death-inducing signaling complex
LCL	Lymphoblastoid cell line
EBNA	EBV-encoded nuclear antigen
LMP	Latent membrane protein
BL	Burkitt lymphoma
PTLD	Post-transplantation lymphoproliferative disorders
NHL	Non-Hodgkin lymphoma
DLBCL	Diffuse large B cell lymphoma
CB	Centroblastic
IB	Immunoblastic
PCNSL	Primary central nervous system lymphoma
T/NK	T/natural killer
HL	Hodgkin lymphoma
NPC	Nasopharyngeal carcinoma
CR2	Complement receptor type 2
PKC	Protein kinase C
LCL	Lymphoblastoid cell lines
PBMC	Peripheral blood mononuclear cells
TLR	Toll-like receptor

CTAR	C-Terminal-activating region
BCR	B cell receptor
MAP	Mitogen-activated protein
HEL	Hen egg lysozyme
Sm	Ribonucleoprotein Smith

Contents

1 Introduction

The transcription factor NF-κB mediates inducible expression of a large number of genes involved in immune and inflammatory responses, cell proliferation and survival, and many other biological processes (Hayden and Ghosh 2008; Vallabhapurapu and Karin 2009). NF-κB represents a family of structurally related DNA-binding proteins, which in mammals includes RelA/p65, RelB, c-Rel, NF-κB1/p50, and NF-κB2/p52. The different NF-κB members can function as various homodimers and heterodimers that transactivate target genes bearing a κB enhancer sequence. Additionally, NF-κB also regulates gene expression via an epigenetic mechanism (Dong et al. 2008). The primary mechanism of NF-κB regulation involves its cytoplasmic sequestration by the inhibitory κB (IκB) family of proteins, including IκBα and homologous ankyrin repeat-containing proteins (Baldwin 1996). NF-κB1 and NF-κB2 are produced as precursor proteins, p105 and p100, which contain a C-terminal IκB-homologous portion and function as atypical IκB molecules (Beinke and Ley 2004). The canonical pathway of NF-κB activation involves rapid phosphorylation and degradation of the prototypical IκB member, IκBα, and concomitant nuclear translocation of p50-containing NF-κB dimeric complexes (Karin and Ben-Neriah 2000). This NF-κB signaling pathway is induced by diverse cellular stimuli and mediates pleiotropic biological functions. NF-κB activation in specific cell types, such as B lymphocytes and lymphoid stromal cells, also involves a noncanonical pathway that is dependent on site-specific phosphorylation and processing of the NF-κB2 precursor protein p100 (Xiao et al. 2001b). This atypical pathway is specifically elicited by a subset of immune receptors that belong to the TNF receptor superfamily and mediates nuclear accumulation of p52/RelB dimer (Claudio et al. 2002; Coope et al. 2002; Dejardin et al. 2002; Kayagaki et al. 2002; Novack et al. 2003).

A central step in NF-κB signaling is activation of the IκB kinase (IKK). The IKK that mediates canonical NF-κB signaling pathway is composed of two catalytic subunits, IKKα and IKKβ, and a regulatory subunit, NEMO (also known as IKKγ and FIP-3) (Karin and Ben-Neriah 2000). Activation of the noncanonical NF-κB does not require IKKβ or NEMO but relies on IKKα as well as its upstream kinase NIK (Senftleben et al. 2001; Xiao et al. 2001b). Consistently, IKKα efficiently phosphorylates the C-terminal region of p100 (Senftleben et al. 2001). Under physiological conditions, NF-κB activation occurs transiently when cells receive a stimulus. This is due to the negative regulation of NF-κB signaling at multiple levels. However, the NF-κB pathway is constitutively activated in various cancer cells (Sun and Xiao 2003). The deregulated NF-κB activation may involve genetic mutations of regulatory factors or persistent stimulation of NF-κB signaling by pathogens (Sun and Xiao 2003). In particular, the NF-κB signaling pathway is a major cellular target of several human oncogenic viruses, including the human T cell leukemia virus type 1 (HTLV1), the Kaposi sarcoma-associated herpesvirus (KSHV), and the Epstein–Bar virus (EBV). These viruses encode specific proteins that deregulate the NF-κB signaling pathway. In this review, we will discuss the molecular mechanisms by which the viral oncoproteins induce persistent NF-κB activation.

2 NF-κB Activation by HTLV1

2.1 HTLV1 and Adult T Cell Leukemia

HTLV1 belongs to the Delta retrovirus genera, which also includes the HTLV1-related virus HTLV2, the simian T cell leukemia virus type 1, and the bovine leukemia virus (Burmeister 2001). HTLV1 is the etiologic agent of adult T cell leukemia (ATL), an acute malignancy of $CD4^+$ T cells (Poiesz et al. 1980; Takatsuki 2005; Yoshida et al. 1982). This pathogen is endemic in certain areas of the world, including Southern Japan, Caribbean islands, South America, and sub-Saharan Africa (Verdonck et al. 2007). HTLV1 transmission occurs primarily via sexual contact, blood transfusion, and breast-feeding. An estimated 20 million people worldwide are infected with HTLV1, among which about 4% (6% male and 2% female) are expected to develop ATL (Taylor and Matsuoka 2005).

The major clinical features of ATL include the presence of $CD4^+CD25^+$ leukemic T cells with flower-shaped nuclei in peripheral blood, skin lesion with infiltrated leukemic T cells, hypercalcemia, and lymphadenopathy (Yasunaga and Matsuoka 2007). The development of ATL in HTLV1-infected individuals follows a long clinical latency (20–30 years), and the disease progress can be divided into four stages: asymptomatic, pre-ATL, chronic/smouldering ATL, and acute ATL (Yasunaga and Matsuoka 2007; Yoshida 2001). The low frequency and long clinical latency of ATL are a consequence of the oncogenic mechanism of HTLV1. Unlike the acute transforming retroviruses of animals (Burmeister 2001), HTLV1 lacks a typical oncogene of cellular origin and induces T cell transformation through a so-called "transactivating" mechanism that involves aberrant induction of cellular genes regulating T cell growth and survival (Matsuoka 2003). HTLV1 infection stimulates T cells to express the T cell growth factor interleukin-2 (IL-2) (Maruyama et al. 1987; Siekevitz et al. 1987) and the α subunit of its high-affinity receptor complex (CD25 or IL-2Rα) (Cross et al. 1987; Inoue et al. 1986; Siekevitz et al. 1987). In addition, HTLV1 induces the abnormal expression of various other cytokines, apoptosis inhibitors, cell cycle regulators, and proto-oncogenes (de La Fuente et al. 2000; Harhaj et al. 1999; Koga et al. 2004; Mori et al. 2002; Pise-Masison et al. 2002; Sasaki et al. 2005; Sinha-Datta et al. 2004; Tsukasaki et al. 2004). It is generally believed that induction of ATL by HTLV1 involves an early phase of polyclonal T cell proliferation and acquisition of anti-apoptotic ability, followed by T cell immortalization characterized by indefinite proliferation in the presence of the T cell growth factor IL-2. Over time, genetic and epigenetic abnormalities accumulate in the immortalized T cells, which promote the generation of a transformed T cell clone that grows independently of IL-2 and contributes to leukemogenesis (Matsuoka and Jeang 2007; Yoshida 2001).

2.2 Tax as a Primary Oncogenic Mediator of HTLV1

In addition to the structural genes common to all retroviruses, the HTLV1 genome contains a region termed pX, which encodes two regulatory proteins, Tax and Rex, as well as a number of accessory proteins (Matsuoka and Jeang 2007). Several of these pX-encoded proteins display signaling functions, with the most notable one being the 40-kDa Tax protein. Tax serves as the transactivator of HTLV1-encoded genes and, thus, is required for viral replication (Franchini et al. 2003; Jeang 2001;

Yoshida 2001). Moreover, Tax is largely responsible for the induction of cellular gene expression by HTLV1 (Ng et al. 2001; Sun and Ballard 1999). Strong evidence suggests that Tax is the primary oncogenic mediator of HTLV1 (Franchini et al. 2003). Studies using an HTLV1 molecular clone demonstrate that Tax is essential for the in vitro induction of T cell immortalization by HTLV1 (Robek and Ratner 1999). Furthermore, expression of Tax in the absence of other HTLV1 gene products is sufficient to immortalize human CD4+ cord blood T cells and transform fibroblasts in cell culture (Grassmann et al. 1992, 1989; Pozzatti et al. 1990; Tanaka et al. 1990). The in vivo oncogenic potential of Tax has been firmly demonstrated using animal models (Lairmore et al. 2005). Transgenic expression of Tax using HTLV1 long-terminal repeat (LTR) or cellular promoters induces different types of tumors in mice (Lairmore et al. 2005). Of particular interest are transgenic mice that express Tax under the control of the T cell-specific Lck distal promoter. At old ages, a proportion of these mice spontaneously develop pre-T cell leukemia and mature T cell leukemia (Hasegawa et al. 2006; Ohsugi et al. 2007). As seen with ATL patients, the clinical latency of the Tax-transgenic mice is extremely long, which is probably why T cell leukemia was not detected in some other studies using similar mouse models (Lairmore et al. 2005). In some cases, the severe inflammation of the Tax-transgenic mice causes early lethality, which precludes the examination of tumorigenesis at old ages (Kwon et al. 2005). Notwithstanding, these studies establish Tax as a primary oncogenic mediator of HTLV1.

2.3 Persistent Activation of NF-κB by Tax

Despite its potent gene induction function, Tax is not an intrinsic transcription factor due to its lack of a DNA-binding domain. Instead, Tax induces target gene expression by modulation of cellular transcription factors, most notably members of the CREB/ATF and NF-κB families (Sun and Ballard 1999). Tax directly interacts with CREB/ATF to form a transcription factor complex that activates the transcription of HTLV1-encoded genes through binding to Tax-responsive enhancer elements within the viral LTR (Suzuki et al. 1993; Zhao and Giam 1991; Zhao and Giam 1992). On the other hand, Tax stimulates the nuclear translocation of NF-κB, which is largely responsible for the induction of various cellular genes (Sun and Ballard 1999). In contrast to its tight regulation in normal T cells, NF-κB is constitutively activated in HTLV1-transformed and Tax-expressing cells. NF-κB activation is also a hallmark of tumor cells isolated from Tax-transgenic mice (Lairmore et al. 2005). Inhibition of NF-κB by antisense oligonucleotides inhibits the growth of Tax-transformed cells and causes tumor regression in Tax-transgenic mice (Kitajima et al. 1992). Studies using an infectious HTLV1 molecular clone further demonstrate that the NF-κB-activating function of Tax is required for HTLV1-induced immortalization of human T cells (Robek and Ratner 1999).

A hallmark of Tax-stimulated NF-κB activation is the involvement of both canonical and noncanonical pathways (Sun and Yamaoka 2005). Under normal conditions, stimulation of T cells by mitogens or the T cell receptor (TCR) signal does not lead to strong activation of the noncanonical NF-κB (Xiao et al. 2001a). Remarkably, Tax expression in both T cells and nonlymphoid cells results in potent induction of noncanonical NF-κB signaling, characterized by processing of p100 and activation of p52-containing NF-κB dimers (Xiao et al. 2001a). Recent evidence suggests that Tax, but not the HTLV2-encoded Tax2 protein, activates the noncanonical NF-κB pathway, although both Tax and Tax2 activate the canonical NF-κB pathway (Higuchi et al. 2007). This finding has important implications, since HTLV1, but not HTLV2, is etiologically linked to human malignancies (Feuer and Green 2005). At least in vitro, the ability of Tax to activate noncanonical NF-κB is required for Tax-mediated induction of T cell transformation, as determined by the conversion of a T cell line from IL-2 dependent to IL-2 independent growth (Higuchi et al. 2007). As will be discussed in a following section, activation of the noncanonical NF-κB pathway is also a major feature in freshly isolated ATL cells.

2.4 Targeting IKK Signaling Components by Tax

Activation of NF-κB by TCR and the CD28 costimulatory molecule involves the transient assembly of a signaling complex, composed of the scaffold protein Carma1, the adaptor protein Bcl10, the paracaspase Malt1, a yet-to-be characterized E3 ubiquitin ligase, and the lysine 63 (K63)-specific ubiquitin-conjugating enzyme (E2) dimer Ubc13/Uev1 (Fig. 1). K63-linked ubiquitin chains facilitate the recruitment and activation of IKK and its activating kinase, Tak1. Both NEMO and the Tak1-binding protein 2 (TAB 2) contain a ubiquitin-association (UBA) domain, which mediates the ubiquitin-dependent IKK/Tak1 recruitment (Skaug et al. 2009). Due to the presence of multiple negative regulators, IKK activation by TCR and other immune receptors occurs transiently (Coornaert et al. 2009; Sun 2009; Sun and Ley 2008). However, IKK is constitutively activated in HTLV1-infected T cells and Tax-transfected cells (Chu et al. 1998; Geleziunas et al. 1998; Sun and Ballard 1999; Uhlik et al. 1998; Yin et al. 1998). Strong evidence suggests that Tax-mediated persistent activation of IKK involves stable assembly of a Tax/IKK signaling complex (Fig. 1). The assembly of this virus-specific signaling complex requires physical interaction between Tax and the IKK regulatory subunit, NEMO (Chu et al. 1999; Harhaj and Sun 1999; Jin et al. 1999). NEMO has two homologous leucine zipper (LZ) domains that are required for interaction with Tax (Xiao et al. 2000). Although Tax does not contain a typical LZ domain, it has a leucine-rich repeat region that is critical for interaction with NEMO (Xiao et al. 2000). Point mutations of the leucines or a conserved upstream motif of this region of Tax abolishes its binding to NEMO. Studies using Tax mutants and NEMO–Tax chimera proteins clearly demonstrate an adaptor function of NEMO in the

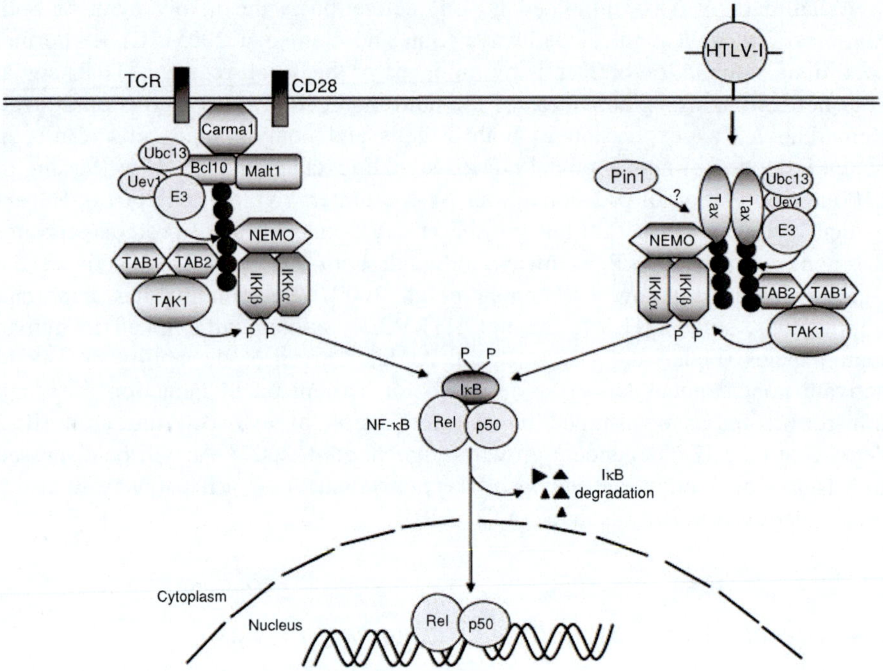

Fig. 1 Canonical NF-κB activation by TCR/CD28 and HTLV1 Tax. Canonical NF-κB activation by the T cell receptor (*TCR*) and CD28 costimulatory molecule involves transient assembly of an intermediate signaling complex composed of Carma1, Bcl10, and Malt1. This so-called CBM complex is also associated with the ubiquitin-conjugating enzyme (E2) Ubc13/Uev1 and a yet-to-be characterized E3 ubiquitin ligase. Within this signaling complex, Bcl10 and probably also Malt1 are conjugated with K63-linked ubiquitin chains that function as a platform to recruit the IKK and Tak1 complexes for their activation. Tax forms a stable complex with IKK and Tak1 and thereby persistently activates these kinases and NF-κB. This viral pathway involves K63 type of ubiquitination of Tax, although how ubiquitination regulates the Tax-specific NF-κB signaling is less clear. Ubiquitination, and possibly Pin1-mediated isomerization, of Tax may facilitate the binding of Tax to NEMO. It is also possible that Tax ubiquitination facilitates its binding by the Tak1 complex via the ubiquitin-association function of Tab 2

recruitment of Tax to the IKK catalytic subunits (Xiao et al. 2000; Xiao and Sun 2000). Together, these studies establish the Tax/IKK physical association as a mechanism by which Tax persistently activates NF-κB.

The Tax–NEMO binding appears to occur directly, since it has also been detected by yeast two-hybrid assays (Jin et al. 1999). However, optimal Tax–NEMO interaction may require additional cellular factors or involve post-translational modifications of Tax or NEMO (Fig. 1). As will be discussed in a following section, ubiquitination of Tax has been suggested to promote Tax/NEMO binding (Nasr et al. 2006). A recent study reveals that the stable association of Tax with NEMO also requires a peptidylproline *cis-trans*-isomerase, Pin1 (Peloponese et al. 2009). Pin1 is known to isomerize phosphorylated serine/threonine-proline bonds in target proteins, an action that may modulate the activity of signaling molecules by causing their conformational changes (Lu and Zhou 2007). Pin1 is over expressed in Tax-expressing and HTLV1-transformed T cell lines and is required for Tax-mediated NF-κB activation (Peloponese et al. 2009). Since Pin1 binds to Tax, it is possible that Pin1 promotes Tax–NEMO association through isomerization of Tax (Fig. 1). However, it is currently unclear whether the enzymatic activity of Pin1 is essential for promoting the Tax–NEMO interaction.

How the Tax–IKK physical association leads to IKK activation is incompletely understood. One possible mechanism is Tax-stimulated oligomerization of NEMO, which may facilitate the catalytic activation of IKK catalytic subunits (Huang et al. 2002). However, the IKK oligomerization is unlikely sufficient for triggering its catalytic activity, since upstream kinases are also required for Tax-stimulated IKK activation (Wu and Sun 2007; Yin et al. 1998). In particular, Tax physically associates with and stimulates the catalytic activity of the IKK-activating kinase Tak1 (Wu and Sun 2007) (Fig. 1). Tak1 is constitutively activated in both Tax-transfected and HTLV1-infected cells (Wu and Sun 2007; Yu et al. 2008). Tax is physically assembled into the Tak1/IKK complex in HTLV1-infected T cells. In transfected cells, Tax not only activates Tak1 but also induces its association with the IKK complex (Wu and Sun 2007). Tak1 activation by cellular signals involves the Tak1-associated ubiquitin-binding protein TAB 2 (Adhikari et al. 2007). Since TAB 2 is also involved in Tax-mediated activation of Tak1 and NF-κB (Yu et al. 2008), it suggests the possible involvement of ubiquitination in the association between Tax and the Tak1 complex (Fig. 1). It is also likely that the Tax-mediated persistent IKK activation involves Tax-stimulated assembly of Tak1/IKK complex (Fig. 1).

IKK activation by antigen receptors involves its recruitment into lipid raft and the central region of the immunological synapse (Hara et al. 2004; Khoshnan et al. 2000; Su et al. 2002). The lipid-raft relocalization of IKK is mediated by the scaffold protein Carma1 (Hara et al. 2004), which constitutively associates with lipid raft and recruits downstream signaling factors upon phosphorylation by PKCtheta (Gaide et al. 2002; Matsumoto et al. 2005; Sommer et al. 2005). Interestingly, Tax possesses lipid raft-associating function, and in HTLV1-transformed T cell lines, the Tax/IKK complex is constitutively present in the Golgi-associated lipid raft microdomains (Huang et al. 2009). It would be important to examine whether the Tax-mediated lipid raft recruitment of IKK is independent of Carma1.

2.5 Tax-Specific Mechanism of Noncanonical NF-κB Activation

Under physiological conditions, active processing of p100 (the central step of noncanonical NF-κB signaling) occurs in B cells but not in T cells. This is because of the selective response of the noncanonical NF-κB signaling pathway to specific signals, including those delivered by CD40 and BAFF on B cells (Pomerantz and

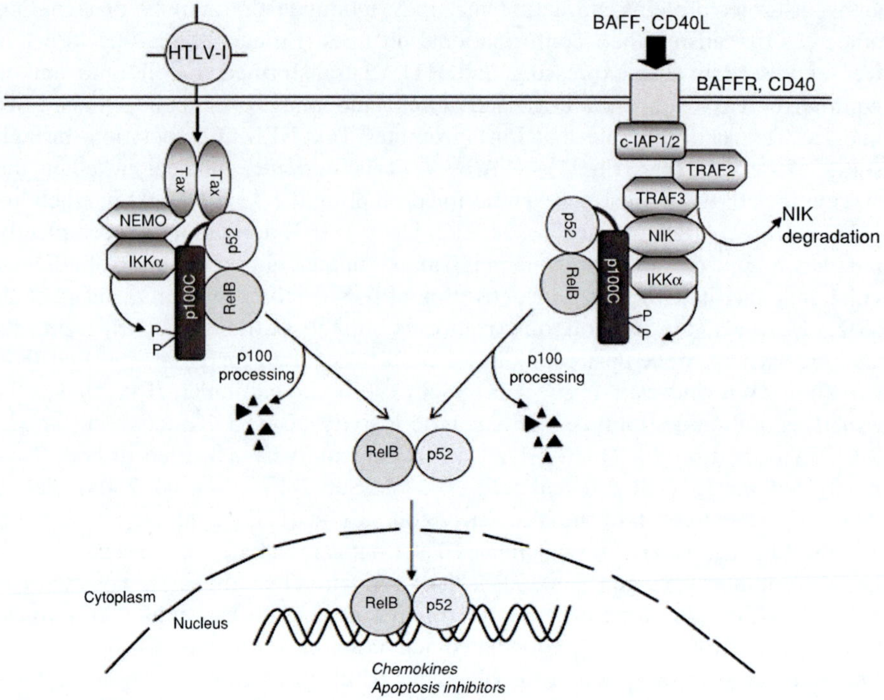

Fig. 2 Tax-specific noncanonical NF-κB pathway. Noncanonical NF-κB signaling pathway is stimulated in B cells by the BAFFR and CD40 signals. This pathway is negatively regulated by TRAF3, which recruits the E3 ubiquitin ligase c-IAP1 or c-IAP2 via TRAF2 and induces ubiquitin-dependent degradation of NIK. The receptor signals induce degradation of TRAF3 and TRAF2, leading to accumulation of NIK and NIK/IKKα-mediated p100 C-terminal phosphorylation. The phosphorylated p100 is then processed through the ubiquitin/proteasome pathway and produce the mature NF-κB2 p52 as a dimer with RelB. Under normal conditions, active processing of p100 does not occur in T cells. However, in HTLV1 infected T cells, Tax initiates an active noncanonical NF-κB pathway by bridging p100 and IKKα. In contrast to the cellular pathway, which is independent of NEMO, the viral pathway requires NEMO, which may function as an adaptor for Tax/IKKα association

Baltimore 2002) (Fig. 2). The active processing of p100 in HTLV1-transformed T cells is mediated by a Tax-specific signaling mechanism that has both similarities and major differences from the cellular mechanism (Xiao et al. 2001a) (Fig. 2). As seen with cellular signals, Tax-stimulated p100 processing requires its C-terminal phosphorylation by IKKα. However, the Tax-specific pathway does not seem to require NIK, which is a central component of the cellular pathway (Xiao et al. 2001a, b). Furthermore, although NEMO is dispensable for the induction of p100 processing by cellular signals, this IKK regulatory subunit is essential for the Tax-specific noncanonical NF-κB pathway (Senftleben et al. 2001; Xiao et al. 2001a). A major function of NEMO in the Tax-specific pathway is to serve as an adaptor in the assembly of the Tax/IKKα signaling complex (Fig. 2). Another unique feature of Tax-stimulated p100 processing is the requirement of Tax/p100 physical interaction (Fig. 2). Tax forms a stable complex with p100 in both HTLV1-transformed T cells and Tax-transfected cells (Béraud et al. 1994), and this molecular interaction requires two N-terminal alpha helices of p100 and is essential for Tax-stimulated p100 processing (Xiao et al. 2001a). The Tax/p100 interaction may allow Tax to recruit p100 to IKKα for phosphorylation. In both transfected cells and HTLV1-transformed T cells, Tax is present in a complex that contains p100, IKKα, and NEMO. Like Tax, NIK physically interacts with both IKKα and p100 and induces IKKα/p100 complex formation (Xiao et al. 2004). However, unlike Tax, NIK binds to IKKα independently of NEMO, which explains why the Tax-specific pathway, but not the cellular pathway, requires NEMO (Fig. 2). Another function of NIK is to stimulate the catalytic activity of IKKα. Since NIK seems to be dispensable for Tax-stimulated p100 processing (Xiao et al. 2001a), it is unclear whether Tax-mediated activation of IKKα involves a different upstream kinase.

2.6 Ubiquitination in Tax-Mediated IKK/NF-κB Activation

Ubiquitination has emerged as a central mechanism that mediates activation of the NF-κB signaling pathway (Chen 2005; Sun and Ley 2008). Polyubiquitin chains are formed through linkage of the carboxy-terminal glycine residue of one ubiquitin to an internal lysine (K) residue of another ubiquitin, with K48- and K63-linked polyubiquitin chains been the most extensively studied. Whereas lysine 48 (K48)-linked polyubiquitin chains mediate protein degradation by 26S proteasome (Chau et al. 1989), K63-linked polyubiquitin chains are involved in assembly of signal transduction complexes (Chen 2005; Sun and Ley 2008). Activation of IKK is associated with K63-linked ubiquitination of NEMO as well as specific upstream adaptors, such as TRAF6 and RIP1 (Chen et al. 2006; Sun et al. 2004; Zhou et al. 2004). Ubiquitinated adaptors serve as a platform that recruits IKK and the IKK-activating kinase, Tak1, for their activation (Ea et al. 2006; Li et al. 2006; Wu et al. 2006) (Fig. 1).

Strong evidence suggests that Tax-mediated IKK activation also involves ubiquitination. Tax undergoes polyubiquitination in both transfected cells and HTLV1-transformed T cells (Lamsoul et al. 2005; Nasr et al. 2006). The ubiquitination of Tax appears to be required for its association with the IKK complex and induction of NF-κB nuclear translocation. Tax also undergoes sumoylation, which regulates the colocalization of Tax with p300 and NF-κB RelA in nuclear bodies and full NF-κB transcriptional activation (Lamsoul et al. 2005; Nasr et al. 2006). The ubiquitin chains conjugated on Tax are predominantly K63-linked, and consistently, the Tax ubiquitination is largely dependent on the K63-specific ubiquitin-conjugating enzyme Ubc13 (Shembade et al. 2007b) (Fig. 1). Ubiquitination of Tax seems to be important for Tax–NEMO physical interaction (Nasr et al. 2006). NEMO interaction with cellular activators, such as RIP1 and TRAF6, is also dependent on K63-linked ubiquitination (Ea et al. 2006; Li et al. 2006; Wu et al. 2006). NEMO has a UBA motif that facilitates NEMO binding to ubiquitinated RIP1. However, the ubiquitin-binding function of NEMO is dispensable for Tax-mediated activation of NF-κB (Wu and Sun 2007). Thus, it remains unclear how Tax ubiquitination promotes its association with NEMO and mediates activation of NF-κB.

Another potential function of Tax ubiquitination is to target this viral protein, as well as its associated IKK complex, to specific cellular compartments. In both HTLV1-infected and Tax-expressing T cell lines, Tax and IKK are colocalized in perinuclear "hot spots" associated with the Golgi (Harhaj et al. 2007). This signaling event, which is induced by Tax, requires Tax–NEMO interaction and correlates with the NF-κB-activation activity of Tax. Tax ubiquitination appears to be important for relocalization of IKK into the Golgi-signaling complex, since a Tax mutant lacking its major ubiquitination-acceptor sites is defective in this function (Harhaj et al. 2007). Another study suggests that the Tax/IKK complex is present in the lipid raft microdomains of the Golgi, suggesting a lipid raft-dependent mechanism of IKK activation (Huang et al. 2009). It has also been suggested that Tax ubiquitination may promote the localization of Tax to the centrosome (Kfoury et al. 2008), a microtubule structure that regulates not only mitosis but also multiple other cellular functions, including signal transduction (Doxsey et al. 2005). The K63-ubiquitinated Tax seems to colocalize with NEMO in the centrosome, suggesting the possibility that Tax activation of IKK occurs at centrosome (Kfoury et al. 2008).

How Tax ubiquitination is regulated is still poorly understood, but a potential mechanism is suggested by the recent finding that ubiquitinated Tax is bound by NEMO-related protein (NRP) (Journo et al. 2009). NRP was originally identified as an apoptosis-regulatory protein, FIP-2, that binds to the adenoviral protein E3-14.7K (Li et al. 1998). More recently, NRP was shown to be mutated in patients with open-angle glaucoma, and therefore it was also named optineurin (Rezaie et al. 2002). Like NEMO, NRP contains a UBA motif, which is required for interaction with ubiquitinated Tax (Journo et al. 2009). NRP appears to stabilize the polyubiquitination chains of Tax and, thereby, promote Tax-stimulated NF-κB signaling (Journo et al. 2009). NRP also interacts with TAX1BP1, and these two proteins cooperate to enhance Tax ubiquitination and Tax-mediated NF-κB activation. This latter finding is unexpected, since TAX1BP1 is known to promote deubiquitination and negatively regulate NF-κB activation by cellular stimuli (Shembade et al. 2007a). Tax1BP1 functions as an adaptor of A20 and is required for A20-mediated deubiquitination of important NF-κB signaling components, RIP1 and TRAF6 (Shembade et al. 2007a). Tax1BP1 also recruits the K48-specific ubiquitin ligase Itch to A20, thereby mediating the degradation of RIP1 and termination of TNFα-stimulated NF-κB activation (Shembade et al. 2008). It is likely that Tax may dysregulate the function of Tax1BP1 and prevent its participation in the A20 ubiquitin editing function. This idea is supported by the finding that Tax disrupts the complex assembly between Tax1BP1, A20, and Itch

(Shembade et al. 2008). Since Tax1BP1 binds to Tax, it is possible that Tax1BP1 promotes Tax ubiquitination by recruiting an E3 ubiquitin ligase to Tax.

In addition to inducing polyubiquitination of NEMO, Tax induces monoubiquitination of the IKK catalytic subunit IKKβ (Carter et al. 2003). The IKKβ monoubiquitination, which can also be stimulated by cellular signals, is triggered by its phosphorylation at Ser-177/Ser-181 within the T loop (Carter et al. 2005). The T-loop phosphorylation of IKKβ recruits a ubiquitin ligase Ro52 (also called TRIM21), which catalyzes monoubiquitination of IKKβ in cooperation with the ubiquitin-conjugating enzyme UbcH5b (Wada et al. 2009). Fusion of IKKβ with ubiquitin inhibits IKKβ function, suggesting a negative role of monoubiquitination in IKKβ regulation (Wada et al. 2009). Consistently, Ro52 overexpression suppresses IKKβ-mediated NF-κB activation, and Ro52-deficient embryonic fibroblasts display hyperactivation of NF-κB in response to toll-like receptor stimulation (Yoshimi et al. 2009). It will be important to examine whether Ro52 knockout or knockdown attenuates Tax-stimulated IKKβ monoubiquitination and promotes Tax-mediated IKK activation.

2.7 Tax-Independent Activation of NF-κB in ATL Cells

Although Tax is essential for HTLV1-induced T cell transformation, this viral gene product may not be required for the late stage of HTLV1 leukemogenesis. Freshly isolated ATL cells often lack detectable expression of viral gene products, including Tax, which is thought to be due to the antiviral immune surveillance (Horie 2007; Sun and Yamaoka 2005). Interestingly, the Tax-negative ATL cells still display constitutive NF-κB activity, thus emphasizing a role for NF-κB in regulating both the initiation and maintenance of HTLV1-induced leukemogenesis (Hironaka et al. 2004). It is currently unclear how the Tax-independent NF-κB activation is mediated in ATL cells, but it appears to involve constitutive activation of IKK (Hironaka et al. 2004). Expression of a dominant-negative IKKα, but not dominant-negative IKKβ or NEMO, inhibits the constitutive NF-κB activity in ATL cells. Consistently, the ATL cells display elevated levels of p52, a product of the noncanonical NF-κB pathway mediated by IKKα (Hironaka et al. 2004). A more recent study further reveals that the IKKα-activating kinase, NIK (NF-κB inducing kinase), is overexpressed in ATL cells derived from a large proportion of patients (Saitoh et al. 2008). Deregulated expression of NIK may contribute to the Tax-independent activation of NF-κB in at least some of the ATL cells. Of note, Tax-dependent activation of the noncanonical NF-κB seems to be independent of NIK but is dependent on NEMO (Xiao et al. 2001a). This is because Tax physically targets IKKα via the adaptor function of NEMO. Thus, NIK is an attractive therapeutic target for treating Tax-negative ATLs, although inhibition of NIK may not be sufficient for blocking NF-κB in Tax-positive ATL cells.

Since NIK overexpression was not detected in some of the ATL cells, additional mechanism is obviously involved in the Tax-independent NF-κB activation.

It would be important to examine whether the rest of the ATL cells have overexpression or activation of other IKK-activating kinases, such as MEKK1, MEKK3, Tak1, and Cot (also known as Tpl2). All of these kinases are potent IKK activators, although only some of them display non-redundant physiological IKK-regulatory functions (Sun and Xiao 2003). In fact, both Cot and Tak1 are constitutively activated in Tax-positive HTLV1-transformed T cell lines (Babu et al. 2006; Wu and Sun 2007), although their expression level and activity in freshly isolated ATL cells have not been analyzed.

Given the complex nature of the HTLV1 genome, the involvement of a yet-to-be characterized viral gene product in Tax-independent NF-κB activation is also a possibility. Recent studies have led to the identification of a novel HTLV1 gene product, HTLV1 basic leucine zipper (HBZ), which is encoded by an antisense mRNA transcribed from the 3′LTR (Matsuoka and Green 2009; Satou et al. 2006). Unlike other viral gene products, HBZ is consistently expressed in HTLV1-transformed T cell lines and freshly isolated ATL cells, implying an important role in leukemogenesis (Matsuoka and Green 2009). HBZ expression enhances the proliferation capacity of HTLV1-infected T cells in vitro and sensitizes T cell activation in transgenic mice (Arnold et al. 2008; Satou et al. 2006). Surprisingly, despite its growth-stimulatory function, HBZ inhibits Tax-stimulated canonical, although not noncanonical, NF-κB activation under overexpression conditions (Zhao et al. 2009). HBZ acts through promoting the ubiquitination and subsequent degradation of RelA. It will be interesting to examine whether RNAi suppression of HBZ expression in ATL cells affects the Tax-independent activation of NF-κB, particularly the noncanonical pathway.

2.8 NF-κB in HTLV1-Stimulated T Cell Transformation

A major pathological characteristic of HTLV1-transformed T cells is their high resistance to apoptosis induction by different mechanisms (Taylor and Nicot 2008). It is generally believed that apoptosis inhibition contributes to both HTLV1-mediated T cell transformation and the resistance of the ATL cells to conventional chemotherapies. The HTLV1-infected and Tax-expressing cells overexpress various anti-apoptotic genes, such as c-IAP1, c-IAP2, c-FLIP, Bcl-XL, and survivin (Harhaj et al. 1999; Okamoto et al. 2006; Sanda et al. 2006; Tsukahara et al. 1999; Wäldele et al. 2006). Since these survival genes are typical targets of the NF-κB signaling pathway, it is likely that the constitutive NF-κB activation is responsible for the anti-apoptotic phenotype of HTLV1-transformed T cells. This idea has indeed been confirmed by a number of studies (Portis et al. 2001; Taylor and Nicot 2008; Tsukahara et al. 1999; Wäldele et al. 2006). Tax-mediated apoptosis inhibition also involves activation of PI3 kinase (PI3K) and its downstream survival kinase AKT (Jeong et al. 2005b; Liu et al. 2001). AKT promotes cell survival by activating NF-κB, which in turn induces expression of apoptosis inhibitors (Jeong et al. 2005b). Recent evidence suggests that AKT and

NF-κB may be mutually regulated. AKT activation by Tax involves NF-κB, which promotes the activation of PI3K and AKT through suppressing the expression of PI3K-inhibitory phosphatases, PTEN and SHIP-1 (Fukuda et al. 2009).

Another potential mechanism by which NF-κB promotes HTLV1-mediated T cell transformation is inhibition of the tumor-suppressor p53. In HLTV1-transformed T cells, p53 is functionally inactive despite its competent expression and lack of structural alterations (Cereseto et al. 1996; Gartenhaus and Wang 1995; Pise-Masison et al. 1998; Reid et al. 1993; Takemoto et al. 2000). The p53 inactivation is mediated by Tax and involves activation of NF-κB (Pise-Masison and Brady 2005). Tax induces phosphorylation of the NF-κB component RelA at serine-536, which promotes the physical interaction between RelA and p53 and, thereby, inactivation of the transactivation function of p53 (Jeong et al. 2005a). The Tax-mediated RelA phosphorylation and p53 inactivation involve both IKKβ and AKT, although the precise underlying mechanism has not been clearly defined (Jeong et al. 2005a, b). These findings suggest the intriguing possibility that IKK inhibitors may function as a double sword in ATL therapy, since they may both block NF-κB activation and restore the function of p53.

Tumorigenesis is often promoted by chronic inflammation, a pathologic process that is largely dependent on NF-κB (Karin and Greten 2005). Inflammation is a typical feature of HTLV1-infected patients and Tax-transgenic mice (Kwon et al. 2005; Peloponese et al. 2006). Whether inflammation contributes to development of ATL is unclear. Nevertheless, a recent study suggests that Tax-induced inflammation precedes the onset of lymphoma formation in mice (Rauch et al. 2009). As seen with tumorigenesis, Tax-induced inflammation in mice is dependent on NF-κB activation (Kwon et al. 2005). Therefore, it is likely that NF-κB promotes HTLV1-mediated T cell malignancy via different mechanisms, including inhibition of apoptosis, repression of tumor suppressors, and induction of inflammation.

3 NF-κB Activation by KSHV

3.1 Diseases Associated with KSHV Infection

KSHV, also called human herpesvirus 8 (HHV-8), is found invariably in Kaposi's sarcoma (Chang et al. 1994; Boshoff and Weiss 1998) and in several lymphoproliferative disorders, that include primary effusion lymphoma (PEL) (Cesarman et al. 1995a), multicentric Castleman's disease (MCD) (Soulier et al. 1995) and MCD-associated plasmablastic lymphoma (Dupin et al. 2000).

3.1.1 Kaposi's Sarcoma (KS)

Compelling evidence indicates that KSHV is an etiologic agent for KS (Chang et al. 1994). Over 22 cohort and 80 case–control epidemiologic studies have confirmed the association between KSHV and KS (Bouvard et al. 2009). KS is the most common cancer in HIV-infected individuals, and it is currently one of the most common malignancies in many subequatorial African countries, where endemic KS had been relatively common even before the epidemic of HIV/AIDS (Parkin 2006; Sinfield et al. 2007). Although the incidence of AIDS–KS in the Western world has declined since the widespread implementation of highly active antiretroviral treatment (HAART), it remains increased as compared to the pre-AIDS era (Eltom et al. 2002).

Four clinical–epidemiological forms of KS have been described, which are: (1) sporadic or European; (2) endemic or African; (3) epidemic or AIDS-related; (4) iatrogenic (associated with therapeutic immunosuppression as in transplant recipients). These four forms have indistinguishable histologic features. KS is composed of a variable mixture of irregularly shaped, round capillary and slit-like vascular spaces that are lined by endothelial cells, and spindle-shaped cells accompanied by an inflammatory cell infiltrate that always includes macrophages and lymphocytes. The spindle cells are of lymphatic endothelial origin, and considered to be the tumor cells. These cells sometimes line vascular spaces, and sometimes form sheets. A variable proportion of these spindle cells contain KSHV, which can be detected by immunohistochemistry using monoclonal antibodies to viral latency-associated nuclear antigen (LANA) (Katano et al. 1999; Kellam et al. 1999; Parravicini et al. 2000).

3.1.2 Primary Effusion Lymphomas (PEL)

Primary effusion lymphomas are a rare subset of malignant lymphomas with distinctive and unusual clinicopathologic features, including their presentation as lymphomatous effusions in body cavities, therefore being initially called body-cavity-based lymphomas (Cesarman et al. 1995a; Nador et al. 1996). While more common in HIV-positive males, PELs also occur in HIV-negative men and women (Nador et al. 1995; Said et al. 1996). These lymphomas contain KSHV, and the presence of this virus has become a diagnostic criterion for PEL. In addition, over 90% are also co-infected with EBV. The presence of KSHV in this subset of lymphomas allowed the development of cell lines that have been used as a tool for its propagation, characterization of the viral life cycle, and for serologic assays (Arvanitakis et al. 1996; Boshoff et al. 1998; Cesarman et al. 1995b; Renne et al. 1996). Purified virus from PEL cell lines has been used to demonstrate its ability to infect B cells (Mesri et al. 1996; Rappocciolo et al. 2008) and endothelial cells (Cannon et al. 2000; Flore et al. 1998; Moses et al. 1999).

Some non-Hodgkin's lymphomas without an effusion component have also been found to contain KSHV. They usually present as solid extranodal lymphomas and are diagnosed as diffuse large cell, immunoblastic, or anaplastic large cell lymphomas, in which the presence of KSHV can be demonstrated in practically all the tumor cells by immunohistochemistry, and confirmed by molecular techniques (Carbone et al. 2005; Chadburn et al. 2004; Deloose et al. 2005;

Engels et al. 2003). These lymphomas appear to fall in the spectrum of PEL, as they usually lack expression of B cell antigens and immunoglobulin, they have a similar morphology, and they are frequently co-infected with EBV.

3.1.3 Multicentric Castleman's Disease

Castleman's disease is a poorly understood atypical lymphoproliferative disorder, usually described as a polyclonal, non-neoplastic condition. Two distinct histopathologic subtypes had been reported before the identification of KSHV: the hyaline vascular type, by far more common, and the plasma cell type (Hall et al. 1989). However, mixed types exist, and it is not always possible to distinguish these. Clinically, Castleman's disease can be localized, or the patient may have multiple enlarged lymph nodes, therefore called "multicentric" MCD. Approximately 90% of patients with MCD have the plasma cell type morphology. These patients have a variety of constitutional symptoms and frequently develop malignancies, most commonly KS and NHL, consistent with an association with KSHV infection (Soulier et al. 1995). In fact, the presence of a single lymph node containing KS and Castleman's disease is not uncommon in HIV-positive patients. Notably, MCD, also called multicentric angiofollicular hyperplasia, is characterized by a vascular proliferation, which is reminiscent of KS.

Since the identification of KSHV in MCD, the understanding of the histology of this disease has changed. KSHV has been reported in MCD with both hyaline vascular and plasma cell morphology (Larroche et al. 2002), but it appears that the majority of cases described in the literature more closely resemble the plasma cell type of MCD. One study reported that the KSHV-positive cases showed the highest intensity of angiosclerosis and germinal center and perifollicular vascular proliferation, while plasmacytosis is less pronounced than in the KSHV-negative cases of the plasma cell type (Suda et al. 2001). We now believe that the KSHV-positive cases represent a distinct morphologic variant, resembling more the plasma cell type, but in addition showing the presence of larger cells in the mantle zones, which are approximately twice the size of mantle zone lymphocytes, and characterized by a moderate amount of amphophilic cytoplasm and a large vesicular nucleus containing prominent nucleoli. These cells have been called plasmablasts, although they frequently have immunoblastic features (Dupin et al. 2000). These cells can be numerous, coalesce and form microlymphomas or frank plasmablastic lymphomas, and they contain KSHV which can be detected by immunohistochemistry for KSHV LANA (Dupin et al. 1999). These KSHV-infected plasmablasts are B cells that for some unknown reason are monotypic but polyclonal, almost invariably expressing IgMλ (Du et al. 2001). One study showed that KSHV-positive endothelial cells can also be found in MCD lymph nodes, in both HIV-positive and -negative patients (Brousset et al. 2001). In addition antibodies to vIL-6 are useful, as this viral protein is also frequently expressed in MCD in scattered plasmablasts surrounding the lymphoid follicles (Cannon et al. 1999; Parravicini et al. 1997; Staskus et al. 1999), and expression of this viral cytokine may confer a worse prognosis (Menke et al. 2002). Lytic antigens are also expressed more frequently in KSHV-infected cells in MCD that in other disorders associated with this virus, suggesting that lytic viral replication may be a feature of MCD (Katano et al. 2000).

3.1.4 Plasmablastic Lymphomas Associated with MCD

Plasmablastic lymphomas associated with multicentric Castleman's disease have also been described in HIV-positive patients (Dupin et al. 2000). While these plasmablastic lymphomas are KSHV positive, they differ from PEL in a number of ways. Plasmablastic lymphomas are EBV negative, do not contain mutations in the Ig genes, and are thought to arise from naïve IgM lambda-expressing B cells rather than terminally differentiated B cells (Du et al. 2001). In addition, KSHV has been documented in germinotropic lymphoproliferative disorders in HIV-negative patients (Du et al. 2002), suggesting that this virus is present in a heterogenous but distinct group of lymphoproliferative diseases, and may be more common than initially thought.

3.2 KSHV Latent and Lytic Infection

The majority of cells in PEL and KS lesions are latently infected by KSHV. Latency allows the virus to remain in the infected cell, ensuring that the cell survives and is not recognized as infected by the host immune system. Upon initial infection, KSHV produces viral proteins that inhibit innate antiviral responses, and subsequently during latency it produces a protein (LANA) that ensures maintenance of viral DNA in the form of extrachromosomal circles, called episomes, in dividing cells. It also produces proteins during latency that promote proliferation and survival of the infected cells, thereby having the potential of promoting tumorigenesis. PEL cell lines have been used to classify KSHV viral gene expression. Upon stimulation with butyrate or phorbol esters, PEL cells are induced to express lytic viral genes (Miller et al. 1997; Renne et al. 1996). Early lytic genes include those coding for viral proteins required for DNA replication or viral gene expression, whereas late lytic genes are those coding for viral structural proteins, like envelope and capsid proteins, required for assembly of viral particles (virions). The genes expressed during latency, and therefore constitutively in most PEL cells and KS spindle cells, include LANA, viral cyclin (vCYC), viral FLIP (FLICE inhibitor protein, vFLIP) (Dittmer et al. 1998; Dupin et al. 1999; Rainbow et al. 1997; Reed et al. 1998; Sturzl et al. 1999), as well as the viral-encoded miRNAs (Cai et al. 2005; Pfeffer et al. 2005; Samols et al. 2005). LANA, vCYC and vFLIP are expressed from the same promoter and at least two alternatively spliced mRNAs (Nakamura et al. 2003; Sarid et al. 1999). Certain viral genes could have a latent expression pattern in PEL but not in KS, like vIL-6 and IRF-3

(LANA2) (Cannon et al. 1999; Rivas et al. 2001). Another series of transcripts, called kaposins (or T0.7), are expressed in latently infected PEL cells, and of the potential proteins in this locus, Kaposin B has been reported to be expressed in some, but not all latently infected PELs (Sadler et al. 1999). Apart from vCYC and vFLIP, most of the cellular orthologues encoded by KSHV and pirated from the host genome, are only expressed during lytic reactivation.

3.3 NF-κB in KSHV Infection and Reactivation

There is an essential interrelationship between the KSHV life cycle and the NF-κB pathway, where the virus can affect NF-κB activity and in turn NF-κB signaling can affect viral latency, both directly by binding to viral promoters and indirectly though cellular gene expression.

3.3.1 NF-κB During KSHV Binding and Entry

NF-κB activation has been found to occur as early as 5 min after KSHV infection, and binding of the virus to the receptors in the cell surface can itself play a role in this activation. KSHV also contains a viral tegument protein (encoded by ORF75) that has been shown to activate NF-κB (Konrad et al. 2009). This tegument protein may contribute to NF-κB activation immediately after infection and independently of new protein synthesis, but the exact mechanism remains to be elucidated. The NF-κB activation induced immediately after infection stimulates the expression of viral genes, including a cluster of latent genes that are controlled from a single latent promoter, and include LANA, vCYC and vFLIP, as well as many cellular genes that play a role in the establishment of latency (Sadagopan et al. 2007).

3.3.2 NF-κB During KSHV Latency

NF-κB activity is essential for the survival of latently KSHV-infected PEL cells; selective inhibition of this pathway, results in downregulation of a very specific set of anti-apoptotic genes, apoptosis of cells in culture, and tumor responses in mice (Keller et al. 2000, 2006). vFLIP has been identified as the major latent activator of NF-κB in KSHV-infected cells (Chaudhary et al. 1999a; Guasparri et al. 2004). Recently, a comprehensive screening for potential KSHV modulators of the NF-κB pathway performed by Konrad et al. (2009) confirmed vFLIP as the most important activator, followed by the product of viral ORF75, which as mentioned above is a tegument protein (Konrad et al. 2009). KSHV vFLIP and the ORF75 product seem to cooperate for NF-κB activation in vitro, but it is unclear whether they can be expressed concomitantly in naturally occurring infection.

In contrast, vIRF3 (LANA2), encoded by ORF K10.5, was reported to inhibit NF-κB by binding to IKKβ (Seo et al. 2004). This protein is expressed during latency in PEL cells, but not in KS. Binding of vIRF3 to IKKβ was demonstrated by coimmunoprecipitation in transfected 293T cells, but could not be shown in a naturally infected PEL cell lines, so that its role as an NF-κB inhibitor in natural infection is unclear. Nevertheless, a screening for potential KSHV modulators confirmed the inhibitory potential of vIRF3 in 293T cells (Konrad et al. 2009).

3.3.3 NF-κB in KSHV Lytic Reactivation

Viral lytic reactivation requires NF-κB downregulation (Brown et al. 2003). The major protein involved in the switch from latency to lytic reactivation in KSHV is RTA, encoded by ORF50. vFLIP inhibits the expression of lytic genes through a NF-κB-mediated suppression of the AP-1 pathway, which has a detrimental effect on KSHV RTA activity (Seo et al. 2004). It has been shown that cellular components of the NF-κB cascade are per se negative regulators of KSHV RTA in almost all viral promoters, another mechanism for maintenance of viral latency. This effect seems to be related to the availability of RBP-Jk, a cellular transcriptional regulator. The RBP-Jk binding core sequence is relatively common in the KSHV genome, and even more frequent among the KSHV RTA-responsive promoters. Activation of NF-κB prevents RBP-Jk from anchoring KSHV RTA to the lytic viral promoters, and thereby suppresses their expression (Izumiya et al. 2009). While NF-κB inhibits expression of lytic viral proteins, the lytic viral proteins encoded by ORFs K1, K9, and K14 have been reported to inhibit NF-κB in transfected 293T cells. The K1 protein was shown to suppress both vFLIP and ORF75-mediated NF-κB activation in a dose-dependent fashion (Konrad et al. 2009). Intriguingly, it was previously reported that K1 expression in transfected BC-3 cells actually *induces* NF-κB-dependent promoter activity in luciferase reporter assays (Samaniego et al. 2001). The same group also reported increased NF-κB activity in B lymphocytes from K1-transgenic mice compared to non-transgenic animals (Prakash et al. 2002). The apparent conflicting information in these studies may be attributable to the distinct experimental methods and models used.

Apparently paradoxically, once lytic reactivation takes place, some lytic viral proteins may actually upregulate NF-κB and counterbalance the expression of other viral lytic genes. One possible explanation for this phenomenon is that a new increase in NF-κB activity might be required to induce expression of anti-apoptotic genes during the lytic cycle, perhaps necessary to increase cell viability long enough to accomplish maximum virion production and release. The KSHV G-protein coupled receptor (vGPCR; KSHV ORF74), for instance, is a lytic protein that can potently activate the NF-κB pathway in PEL (Cannon and Cesarman 2004) and in endothelial cells (Martin et al. 2008). While vGPCR is a lytic gene, it has been shown to inhibit the KSHV lytic cycle consistent with a

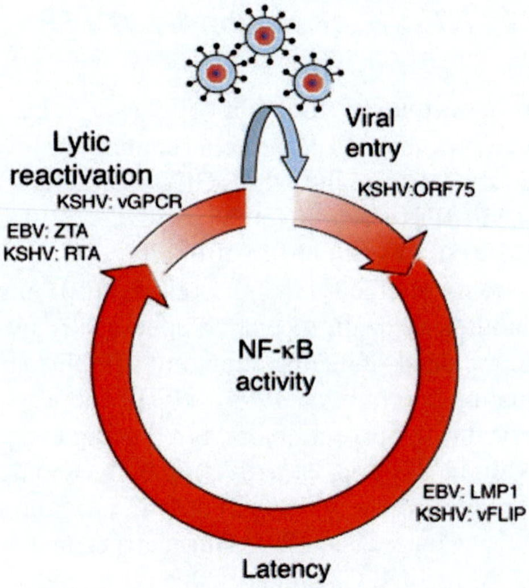

Fig. 3 Model for the NF-κB activity kinetics throughout the course KSHV or EBV infection. Viral entry can trigger NF-κB activation, which can be caused by receptor binding and activity of the tegument protein encoded in ORF75 or KSHV. NF-κB induces expression of latent genes, such as EBV LMP1 and KSHV vFLIP, that in turn contribute to constitutive activation of the NF-κB pathway in the latently infected cells. Viral latency persists for a variable period of time, until unknown triggers downregulate NF-κB signaling and/or perturb the latent/lytic phase homeostasis. Consequently, a proportional increment in the expression of the EBV ZTA, EBV RTA and KSHV RTA major viral lytic activators occurs, which in turn further downregulates NF-κB, thereby propagating the lytic cascade. Once a biological threshold is reached, the latent–lytic switch is completed and viral replication occurs. Later in the lytic cascade, the expression of some viral lytic genes, such as KSHV vGPCR, may contribute to a new wave of NF-κB activation, which may have a role in extending the cell lifespan sufficiently to allow release of new viral particles until cytopathic effects of viral infection cause cell death

negative regulatory role of NF-κB in lytic viral gene expression (Cannon et al. 2006).

An additional role for NF-κB has also been shown during the post-entry replicative steps of KSHV and during virion maturation (Sgarbanti et al. 2004). The abolishment of NF-κB activation with a super-repressor $I\kappa B\alpha^{2N\Delta4}$ in a KSHV-infected PEL cell line treated with an inducer of lytic replication causes a striking negative effect in the production of KSHV viral particles. Although viral particles derived from $I\kappa B\alpha^{2N\Delta4}$-transfected PEL cells entered endothelial cells, activation of NF-κB was found to be impaired, leading to defective viral gene expression and impaired establishment of infection.

We believe that the dynamics of NF-κB infection and viral replication are tightly co-regulated, and this control is important for establishment of latency, viral replication as evasion of immune responses. A model of NF-κB activity in the context of the KSHV life cycle is illustrated in Fig. 3.

3.4 Mechanism of NF-κB Activation by vFLIP

KSHV vFLIP is part of a group of viral and cellular proteins that are inhibitors of death receptor-induced apoptosis. FLIP proteins contain two death effector domains (DED) and have been shown to inhibit DED–DED interactions between FADD and procaspases 8 and 10. vFLIP is essential for the survival of PEL cells (Guasparri et al. 2004; Godfrey et al. 2005). vFLIP appears to inhibit cell death by several mechanisms. It may be able to do it directly, like the cellular FLIP proteins, by competing with caspase 8 for binding to death receptors, specifically by interacting with the FADD component of the death-inducing signaling complex (DISC) via one of two conserved DED domains (Djerbi et al. 1999). vFLIP can also suppress autophagy, which was shown to be due to prevention of Atg3 binding and processing of LC3 by vFLIP (Lee et al. 2009). In addition, by activating both canonical and noncanonical NF-κB pathways, expression of a full anti-apoptotic program is induced by vFLIP (Chaudhary et al. 1999b; Chugh et al. 2005; Guasparri et al. 2004; Keller et al. 2000, 2006; Liu et al. 2002; Matta and Chaudhary 2004) (Fig. 4).

The mechanism by which vFLIP induces NF-κB is incompletely understood, but we have acquired significant insights based on our understanding of the NF-κB

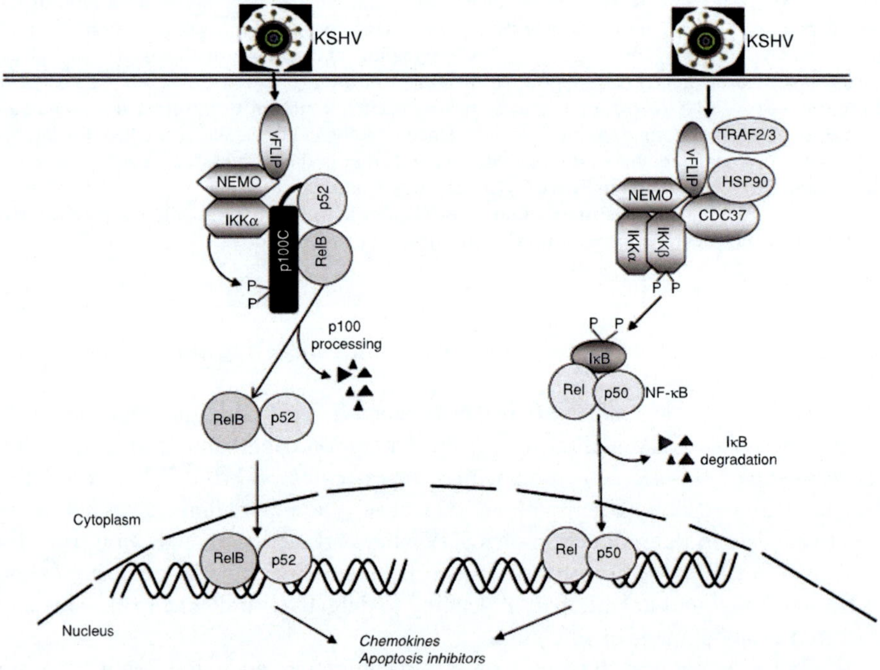

Fig. 4 NF-κB activation by KSHV vFLIP. The vFLIP protein encoded by KSHV can induce both the canonical (*right*) and noncanonical (*left*) NF-κB pathways. Direct binding of vFLIP to NEMO results in activation of IKKα and IKKβ, which in turn lead to cleavage of p100 and phosphorylation of IκB to induce nuclear translocation of RelB/p52 and Rel (p65)/p50 complexes, respectively

pathway and of the interaction of vFLIP with specific cellular proteins in this pathway. vFLIP is present in the IKK complex or signalosome, the kinases IKKα and IKKβ, and the regulatory subunit NEMO. This complex also includes Hsp90 and cdc37 (Chen et al. 2002a). vFLIP binds directly to NEMO (Field et al. 2003; Guasparri et al. 2006; Liu et al. 2002). TRAF2 and 3 can also be found in this complex and appear to be involved in signaling in some experimental conditions (Chaudhary et al. 1999b; Guasparri et al. 2006), but not others (Matta et al. 2007). RIP and NIK are not in the vFLIP-containing complexes, and appear to be dispensable for NF-κB activation (Chaudhary et al. 1999b).

The structure of vFLIP binding to NEMO has been solved (Bagneris et al. 2008). The region of NEMO recognized by vFLIP was mapped to the HLX2 alpha helical domain, which forms a nonstandard intermolecular coiled coil composed of two IKKγ monomers in a parallel arrangement. A model for vFLIP activation of NEMO was proposed based on the crystal structure where inactive NEMO is in a helical bundle conformation but transitions to an open conformation upon an intermolecular coiled-coil formation catalyzed by vFLIP. This configuration, stabilized by vFLIP, was proposed to induce recruitment of the IKKβ and/or IKKα kinases for phosphorylation and subsequent phosphorylation of the IκBs. While inactivation of this complex in normal cells involves the recruitment of phosphatases or other proteins that restore the resting conformation of NEMO, these may be prevented from engaging with NEMO due to the presence of vFLIP, leading to constitutive activation of NF-κB.

3.5 Role of NF-κB in KSHV-Mediated Oncogenesis

The relevance of the NF-κB pathway in KSHV-mediated lymphomagenesis has been provided by studies using a pharmacological inhibitor called Bay11-7082 (Keller et al. 2006). These studies have shown that elimination of NF-κB activity induces apoptosis of PEL cell lines in vitro and in mice, indicating that this is an essential pathway that is induced by viral oncoproteins. Confirmation that vFLIP plays a central role in activating NF-κB, which in turn is essential for the survival of infected lymphoma cells, comes from experiments using RNA interference, where elimination of vFLIP results in decrease of NF-κB and apoptosis of PEL cells and inhibition of tumor growth in mice (Guasparri et al. 2004; Godfrey et al. 2005).

4 NF-κB Activation by EBV

4.1 EBV Infection in Healthy Humans and EBV Life Cycle

EBV infection is practically ubiquitous in healthy adults, so it has been challenging to establish the exact role of this virus in lymphomagenesis. Nevertheless, extensive epidemiologic and experimental data support the notion that EBV is an

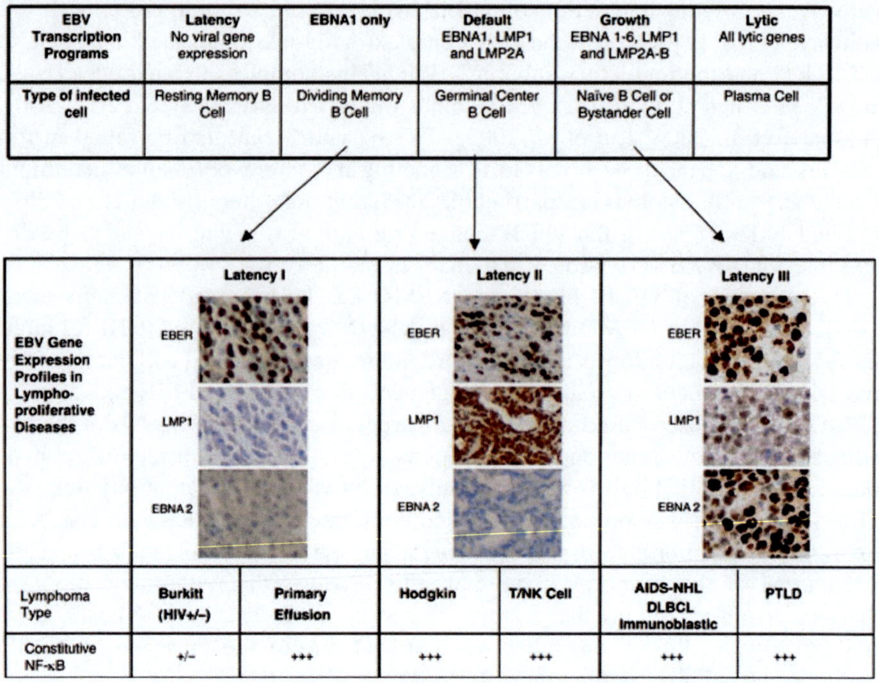

Fig. 5 Patterns of EBV latent gene expression in healthy individuals and in malignant lymphomas. The patterns of EBV gene expression infection described in different B cell subsets are shown in the *upper table*. Corresponding expression profiles in malignant lymphomas have been designated Latencies I, II, and III, and are shown in the *lower table*. EBER in situ hybridization is used to detect the presence of EBV, immunohistochemical positivity for LMP1 denotes latency II or III, and EBNA 2 protein expression together with LMP1 is indicative of latency III. Those lymphomas expressing LMP1 have constitutive NF-κB activity, while in other lymphomas this activity may be present but more variable and sometimes induced by exogenous signals, such as that induced by CD40, BAFF and APRIL or by cellular genetic alterations, such as inactivating mutations of A20 or CARD11. Primary effusion lymphomas, while not expressing LMP1, also contain KSHV which induces NF-κB through expression of vFLIP

oncogenic virus, which is supported by the well established fact that EBV can infect and transform normal human B cells in vitro, resulting in their "immortalization" and leading to continuously growing lymphoblastoid cell lines (LCLs) (Rickinson and Kieff 1996). EBV establishes a lifelong infection in the vast majority of people without causing any disease. Careful analysis of expression patterns in different tissues from EBV-infected immunocompetent individuals led to the description of five different transcription programs that are used to establish and maintain EBV infection (Fig. 5); reviewed by (Thorley-Lawson 2001; Thorley-Lawson and Gross 2004). Most of the same transcriptional programs are recapitulated in lymphomas and lymphoproliferative diseases.

When EBV first infects a naïve B cell in a healthy individual, a transient "growth program" is established, where EBV expresses EBNA 1–6, as well as

LMP1, LMP2A and LMP2B. These proteins force the infected cells to become proliferating B cell blasts, probably allowing EBV infection to be propagated. In vitro generated LCLs express this growth program indefinitely. However, since many of these proteins are antigenic, this state is only transient in immunocompetent individuals. As soon as an immune response is established, most of the cells with this program are eliminated, or otherwise switch to a "default program" of EBV expression, where only EBNA1, LMP1 and LMP2A are expressed. This stage is also temporary because LMP1 and LMP2A mimic CD40 and antigen-receptor signaling, respectively, thereby inducing the B cells in peripheral lymphoid organs to behave like germinal center B cells and differentiate into resting memory B cells (Babcock et al. 2000; Laichalk et al. 2002). These infected cells in turn switch to a "latency program" where no viral genes are expressed, allowing lifetime persistence of EBV. Dividing peripheral blood infected memory B cells express only EBNA1, which is not immunogenic but allows the EBV episome to segregate and be propagated in dividing cells. Differentiation of memory B cells into plasma cells induces lytic replication, mediated by expression of the plasma cell transcription factor XBP-1, which induces expression of EBV ZTA initiating the lytic cascade (further described in Sect. 4.5) (Bhende et al. 2007; Laichalk and Thorley-Lawson 2005; Sun and Thorley-Lawson 2007). Differentiation of B cells into plasma cells frequently occurs in lymphoid tissues near mucosal surfaces, notably in the Weldeyer's ring, leading to viral shedding in saliva.

4.2 Diseases Caused by EBV Infection

Three different patterns of EBV expression have been described in infected cells in lymphoproliferative disorders: Latency I, II or III, illustrated in Fig. 5 (Kieff 1996; Rickinson and Kieff 1996). In Latency I, EBNA1 is the major viral protein produced. In the other extreme is Latency III, which corresponds to the "growth program" and involves the unrestricted expression of all nine latent genes including six EBV-encoded nuclear antigens (EBNA1-6) (Kieff 1996) and three latent membrane proteins (LMP1, LMP2A, and LMP2B). Latency II corresponds to the "default program", and consists of expression of EBNA1 and varying amounts of the three LMP proteins.

Because EBNA proteins are immunogenic, with the exception of EBNA1, an important feature of Latency III is the recognition and elimination of the EBV-infected cells by the immune system. Therefore, lymphomas with unrestricted EBV latency are generally only encountered in immunodeficient individuals. In contrast, most lymphomas in immunocompetent hosts will have Latency I or II, because downregulation of the immunogenic EBNA proteins is an important mechanism of immune evasion by EBV (Rickinson and Kieff 1996).

Acute infection with EBV is frequently asymptomatic, but in some instances leads to infectious mononucleosis. Age of infection, viral dosage upon original infection and immune responses are thought to determine whether primary infection is symptomatic in some individuals but not others. While infectious mononucleosis is usually self-limited, in rare instances chronic active EBV can develop. In addition, in the context of congenital or acquired immunodeficiency, a variety of lymphoproliferative disorders may develop. EBV is well known to be associated with the following malignancies:

4.2.1 Burkitt's Lymphoma (BL)

Epstein–Barr virus is invariably present in African (endemic) BL, but is found only in a minority of sporadic cases. Most of our understanding of EBV gene expression was originally derived from the study of BL cell lines; however, in vivo expression has also been examined in endemic BL tissue biopsies (Tao et al. 1998). EBV-positive BLs have EBNA1, and usually LMP2A, transcripts, in the absence of lytic transcripts or other latent transcripts. A subset of BL has a deletion of EBNA2, and in these cases there is expression of EBNA3A-C (Kelly et al. 2002, 2005).

Translocation of c-myc into one of the immunoglobulin loci is considered by some to be a prerequisite for classification of a lymphoma as BL or atypical BL. The most common translocation is a t(8;14), involving the c-myc and immunoglobulin heavy chain genes, but in 10% of the cases it can involve c-myc and one of the light chain genes. It is thought that this translocation leads to deregulated expression of the c-myc gene. Mutations of the c-myc locus also occur in Burkitt lymphoma, and these may also lead to abnormal expression. Gene expression profiling experiments have concluded that there are cases with a typical and unique BL signature, while other cases are more heterogenous (Dave et al. 2006; Hummel et al. 2006). The latter tend to have more complex karyotypes than the former, where usually translocations involving c-myc are the only detectable cytogenetic abnormality.

4.2.2 Post-Transplantation Lymphoproliferative Disorder

Post-transplantation lymphoproliferative disorders (PTLDs) develop in the setting of iatrogenic immunosuppression following solid organ transplantation or allogeneic bone marrow transplantation. The incidence of these lesions varies based on the type of organ transplanted as well as on the type and amount of immunosuppression employed. As with other immunodeficiency-related lymphoproliferative disorders, the development of PTLDs is highly associated with EBV infection. The relative incidence of these lesions is higher in patients who are EBV negative at the time of transplantation and become infected when already immunosuppressed. Most PTLDs exhibit type III latency, with the exception of the monomorphic lesions, which often exhibit the latency type I pattern of EBV gene expression, and also often carry cellular genetic alterations in oncogenes and tumor-suppressor genes and thereby may be less dependent on EBV (Knowles et al. 1995).

4.2.3 AIDS-Related Non-Hodgkin's Lymphomas

The incidence of non-Hodgkin's lymphomas (NHL) in HIV-positive individuals is estimated to be between 4 and 10%, but the incidence of at least some subsets has decreased with combination antiretroviral therapy. The incidence of Hodgkin's lymphoma is somewhat increased in HIV-infected individuals, but it is not considered to be an AIDS-defining condition. The pathogenesis of NHL in the context AIDS is complex and thought to be related to disrupted immune surveillance, chronic antigenic stimulation, genetic alterations, cytokine dysregulation and herpes virus infection (Carbone 2003; Carbone et al. 1998; Knowles 2001). Although HIV-related lymphomas are almost always of B cell origin, they are morphologically diverse. Several subtypes are similar to lymphomas occurring in immunocompetent patients, while others preferentially develop in the context of AIDS. HIV-related lymphomas can be classified by morphology (as in the WHO classification), and/or by primary site of presentation (i.e. systemic, primary central nervous system, body cavity) (Carbone et al. 2009; Knowles 2001; Raphaël et al. 2008).

Lymphomas also Occurring in Immunocompetent Patients

HIV-related BL includes cases exhibiting the features of classical BL (described above), those showing plasmacytoid differentiation and those exhibiting features of atypical Burkitt/Burkitt-like lymphoma. In terms of EBV infection, AIDS-related BL resembles sporadic BL, with around 30% of cases being positive. Diffuse large B cell lymphoma (DLBCL) can be divided into centroblastic (CB) and immunoblastic (IB) categories. While these morphologically and immunophenotypically resemble lesions found in immunocompetent individuals, the frequent association with EBV is almost exclusive of immunodeficient patients. The IB type is more frequently associated with EBV infection, and patients with these lymphomas are usually significantly immunosuppressed with low CD4 counts (median $< 100 \times 10^6$/L) and approximately one-third have been previously diagnosed with an AIDS-defining illness. This degree of immune dysfunction allows EBV to be the driving proliferative force, with expression of the oncogenic but also immunogenic LMP and EBNA proteins. In addition, while DLBCL express adhesion molecules that are important for immune recognition, BLs do not. These observations suggest that defective EBV immunity is involved in the pathogenesis of DLBCLs (Kersten et al. 1998).

Lymphomas Occurring Primarily in HIV-Positive Patients

Primary central nervous system lymphomas (PCNSL) differ from systemic DLBCLs, with the majority of cases exhibiting IB morphology and EBV-positivity. According to one study, PCNSL can be divided into two categories:

those with immunoblastic features, which express LMP-1 in conjunction with BCL-2 but no BCL-6 expression, and those with a large, noncleaved cell morphology, which do not express LMP-1 or BCL-2, but express BCL-6 (Larocca et al. 1998). Another type of lymphoma described in the context of HIV infection is the plasmablastic lymphoma of the oral cavity. It has features similar to IB lymphomas, but is less heterogeneous and polymorphic. A majority of these are associated with EBV infection. Polymorphic B cell lymphomas (PTLD-like) are extremely rare lesions but morphologically resemble polymorphic PTLDs. The last category of lymphoma predominantly occurring in HIV-positive patients is primary effusion lymphoma. The latter, while positive for EBV, also contains KSHV, and was discussed in the previous section.

4.2.4 T/natural Killer Cell Lymphomas

The angiocentric (nasal and nasal-type) T/natural killer (T/NK)-cell lymphomas are always associated with EBV infection (Jaffe et al. 1999). These have a high prevalence in Asia, but cases from other countries have also shown an association with EBV (Elenitoba-Johnson et al. 1998). Studies on cell lines indicate that T/NK cell lymphomas have a Latency II (Kanegane et al. 1998; Tsuchiyama et al. 1998). Although EBV has also been reported to be present in peripheral T cell lymphomas, it has been shown to be preferentially localized in B cells rather than the neoplastic T cells (Ho et al. 1998).

4.2.5 Hodgkin's Lymphoma (HL)

EBV is present in approximately 40% of cases of HL in Western countries and more frequently in developing countries and in younger patients (Harris 1998). HL results from a monoclonal expansion of B cells containing somatic hypermutations of the immunoglobulin genes. These mutations may be "crippling", resulting in lack of antigen-receptor expression. Therefore, the Hodgkin's Reed–Sternberg cells are derived from germinal B cells destined to undergo apoptosis, but they are postulated to be protected by some transforming event, such as EBV (Küppers and Rajewsky 1998). In HL, EBV establishes Latency II within HRS cells, with expression of LMP-1 and LMP2, which are subdominant targets for CTL recognition.

4.2.6 Nasopharyngeal Carcinoma (NPC)

This type of carcinoma is most common in Cantonese individuals, but also occurs in Arab, and Eskimo populations (Yu and Yuan 2002), and sporadically in the West. EBV is consistently associated with the non-keratinizing and undifferentiated subtypes of nasopharyngeal carcinomas. Biopsies show lesions composed of large neoplastic epithelial cells disposed in a syncytium-like array, admixed with a prominent inflammatory component consisting of normal appearing lymphocytes. This histologic appearance gave rise to the misnomer or lymphoepithelioma. Well-differentiated carcinomas of the nasopharynx are often EBV associated as well (Pathmanathan et al. 1995). Nasopharyngeal carcinomas express EBV EBNA1, LMP2 and sometimes LMP1, classified as type II latency. Viral DNA is present in plasma in patients with nasopharyngeal carcinoma and has emerged as a highly reliable guide to determining prognosis and monitoring therapy (Lechowicz et al. 2002; Lin et al. 2004; Lo et al. 2000). This DNA is not encapsidated but is fragmented DNA released from tumor cells undergoing apoptosis (Chan et al. 2002). High levels of viral DNA in plasma at the start of therapy has emerged as an important prognostic factor, persistence of high levels in the face of therapy is a marker of relapse or progression (Chan et al. 2002).

4.3 NF-κB Activation During EBV Binding and Entry

To infect naïve B lymphocytes, the major envelope glycoprotein of EBV, gp350/220, binds CD21, which is the complement receptor type 2 (CR2), on the cell surface. Binding to CD21 triggers NF-κB activation, which has been demonstrated by inhibition with a soluble gp105 fragment of EBV gp350/220 protein and with anti-CR2 monoclonal antibody OKB7 (Sugano et al. 1997). This binding results in IκBα phosphorylation by protein kinase C (PKC), followed by its degradation and nuclear accumulation of p50 and RelA hetero- or homo-dimers. As NF-κB is activated, the viral DNA enters the cell nucleus and the transcription of latent viral products can take place, a consequence of triggering NF-κB responsive elements in the EBV Wp promoter (Sugano et al. 1997). Therefore, the EBV binding initiates NF-κB activation, required for successful cell infection. In turn, the NF-κB activity also upregulates the expression of the CD21 molecule (Sugano et al. 1997), which may provide a positive feedback loop to enhance the cell susceptibility to EBV entry.

4.4 NF-κB During Latent EBV Infection

EBV LMP1 protein is required for the establishment of viral latency, although it appears to be expressed only transiently during primary EBV infection in humans. It is found in EBV-immortalized lymphoblastoid cell lines (LCL) in vitro, as well as in the newly infected B lymphocytes during latent infection. LMP1 strongly activates the NF-κB pathway, and in turn it is itself upregulated by NF-κB (Johansson et al. 2009). This creates an amplification loop that keeps steady high levels of NF-κB during EBV latency. EBV LMP1 is important for latency maintenance, and can suppress lytic reactivation by both NF-κB-dependent and

NF-κB-independent pathways (Prince et al. 2003). LMP2 has also been shown to affect NF-κB in EBV-associated lymphomas through indirect mechanisms (Guasparri et al. 2008), as well as in transgenic mice (Swanson-Mungerson et al. 2006).

Paradoxically, the EBNA1 protein was recently demonstrated to downregulate NF-κB in NPC cells by inhibiting the phosphorylation of IKKα/β (Valentine et al. 2010). EBNA1 is expressed in all EBV+ dividing cells, so it may be postulated that EBV has developed a mechanism to downregulate this transcription factor during infection in vivo in order to avoid immune recognition. It is possible that NF-κB is only transiently upregulated during latency but for long-term viral infection, this activity may remain low. However, as this downregulation of NF-κB by EBNA1 has only been reported in epithelial cells, it may be cell-specific and not occurring in latently infected memory B cell reservoirs.

4.5 NF-κB in Lytic Reactivation of EBV Reactivation

EBV encodes an immediate early protein, called ZTA, BZLF1, bZIP or ZEBRA, which is important for the switch to lytic replication. Expression of ZTA is inhibited by NF-κB, specifically by the RelA protein (Fig. 5). In turn, while ZTA induces the nuclear translocation of RelA, it inhibits its transcriptional activity (Morrison and Kenney 2004). Thereby, NF-κB is important to maintain latency, and cellular changes that lead to a reduction of NF-κB can result in expression of ZTA. Conversely, induction of expression of ZTA, for example by induction of XBP-1 during B cell differentiation to plasma cells (Bhende et al. 2007; Laichalk and Thorley-Lawson 2005; Sun and Thorley-Lawson 2007), leads to a reduction of NF-κB which in turn allows higher levels of ZTA expression thereby propagating the lytic cascade.

NF-κB may also play an important role during lytic viral replication by affecting the surrounding non-infected inflammatory cells. The release of the EBV dUTPase, a non-structural viral protein produced during the lytic phase, into the microenvironment of peripheral blood mononuclear cells (PBMC) and monocyte-derived macrophages was shown to activate NF-κB in these cells through the Toll-like receptor (TLR) 2. The EBV dUTPase-driven NF-κB activation ultimately modulates the local immune response as a result of increase in the secretion of cytokines, notably IL-6 and IL-10 (Ariza et al. 2009).

4.6 Mechanism of NF-κB Activation by the Latent Viral Proteins LMP1 and LMP2

LMP1 is the most important EBV product that causes constitutive NF-κB activity in the majority of EBV-associated malignancies, and it is capable of transforming both in vitro (Wang et al. 1985) and in vivo (Homig-Holzel et al. 2008; Kulwichit et al. 1998; Panagopoulos et al. 2004). EBV LMP1 mimics a constitutively activated ligand-independent receptor of the TNF receptor family. It binds TRAFs and recruits TRADD, ultimately inducing the expression of NF-κB-regulated genes that promote cell survival and proliferation (Cahir-McFarland et al. 1999; Gires et al. 1997; Kieser 2008). Although two cytoplasmic carboxy-terminal regions in the LMP1 protein—namely the C-terminal-activating region 1 and 2 (CTAR1 and CTAR2)—are able to activate the NF-κB cascade, CTAR1 is enough for cell transformation due to its unique features in inducing multiple signaling pathways (Mainou et al. 2007). LMP1 associates with TRAF-1 and TRAF-3 in vivo in EBV-associated lymphomas, eventually leading to the downstream activation of NF-κB (Liebowitz 1998). While LMP1 binds several TRAFs, the ones that are essential for NF-κB activation depend on the experimental system used. TRAF-3 (Xie et al. 2004) and TRAF-6 (Luftig et al. 2003) have been found to be involved in LMP1 signaling in murine knockout systems, while in these, TRAF-2 has been shown to be dispensable. In contrast, TRAF2 is essential for NF-κB signaling in EBV-infected lymphoma cell lines (Guasparri et al. 2008). Knockdown of TRAF-2 by RNA interference, but not of the other TRAFs, results in downregulation of NF-κB and apoptotic cell death.

LMP2A is a functional homolog of the B cell receptor (BCR), although it also inhibits antigen-induced activation of the BCR signal transduction cascade which is thought to prevent BCR-induced lytic replication of EBV in LCLs (Miller et al. 1994). LMP2A is not essential for generation of LCLs (Rochford et al. 1997; Speck et al. 1999), but at least according to one study, it does contribute to the efficiency of B cell immortalization (Brielmeier et al. 1996) and has been found to have several effects on B cells. Experiments with transgenic mice expressing LMP2A targeting expression to the B cell lineage showed that LMP2A sends survival signals and allows B cells to bypass developmental checkpoints and escape the bone marrow to colonize peripheral lymphoid organs (Caldwell et al. 1998, 2000; Merchant et al. 2000). These functions are mediated by an ITAM motif, through which LMP2A activates PI3K > Akt- > mTOR signaling in B lymphocytes by activating members of the Src family of tyrosine kinases, and also associates with the BCR signaling effector Syk kinase, a mechanism through which it induces epithelial cell migration (Fruehling and Longnecker 1997; Fukuda and Longnecker 2007; Lu et al. 2006; Moody et al. 2005; Swart et al. 2000). LMP2A can also engage the JNK mitogen-activated protein (MAP) kinase and beta-catenin signaling pathways (Chen et al. 2002b; Morrison et al. 2003). While transfected LMP2 has not been reported to activate NF-κB, two recent studies have shown activation of NF-κB by LMP2A by evaluating the role of this viral protein in conjunction with known BCR signals in double transgenic mice expressing LMP2A and BCR restricted to hen egg lysozyme (HEL) or ribonucleoprotein Smith (Sm) (Swanson-Mungerson et al. 2005; Wang et al. 2006). Both of these studies found that B cells expressing LMP2A in vivo display constitutive NF-κB activity, as compared to LMP2A-negative control B cells. LMP2A signaling appears not to affect B cell proliferation in vivo (Rochford et al. 1997), but rather provides survival signals in BCR-negative B cells (Caldwell et al. 2000). Although LMP2A cannot activate NF-κB on its own, its ability augment signaling from LMP1 by increasing its half-life has been reported (Dawson et al. 2001). In contrast, a different study found that LMP2A inhibits NF-κB activity in carcinoma cell lines infected in vitro with wild-type recombinant EBV, as compared with virus in which LMP2A was deleted (Stewart et al. 2004). In LCLs and EBV-infected lymphoma cell lines, LMP2A was found to be essential for NF-κB signaling, as knockdown of this viral protein resulted in suppression of NF-κB (Guasparri et al. 2008). However, in contrast to the previous study by Dawson et al. (2001), this effect was not mediated by LMP1 stabilization, but rather by the transcriptional control of TRAF-2 mediated by LMP2A-induced signaling (Guasparri et al. 2008). In the absence of LMP2A, TRAF-2 transcription is downregulated and LMP1 signaling is impaired.

4.7 Role of NF-κB in EBV-Mediated Oncogenesis

The relevance of the NF-κB pathway in EBV-mediated lymphomagenesis has been supported by studies in which inhibition of NF-κB using an IκB phosphorylation-deficient mutant which sequesters NF-κB in the cytoplasm (Cahir-McFarland et al. 2000; Feuillard et al. 2000) or a pharmacological IKK inhibitor called Bay11-7082 (Cahir-McFarland et al. 2004; Keller et al. 2006). These studies have shown that elimination of NF-κB activity induces apoptosis of EBV-infected lymphoma cell lines in vitro and in mice, indicating that this is an essential pathway that is induced by viral oncoproteins. Confirmation that LMP1 plays a central role in activating NF-κB, which in turn is essential for the survival of infected lymphoma cells, comes from experiments using RNA interference, where elimination of LMP1 or LMP2A results in decrease of NF-κB and apoptosis of EBV-infected lymphoma cells (Guasparri et al. 2008).

5 Concluding Remarks

NF-κB is a common cellular target of HTLV1, EBV, and KSHV oncogenic viruses that are etiologically associated with human lymphoid malignancies. Despite their tremendous differences in genomic structure and life cycles, these pathogens share the ability to persistently activate NF-κB via specific viral proteins. HTLV1 Tax protein physically interacts with IKK and activates IKK independently of upstream signaling molecules. Similar to HTLV1 Tax, the KSHV vFLIP protein directly binds NEMO, thereby activating the IKK complex independently of upstream signaling molecules. In contrast, the EBV LMP1 protein interacts with and activates TRAFs, thereby mediating TRAF-dependent NF-κB activation. A common feature of these viral NF-κB inducers is the induction of both canonical and noncanonical NF-κB pathways. Persistent activation of the NF-κB pathways by these human pathogens plays a central role in their induction of host cell transformation. Thus, NF-κB represents an attractive therapeutic target in the treatment of the lymphoid malignancies associated with infection by these viruses.

Acknowledgments Work performed in the authors' laboratories is supported by the National Institutes of Health Grants (AI064639, AI057555, and GM084459 to SCS; CA068939 and CA103646 to EC) and the Starr Cancer Consortium (Award to E.C.).

References

Adhikari A, Xu M, Chen ZJ (2007) Ubiquitin-mediated activation of TAK1 and IKK. Oncogene 26:3214–3226

Ariza ME, Glaser R, Kaumaya PT, Jones C, Williams MV (2009) The EBV-encoded dUTPase activates NF-kappa B through the TLR2 and MyD88-dependent signaling pathway. J Immunol 182:851–859

Arnold J, Zimmerman B, Li M, Lairmore MD, Green PL (2008) Human T-cell leukemia virus type-1 antisense-encoded gene, Hbz, promotes T-lymphocyte proliferation. Blood 112:3788–3797

Arvanitakis L, Mesri EA, Nador R, Said JW, Asch AS, Knowles DM, Cesarman E (1996) Establishment and characterization of a primary effusion (body cavity-based) lymphoma cell line (BC-3) harboring Kaposi's sarcoma-associated herpesvirus (KSHV/HHV-8) in the absence of Epstein–Barr virus. Blood 88:2648–2654

Babcock GJ, Hochberg D, Thorley-Lawson AD (2000) The expression pattern of Epstein–Barr virus latent genes in vivo is dependent upon the differentiation stage of the infected B cell. Immunity 13:497–506

Babu G, Waterfield M, Chang M, Wu X, Sun S-C (2006) Deregulated activation of oncoprotein kinase Tpl2/Cot in HTLV-I-transformed T cells. J Biol Chem 281:14041–14047

Bagneris C, Ageichik AV, Cronin N, Wallace B, Collins M, Boshoff C, Waksman G, Barrett T (2008) Crystal structure of a vFlip–IKKgamma complex: insights into viral activation of the IKK signalosome. Mol Cell 30:620–631

Baldwin A S Jr (1996) The NF-κB and IκB proteins: new discoveries and insights. Annu Rev Immunol 14:649–683

Beinke S, Ley SC (2004) Functions of NF-kappaB1 and NF-kappaB2 in immune cell biology. Biochem J 382:393–409

Béraud C, Sun S-C, Ganchi PA, Ballard DW, Greene WC (1994) Human T-cell leukemia virus type I Tax associates with and is negatively regulated by the NF-κB2 p100 gene product: implications for viral latency. Mol Cell Biol 14:1374–1382

Bhende PM, Dickerson SJ, Sun X, Feng WH, Kenney SC (2007) X-box-binding protein 1 activates lytic Epstein–Barr virus gene expression in combination with protein kinase D. J Virol 81:7363–7370

Boshoff C, Weiss RA (1998) Kaposi's sarcoma-associated herpesvirus. Adv Cancer Res 75: 57–86

Boshoff C, Gao SJ, Healy LE, Matthews S, Thomas AJ, Coignet L, Warnke RA, Strauchen JA, Matutes E, Kamel OW, Moore PS, Weiss RA, Chang Y (1998) Establishing a KSHV+ cell line (BCP-1) from peripheral blood and characterizing its growth in Nod/SCID mice. Blood 91:1671–1679

Bouvard V, Baan R, Straif K, Grosse Y, Secretan B, El Ghissassi F, Benbrahim-Tallaa L, Guha N, Freeman C, Galichet L, Cogliano V (2009) A review of human carcinogens—Part B: biological agents. Lancet Oncol 10:321–322

Brielmeier M, Mautner J, Laux G, Hammerschmidt W (1996) The latent membrane protein 2 gene of Epstein–Barr virus is important for efficient B cell immortalization. J Gen Virol 77(Pt 11):2807–2818

Brousset P, Cesarman E, Meggetto F, Lamant L, Delsol G (2001) Colocalization of the viral interleukin-6 with latent nuclear antigen-1 of human herpesvirus-8 in endothelial spindle cells of Kaposi's sarcoma and lymphoid cells of multicentric Castleman's disease. Hum Pathol 32:95–100

Brown HJ, Song MJ, Deng H, Wu TT, Cheng G, Sun R (2003) NF-kappaB inhibits gammaherpesvirus lytic replication. J Virol 77:8532–8540

Burmeister T (2001) Oncogenic retroviruses in animals and humans. Rev Med Virol 11:369–380

Cahir McFarland ED, Izumi KM, Mosialos G (1999) Epstein–Barr virus transformation: involvement of latent membrane protein 1-mediated activation of NF-kappaB. Oncogene 18:6959–6964

Cahir-McFarland ED, Davidson DM, Schauer SL, Duong J, Kieff E (2000) NF-kappa B inhibition causes spontaneous apoptosis in Epstein–Barr virus-transformed lymphoblastoid cells. Proc Natl Acad Sci USA 97:6055–6060

Cahir-McFarland ED, Carter K, Rosenwald A, Giltnane JM, Henrickson SE, Staudt LM, Kieff E (2004) Role of NF-kappa B in cell survival and transcription of latent membrane protein 1-expressing or Epstein–Barr virus latency III-infected cells. J Virol 78:4108–4119

Cai X, Lu S, Zhang Z, Gonzalez CM, Damania B, Cullen BR (2005) Kaposi's sarcoma-associated herpesvirus expresses an array of viral microRNAs in latently infected cells. Proc Natl Acad Sci USA 102:5570–5575

Caldwell RG, Wilson JB, Anderson SJ, Longnecker R (1998) Epstein–Barr virus LMP2A drives B cell development and survival in the absence of normal B cell receptor signals. Immunity 9:405–411

Caldwell RG, Brown RC, Longnecker R (2000) Epstein–Barr virus LMP2A-induced B-cell survival in two unique classes of EmuLMP2A transgenic mice. J Virol 74:1101–1113

Cannon ML, Cesarman E (2004) The KSHV G protein-coupled receptor signals via multiple pathways to induce transcription factor activation in primary effusion lymphoma cells. Oncogene 23:514–523

Cannon JS, Nicholas J, Orenstein JM, Mann RB, Murray PG, Browning PJ, DiGiuseppe JA, Cesarman E, Hayward GS, Ambinder RF (1999) Heterogeneity of viral IL-6 expression in HHV-8-associated diseases. J Infect Dis 180:824–828

Cannon JS, Ciufo D, Hawkins AL, Griffin CA, Borowitz MJ, Hayward GS, Ambinder RF (2000) A new primary effusion lymphoma-derived cell line yields a highly infectious Kaposi's sarcoma herpesvirus-containing supernatant. J Virol 74:10187–10193

Cannon M, Cesarman E, Boshoff C (2006) KSHV G protein-coupled receptor inhibits lytic gene transcription in primary-effusion lymphoma cells via p21-mediated inhibition of Cdk2. Blood 107:277–284

Carbone A (2003) Emerging pathways in the development of AIDS-related lymphomas. Lancet Oncol 4:22–29

Carbone A, Gaidano G, Gloghini A, Larocca LM, Capello D, Canzonieri V, Antinori A, Tirelli U, Falini B, Dalla-Favera R (1998) Differential expression of BCL-6, CD138/syndecan-1, and Epstein–Barr virus-encoded latent membrane protein-1 identifies distinct histogenetic subsets of acquired immunodeficiency syndrome-related non-Hodgkin's lymphomas. Blood 91: 747–755

Carbone A, Gloghini A, Vaccher E, Cerri M, Gaidano G, Dalla-Favera R, Tirelli U (2005) Kaposi's sarcoma-associated herpesvirus/human herpesvirus type 8-positive solid lymphomas: a tissue-based variant of primary effusion lymphoma. J Mol Diagn 7:17–27

Carbone A, Cesarman E, Spina M, Gloghini A, Schulz TF (2009) HIV-associated lymphomas and gamma-herpesviruses. Blood 113:1213–1224

Carter RS, Pennington KN, Ungurait BJ, Arrate P, Ballard DW (2003) Signal-induced ubiquitination of I kappaB kinase-beta. J Biol Chem 278:48903–48906

Carter RS, Pennington KN, Arrate P, Oltz EM, Ballard DW (2005) Site-specific monoubiquitination of IkappaB kinase IKKbeta regulates its phosphorylation and persistent activation. J Biol Chem 280:43272–43279

Cereseto A, Diella F, Mulloy JC, Cara A, Michieli P, Grassmann R, Franchini G, Klotman ME (1996) p53 functional impairment and high p21waf1/cip1 expression in human T-cell lymphotropic/leukemia virus type I-transformed T cells. Blood 88:1551–1560

Cesarman E, Chang Y, Moore PS, Said JW, Knowles DM (1995a) Kaposi's sarcoma-associated herpesvirus-like DNA sequences in AIDS-related body cavity-based lymphomas. N Engl J Med 332:1186–1191

Cesarman E, Moore PS, Rao P, Inghirami G, Knowles DM, Chang Y (1995b) In vitro establishment and characterization of two acquired immunodeficiency syndrome-related lymphoma cell lines (BC-1 and BC-2) containing Kaposi's sarcoma-associated herpesvirus-like (KSHV) DNA sequences. Blood 86:2708–2714

Chadburn A, Hyjek E, Mathew S, Cesarman E, Said J, Knowles DM (2004) KSHV-positive solid lymphomas represent an extra-cavitary variant of primary effusion lymphoma. Am J Surg Pathol 28:1401–1416

Chan AT, Lo YM, Zee B, Chan LY, Ma BB, Leung SF, Mo F, Lai M, Ho S, Huang DP, Johnson PJ (2002) Plasma Epstein–Barr virus DNA and residual disease after radiotherapy for undifferentiated nasopharyngeal carcinoma. J Natl Cancer Inst 94:1614–1619

Chang Y, Cesarman E, Pessin MS, Lee F, Culpepper J, Knowles DM, Moore PS (1994) Identification of herpesvirus-like DNA sequences in AIDS-associated Kaposi's sarcoma. Science 266:1865–1869

Chau V, Tobias JW, Bachmair A, Marriott D, Ecker DJ, Gonda DK, Varshavsky A (1989) A multiubiquitin chain is confined to specific lysine in a targeted short-lived protein. Science 243:1576–1583

Chaudhary PM, Jasmin A, Eby MT, Hood L (1999a) Modulation of the NF-kappa B pathway by virally encoded death effector domains-containing proteins. Oncogene 18:5738–5746

Chaudhary PM, Jasmin A, Eby MT, Hood L (1999b) Modulation of the NF-kappa B pathway by virally encoded death effector domains-containing proteins. Oncogene 14:5738–5746

Chen ZJ (2005) Ubiquitin signalling in the NF-kappaB pathway. Nat Cell Biol 7:758–765

Chen G, Cao P, Goeddel DV (2002a) TNF-induced recruitment and activation of the IKK complex require Cdc37 and Hsp90. Mol Cell 9:401–410

Chen SY, Lu J, Shih YC, Tsai CH (2002b) Epstein–Barr virus latent membrane protein 2A regulates c-Jun protein through extracellular signal-regulated kinase. J Virol 76:9556–9561

Chen ZJ, Bhoj V, Seth RB (2006) Ubiquitin, TAK1 and IKK: is there a connection? Cell Death Differ 13:687–692

Chu Z-L, DiDonato JA, Hawiger J, Ballard DW (1998) The Tax oncoprotein of human T-cell leukemia virus type 1 associates with and persistently activates IκB kinases containing IKKα and IKKβ. J Biol Chem 273:15891–15894

Chu Z-L, Shin Y-A, Yang J-M, DiDonato JA, Ballard DW (1999) IKKγ mediates the interaction of cellular IκB kinases with the Tax transforming protein of human T cell leukemia virus type 1. J Biol Chem 274:15297–15300

Chugh P, Matta H, Schamus S, Zachariah S, Kumar A, Richardson JA, Smith AL, Chaudhary PM (2005) Constitutive NF-{kappa}B activation, normal Fas-induced apoptosis, and increased incidence of lymphoma in human herpes virus 8 K13 transgenic mice. Proc Natl Acad Sci USA 102:12885–12890

Claudio E, Brown K, Park S, Wang H, Siebenlist U (2002) BAFF-induced NEMO-independent processing of NF-kappaB2 in maturing B cells. Nat Immunol 3:958–965

Coope HJ, Atkinson PG, Huhse B, Belich M, Janzen J, Holman MJ, Klaus GG, Johnston LH, Ley SC (2002) CD40 regulates the processing of NF-kappaB2 p100 to p52. EMBO J 15:5375–5385

Coornaert B, Carpentier I, Beyaert R (2009) A20: central gatekeeper in inflammation and immunity. J Biol Chem 284:8217–8221

Cross SL, Feinberg MB, Wolf JB, Holbrook NJ, Wong-Staal F, Leonard WJ (1987) Regulation of the human interleukin-2 receptor a chain promoter: activation of a non functional promoter by the transactivator gene of HTLV-1. Cell 49:47–56

Dave SS, Fu K, Wright GW, Lam LT, Kluin P, Boerma EJ, Greiner TC, Weisenburger DD, Rosenwald A, Ott G, Muller-Hermelink HK, Gascoyne RD, Delabie J, Rimsza LM, Braziel RM, Grogan TM, Campo E, Jaffe ES, Dave BJ, Sanger W, Bast M, Vose JM, Armitage JO, Connors JM, Smeland EB, Kvaloy S, Holte H, Fisher RI, Miller TP, Montserrat E, Wilson WH, Bahl M, Zhao H, Yang L, Powell J, Simon R, Chan WC, Staudt LM (2006) Molecular diagnosis of Burkitt's lymphoma. N Engl J Med 354:2431–2442

Dawson CW, George JH, Blake SM, Longnecker R, Young LS (2001) The Epstein–Barr virus encoded latent membrane protein 2A augments signaling from latent membrane protein 1. Virology 289:192–207

de La Fuente C, Deng L, Santiago F, Arce L, Wang L, Kashanchi F (2000) Gene expression array of HTLV type 1-infected T cells: up-regulation of transcription factors and cell cycle genes. AIDS Res Hum Retroviruses 16:1695–1700

Dejardin E, Droin NM, Delhase M, Haas E, Cao Y, Makris C, Li ZW, Karin M, Ware CF, Green DR (2002) The lymphotoxin-beta receptor induces different patterns of gene expression via two NF-kappaB pathways. Immunity 17:525–535

Deloose ST, Smit LA, Pals FT, Kersten MJ, van Noesel CJ, Pals ST (2005) High incidence of Kaposi sarcoma-associated herpesvirus infection in HIV-related solid immunoblastic/ plasmablastic diffuse large B-cell lymphoma. Leukemia 19:851–855

Dittmer D, Lagunoff M, Renne R, Staskus K, Haase A, Ganem D (1998) A cluster of latently expressed genes in Kaposi's sarcoma-associated herpesvirus. J Virol 72:8309–8315

Djerbi M, Screpanti V, Catrina AI, Bogen B, Biberfeld P, Grandien A (1999) The inhibitor of death receptor signaling, FLICE-inhibitory protein defines a new class of tumor progression factors. J Exp Med 190:1025–1032 (see comments)

Dong J, Zhong H, Hayden MS, Ghosh G (2008) Repression of gene expression by unphosphorylated NF-κB p65 through epigenetic mechanisms. Genes Dev 22:1159–1173

Doxsey S, McCollum D, Theurkauf W (2005) Centrosomes in cellular regulation. Annu Rev Cell Dev Biol 21:411–434

Du MQ, Liu H, Diss TC, Ye H, Hamoudi RA, Dupin N, Meignin V, Oksenhendler E, Boshoff C, Isaacson PG (2001) Kaposi sarcoma-associated herpesvirus infects monotypic (IgM lambda) but polyclonal naive B cells in Castleman disease and associated lymphoproliferative disorders. Blood 97:2130–2136

Du MQ, Diss TC, Liu H, Ye H, Hamoudi RA, Cabecadas J, Dong HY, Harris NL, Chan JK, Rees JW, Dogan A, Isaacson PG (2002) KSHV- and EBV-associated germinotropic lymphoproliferative disorder. Blood 100:3415–3418

Dupin N, Fisher C, Kellam P, Ariad S, Tulliez M, Franck N, van Marck E, Salmon D, Gorin I, Escande JP, Weiss RA, Alitalo K, Boshoff C (1999) Distribution of human herpesvirus-8 latently infected cells in Kaposi's sarcoma, multicentric Castleman's disease, and primary effusion lymphoma. Proc Natl Acad Sci USA 96:4546–4551

Dupin N, Diss TL, Kellam P, Tulliez M, Du MQ, Sicard D, Weiss RA, Isaacson PG, Boshoff C (2000) HHV-8 is associated with a plasmablastic variant of Castleman disease that is linked to HHV-8-positive plasmablastic lymphoma. Blood 95:1406–1412

Ea CK, Deng L, Xia ZP, Pineda G, Chen ZJ (2006) Activation of IKK by TNFalpha requires site-specific ubiquitination of RIP1 and polyubiquitin binding by NEMO. Mol Cell 22:245–257

Elenitoba-Johnson KS, Zarate-Osorno A, Meneses A, Krenacs L, Kingma DW, Raffeld M, Jaffe ES (1998) Cytotoxic granular protein expression, Epstein–Barr virus strain type, and latent membrane protein-1 oncogene deletions in nasal T-lymphocyte/natural killer cell lymphomas from Mexico. Mod Pathol 11:754–761

Eltom MA, Jemal A, Mbulaiteye SM, Devesa SS, Biggar RJ (2002) Trends in Kaposi's sarcoma and non-Hodgkin's lymphoma incidence in the United States from 1973 through 1998. J Natl Cancer Inst 94:1204–1210

Engels EA, Pittaluga S, Whitby D, Rabkin C, Aoki Y, Jaffe ES, Goedert JJ (2003) Immunoblastic lymphoma in persons with AIDS-associated Kaposi's sarcoma: a role for Kaposi's sarcoma-associated herpesvirus. Mod Pathol 16:424–429

Feuer G, Green PL (2005) Comparative biology of human T-cell lymphotropic virus type 1 (HTLV-1) and HTLV-2. Oncogene 24:5996–6004

Feuillard J, Schuhmacher M, Kohanna S, Asso-Bonnet M, Ledeur F, Joubert-Caron R, Bissieres P, Polack A, Bornkamm GW, Raphael M (2000) Inducible loss of NF-kappaB activity is associated with apoptosis and Bcl-2 down-regulation in Epstein–Barr virus-transformed B lymphocytes. Blood 95:2068–2075

Field N, Low W, Daniels M, Howell S, Daviet L, Boshoff C, Collins M (2003) KSHV vFLIP binds to IKK-gamma to activate IKK. J Cell Sci 116:3721–3728

Flore O, Rafii S, Ely S, O'Leary JJ, Hyjek EM, Cesarman E (1998) Transformation of primary human endothelial cells by Kaposi's sarcoma-associated herpesvirus. Nature 394:588–592

Franchini G, Nicot C, Johnson JM (2003) Seizing of T cells by human T-cell leukemia/lymphoma virus type 1. Adv Cancer Res 89:69–132

Fruehling S, Longnecker R (1997) The immunoreceptor tyrosine-based activation motif of Epstein–Barr virus LMP2A is essential for blocking BCR-mediated signal transduction. Virology 235:241–251

Fukuda M, Longnecker R (2007) Epstein–Barr virus (EBV) Latent membrane protein 2A mediates transformation through constitutive activation of the Ras/PI3-K/Akt Pathway. J Virol 81:9299–9306

Fukuda RI, Tsuchiya K, Suzuki K, Itoh K, Fujita J, Utsunomiya A, Tsuji T (2009) Human T-cell leukemia virus type I tax down-regulates the expression of phosphatidylinositol 3,4,5-trisphosphate inositol phosphatases via the NF-kappaB pathway. J Biol Chem 284:2680–2689

Gaide O, Favier B, Legler DF, Bonnet D, Brissoni B, Valitutti S, Bron C, Tschopp J, Thome M (2002) CARMA1 is a critical lipid raft-associated regulator of TCR-induced NF-kappa B activation. Nat Immunol 3:836–843

Gartenhaus RB, Wang P (1995) Functional inactivation of wild-type p53 protein correlates with loss of IL-2 dependence in HTLV-I transformed human T lymphocytes. Leukemia 9:2082–2086

Geleziunas R, Ferrell S, Lin X, Mu Y, Cunningham E T Jr, Grant M, Connelly MA, Hambor JE, Marcu KB, Greene WC (1998) Human T-cell leukemia virus type 1 Tax induction of NF-κB involves activation of the IkB kinase α (IKKα) and IKKβ cellular kinases. Mol Cell Biol 18:5157–5165

Gires O, Zimber-Strobl U, Gonnella R, Ueffing M, Marschall G, Zeidler R, Pich D, Hammerschmidt W (1997) Latent membrane protein 1 of Epstein–Barr virus mimics a constitutively active receptor molecule. EMBO J 16:6131–6140

Godfrey A, Anderson J, Papanastasiou A, Takeuchi Y, Boshoff C (2005) Inhibiting primary effusion lymphoma by lentiviral vectors encoding short hairpin RNA. Blood 105:2510–2518

Grassmann R, Dengler C, Müller-Fleckenstein I, Fleckenstein B, McGuire K, Dokhelar M-C, Sodroski JG, Haseltine WA (1989) Transformation to continuous growth of primary human T-lymphocytes by human T-cell leukemia virus type I X-region gene transduced by a herpesvirus saimiri vector. Proc Natl Acad Sci USA 86:3351–3355

Grassmann R, Berchtold S, Radant I, Alt M, Fleckenstein B, Sodroski JG, Haseltine WA, Ramstedt U (1992) Role of human T-cell leukemia virus type I x region proteins in immortalization of primary human lymphocytes in culture. J Virol 66:4570–4575

Guasparri I, Keller SA, Cesarman E (2004) KSHV vFLIP is essential for the survival of infected lymphoma cells. J Exp Med 199:993–1003

Guasparri I, Wu H, Cesarman E (2006) The KSHV oncoprotein vFLIP contains a TRAF-interacting motif and requires TRAF2 and TRAF3 for signalling. EMBO Rep 7:114–119

Guasparri I, Bubman D, Cesarman E (2008) EBV LMP2A affects LMP1-mediated NF-kappaB signaling and survival of lymphoma cells by regulating TRAF2 expression. Blood 111:3813–3820

Hall PA, Donaghy M, Cotter FE, Stansfeld AG, Levison DA (1989) An immunohistological and genotypic study of the plasma cell form of Castleman's disease. Histopathology 14:333–346 (discussion 429–432)

Hara H, Bakal C, Wada T, Bouchard D, Rottapel R, Saito T, Penninger JM (2004) The molecular adapter Carma1 controls entry of IkappaB kinase into the central immune synapse. J Exp Med 200:1167–1177

Harhaj EW, Sun S-C (1999) IKKg serves as a docking subunit of the IkB kinase and mediates interaction of IKK with the human T-cell leukemia virus Tax protein. J Biol Chem 274:22911–22914

Harhaj EW, Good L, Xiao G, Sun S-C (1999) Gene expression profiles in HTLV-I-immortalized T cells: deregulated expression of genes involved in apoptosis regulation. Oncogene 18:1341–1349

Harhaj NS, Sun SC, Harhaj EW (2007) Activation of NF-kappa B by the human T cell leukemia virus type I (HTLV-I) tax oncoprotein is associated with ubiquitin-dependent relocalization of IKK. J Biol Chem 282:4185–4192

Harris NL (1998) The many faces of Hodgkin's disease around the world: what have we learned from its pathology? Ann Oncol 9:S45–S56

Hasegawa H, Sawa H, Lewis MJ, Orba Y, Sheehy N, Yamamoto Y, Ichinohe T, Tsunetsugu-Yokota Y, Katano H, Takahashi H, Matsuda J, Sata T, Kurata T, Nagashima K, Hall WW (2006) Thymus-derived leukemia-lymphoma in mice transgenic for the Tax gene of human T-lymphotropic virus type I. Nat Med 12:466–472

Hayden MS, Ghosh S (2008) Shared principles in NF-kappaB signaling. Cell 132:344–362

Higuchi M, Tsubata C, Kondo R, Yoshida S, Takahashi M, Oie M, Tanaka Y, Mahieux R, Matsuoka M, Fujii M (2007) Cooperation of NF-kappaB2/p100 activation and the PDZ domain binding motif signal in human T-cell leukemia virus type 1 (HTLV-1) Tax1 but not HTLV-2 Tax2 is crucial for interleukin-2-independent growth transformation of a T-cell line. J Virol 81:11900–11907

Hironaka N, Mochida K, Mori N, Maeda M, Yamamoto N, Yamaoka S (2004) Tax-independent constitutive IkappaB kinase activation in adult T-cell leukemia cells. Neoplasia 6:266–278

Ho JW, Ho FC, Chan AC, Liang RH, Srivastava G (1998) Frequent detection of Epstein–Barr virus-infected B cells in peripheral T-cell lymphomas. J Pathol 185:79–85

Homig-Holzel C, Hojer C, Rastelli J, Casola S, Strobl LJ, Muller W, Quintanilla-Martinez L, Gewies A, Ruland J, Rajewsky K, Zimber-Strobl U (2008) Constitutive CD40 signaling in B cells selectively activates the noncanonical NF-kappaB pathway and promotes lymphomagenesis. J Exp Med 205:1317–1329

Horie R (2007) NF-kappaB in pathogenesis and treatment of adult T-cell leukemia/lymphoma. Int Rev Immunol 26:269–281

Huang GJ, Zhang ZQ, Jin DY (2002) Stimulation of IKK-gamma oligomerization by the human T-cell leukemia virus oncoprotein Tax. FEBS Lett 531:494–498

Huang J, Ren T, Guan H, Jiang Y, Cheng H (2009) HTLV-1 Tax is a critical lipid raft modulator that hijacks IkappaB kinases to the microdomains for persistent activation of NF-kappaB. J Biol Chem 284:6208–6217

Hummel M, Bentink S, Berger H, Klapper W, Wessendorf S, Barth TF, Bernd HW, Cogliatti SB, Dierlamm J, Feller AC, Hansmann ML, Haralambieva E, Harder L, Hasenclever D, Kuhn M, Lenze D, Lichter P, Martin-Subero JI, Moller P, Muller-Hermelink HK, Ott G, Parwaresch RM, Pott C, Rosenwald A, Rosolowski M, Schwaenen C, Sturzenhofecker B, Szczepanowski M, Trautmann H, Wacker HH, Spang R, Loeffler M, Trumper L, Stein H, Siebert R (2006) A biologic definition of Burkitt's lymphoma from transcriptional and genomic profiling. N Engl J Med 354:2419–2430

Inoue J, Seiki M, Taniguchi T, Tsuru S, Yoshida M (1986) Induction of interleukin-2 receptor gene expression by p40x encoded by human T-cell leukemia virus type I. EMBO J 5:2883–2888

Izumiya Y, Izumiya C, Hsia D, Ellison TJ, Luciw PA, Kung HJ (2009) NF-kappaB serves as a cellular sensor of Kaposi's sarcoma-associated herpesvirus latency and negatively regulates K-Rta by antagonizing the RBP-Jkappa coactivator. J Virol 83:4435–4446

Jaffe ES, Krenacs L, Kumar S, Kingma DW, Raffeld M (1999) Extranodal peripheral T-cell and NK-cell neoplasms. Am J Clin Pathol 111:S46–S55

Jeang KT (2001) Functional activities of the human T-cell leukemia virus type I Tax oncoprotein: cellular signaling through NF-kappa B. Cytokine Growth Factor Rev 12:207–217

Jeong SJ, Pise-Masison CA, Radonovich MF, Park HU, Brady JN (2005a) A Novel NF-{kappa}B Pathway Involving IKK{beta} and p65/RelA Ser-536 phosphorylation results in p53 inhibition in the absence of NF-{kappa}B transcriptional activity. J Biol Chem 280:10326–19332

Jeong SJ, Pise-Masison CA, Radonovich MF, Park HU, Brady JN (2005b) Activated AKT regulates NF-kappaB activation, p53 inhibition and cell survival in HTLV-1-transformed cells. Oncogene 24:6719–6728

Jin D-Y, Giordano V, Kibler KV, Nakano H, Jeang K-T (1999) Role of adaptor function in oncoprotein-mediated activation of NF-κB: HTLV-I Tax interacts directly with IκB kinase γ. J Biol Chem 274:17402–17405

Johansson P, Jansson A, Ruetschi U, Rymo L (2009) Nuclear factor-kappaB binds to the Epstein–Barr virus LMP1 promoter and upregulates its expression. J Virol 83:1393–1401

Journo C, Filipe J, About F, Chevalier SA, Afonso PV, Brady JN, Flynn D, Tangy F, Israël A, Vidalain PO, Mahieux R, Weil R (2009) NRP/optineurin cooperates with TAX1BP1 to potentiate the activation of NF-kappaB by human T-lymphotropic virus type 1 tax protein. PLoS Pathog 5:e1000521

Kanegane H, Yachie A, Miyawaki T, Tosato G (1998) EBV-NK cells interactions and lymphoproliferative disorders. Leuk Lymphoma 29:491–498

Karin M, Ben-Neriah Y (2000) Phosphorylation meets ubiquitination: the control of NF-[kappa]B activity. Annu Rev Immunol 18:621–663

Karin M, Greten FR (2005) NF-kappaB: linking inflammation and immunity to cancer development and progression. Nat Rev Immunol 5:749–759

Katano H, Sato Y, Kurata T, Mori S, Sata T (1999) High expression of HHV-8-encoded ORF73 protein in spindle-shaped cells of Kaposi's sarcoma. Am J Pathol 155:47–52

Katano H, Sato Y, Kurata T, Mori S, Sata T (2000) Expression and localization of human herpesvirus 8-encoded proteins in primary effusion lymphoma, Kaposi's sarcoma, and multicentric Castleman's disease. Virology 269:335–344

Kayagaki N, Yan M, Seshasayee D, Wang H, Lee W, French DM, Grewal IS, Cochran AG, Gordon NC, Yin J, Starovasnik MA, Dixit VM (2002) BAFF/BLyS receptor 3 binds the B cell survival factor BAFF ligand through a discrete surface loop and promotes processing of NF-kappaB2. Immunity 17:515–524

Kellam P, Bourboulia D, Dupin N, Shotton C, Fisher C, Talbot S, Boshoff C, Weiss RA (1999) Characterization of monoclonal antibodies raised against the latent nuclear antigen of human herpesvirus 8. J Virol 73:5149–5155

Keller SA, Schattner EJ, Cesarman E (2000) Inhibition of NF-κB induces apoptosis of KSHV-infected primary effusion lymphoma cells. Blood 96:2537–2542

Keller SA, Hernandez-Hopkins D, Vider J, Ponomarev V, Hyjek E, Schattner EJ, Cesarman E (2006) NF-{kappa}B is essential for progression of KSHV- and EBV-infected lymphomas in vivo. Blood 107:3295–3302

Kelly G, Bell A, Rickinson A (2002) Epstein–Barr virus-associated Burkitt lymphomagenesis selects for downregulation of the nuclear antigen EBNA2. Nat Med 8:1098–1104

Kelly GL, Milner AE, Tierney RJ, Croom-Carter DS, Altmann M, Hammerschmidt W, Bell AI, Rickinson AB (2005) Epstein–Barr virus nuclear antigen 2 (EBNA2) gene deletion is consistently linked with EBNA3A, -3B, and -3C expression in Burkitt's lymphoma cells and with increased resistance to apoptosis. J Virol 79:10709–10717

Kersten MJ, Van Gorp J, Pals ST, Boon F, Van Oers MH (1998) Expression of Epstein–Barr virus latent genes and adhesion molecules in AIDS-related non-Hodgkin's lymphomas: correlation with histology and CD4-cell number. Leuk Lymphoma 30:515–524

Kfoury Y, Nasr R, Favre-Bonvin A, El-Sabban M, Renault N, Giron ML, Setterblad N, Hajj HE, Chiari E, Mikati AG, Hermine O, Saib A, de Thé H, Pique C, Bazarbachi A (2008) Ubiquitylated Tax targets and binds the IKK signalosome at the centrosome. Oncogene 27:1665–1676

Khoshnan A, Bae D, Tindell CA, Nel AE (2000) The physical association of protein kinase C theta with a lipid raft-associated inhibitor of kappa B factor kinase (IKK) complex plays a role in the activation of the NF-kappa B cascade by TCR and CD28. J Immunol 165:6933–6940

Kieff E (1996) Epstein–Barr virus and its replication. In: Fields BN, Knipe DM, Howley PM (eds) Virology. Lippincott–Raven Publishers, Philadelphia, pp 2343-2396

Kieser A (2008) Pursuing different 'TRADDes': TRADD signaling induced by TNF-receptor 1 and the Epstein–Barr virus oncoprotein LMP1. Biol Chem 389:1261–1271

Kitajima I, Shinohara T, Bilakovics J, Brown DA, Xu X, Nerenberg M (1992) Ablation of transplanted HTLV-I Tax-transformed tumors in mice by antisense inhibition of NF-κB. Science 258:1792–1795

Knowles DM (2001) Neoplastic hematopathology. Williams and Wilkins, Baltimore, p 1956

Knowles DM, Cesarman E, Chadburn A, Frizzera G, Chen J, Rose EA, Michler RE (1995) Correlative morphologic and molecular genetic analysis demonstrates three distinct categories of posttransplantation lymphoproliferative disorders. Blood 85:552–565

Koga H, Imada K, Ueda M, Hishizawa M, Uchiyama T (2004) Identification of differentially expressed molecules in adult T-cell leukemia cells proliferating in vivo. Cancer Sci 95:411–417

Konrad A, Wies E, Thurau M, Marquardt G, Naschberger E, Hentschel S, Jochmann R, Schulz TF, Erfle H, Brors B, Lausen B, Neipel F, Sturzl M (2009) A systems biology approach to identify the combination effects of human herpesvirus 8 genes on NF-kappaB activation. J Virol 83:2563–2574

Kulwichit W, Edwards RH, Davenport EM, Baskar JF, Godfrey V, Raab-Traub N (1998) Expression of the Epstein–Barr virus latent membrane protein 1 induces B cell lymphoma in transgenic mice. Proc Natl Acad Sci USA 95:11963–11968

Küppers R, Rajewsky K (1998) The origin of Hodgkin and Reed/Sternberg cells in Hodgkin's disease. Annu Rev Immunol 16:471–493

Kwon H, Ogle L, Benitez B, Bohuslav J, Montano M, Felsher DW, Greene WC (2005) Lethal cutaneous disease in transgenic mice conditionally expressing type I human T cell leukemia virus Tax. J Biol Chem 280:35713–35722

Laichalk LL, Thorley-Lawson DA (2005) Terminal differentiation into plasma cells initiates the replicative cycle of Epstein–Barr virus in vivo. J Virol 79:1296–1307

Laichalk LL, Hochberg D, Babcock GJ, Freeman RB, Thorley-Lawson DA (2002) The dispersal of mucosal memory B cells: evidence from persistent EBV infection. Immunity 16:745–754

Lairmore MD, Silverman L, Ratner L (2005) Animal models for human T-lymphotropic virus type 1 (HTLV-1) infection and transformation. Oncogene 24:6005–6015

Lamsoul I, Lodewick J, Lebrun S, Brasseur R, Burny A, Gaynor RB, Bex F (2005) Exclusive ubiquitination and sumoylation on overlapping lysine residues mediate NF-kappaB activation by the human T-cell leukemia virus tax oncoprotein. Mol Cell Biol 25:10391–10406

Larocca LM, Capello D, Rinelli A, Nori S, Antinori A, Gloghini A, Cingolani A, Migliazza A, Saglio G, Cammilleri-Broet S, Raphael M, Carbone A, Gaidano G (1998) The molecular and phenotypic profile of primary central nervous system lymphoma identifies distinct categories of the disease and is consistent with histogenetic derivation from germinal center-related B cells. Blood 92:1011–1099

Larroche C, Cacoub P, Soulier J, Oksenhendler E, Clauvel JP, Piette JC, Raphael M (2002) Castleman's disease and lymphoma: report of eight cases in HIV-negative patients and literature review. Am J Hematol 69:119–126

Lechowicz MJ, Lin L, Ambinder RF (2002) Epstein–Barr virus DNA in body fluids. Curr Opin Oncol 14:533–537

Lee JS, Li Q, Lee JY, Lee SH, Jeong JH, Lee HR, Chang H, Zhou FC, Gao SJ, Liang C, Jung JU (2009) FLIP-mediated autophagy regulation in cell death control. Nat Cell Biol 11:1355–1362

Li Y, Kang J, Horwitz M (1998) Interaction of an adenovirus E3 14.7-kilodalton protein with a novel tumor necrosis factor alpha-inducible cellular protein containing leucine zipper domains. Mol Cell Biol 18:1601–1610

Li H, Kobayashi M, Blonska M, You Y, Lin X (2006) Ubiquitination of RIP is required for tumor necrosis factor alpha-induced NF-kappaB activation. J Biol Chem 281:13636–13643

Liebowitz D (1998) Epstein–Barr virus and a cellular signaling pathway in lymphomas from immunosuppressed patients. N Engl J Med 338:1413–1421

Lin JC, Wang WY, Chen KY, Wei YH, Liang WM, Jan JS, Jiang RS (2004) Quantification of plasma Epstein–Barr virus DNA in patients with advanced nasopharyngeal carcinoma. N Engl J Med 350:2461–2470

Liu Y, Wang Y, Yamakuchi M, Masuda S, Tokioka T, Yamaoka S, Maruyama I, Kitajima I (2001) Phosphoinositide-3 kinase-PKB/Akt pathway activation is involved in fibroblast Rat-1 transformation by human T-cell leukemia virus type I tax. Oncogene 20:2514–2526

Liu L, Eby MT, Rathore N, Sinha SK, Kumar A, Chaudhary PM (2002) The human herpes virus 8 encoded viral FLICE inhibitory protein physically associates with and persistently activates the IkappaB kinase complex. J Biol Chem 5:5

Lo YM, Chan AT, Chan LY, Leung SF, Lam CW, Huang DP, Johnson PJ (2000) Molecular prognostication of nasopharyngeal carcinoma by quantitative analysis of circulating Epstein–Barr virus DNA. Cancer Res 60:6878–6881

Lu KP, Zhou XZ (2007) The prolyl isomerase PIN1: a pivotal new twist in phosphorylation signalling and disease. Nat Rev Mol Cell Biol 8:904–916

Lu J, Lin WH, Chen SY, Longnecker R, Tsai SC, Chen CL, Tsai CH (2006) Syk tyrosine kinase mediates Epstein–Barr virus latent membrane protein 2A-induced cell migration in epithelial cells. J Biol Chem 281:8806–8814

Luftig M, Prinarakis E, Yasui T, Tsichritzis T, Cahir-McFarland E, Inoue J, Nakano H, Mak TW, Yeh WC, Li X, Akira S, Suzuki N, Suzuki S, Mosialos G, Kieff E (2003) Epstein–Barr virus latent membrane protein 1 activation of NF-kappaB through IRAK1 and TRAF6. Proc Natl Acad Sci USA 100:15595–15600

Mainou BA, Everly D N Jr, Raab-Traub N (2007) Unique signaling properties of CTAR1 in LMP1-mediated transformation. J Virol 81:9680–9692

Martin D, Galisteo R, Ji Y, Montaner S, Gutkind JS (2008) An NF-kappaB gene expression signature contributes to Kaposi's sarcoma virus vGPCR-induced direct and paracrine neoplasia. Oncogene 27:1844–1852

Maruyama M, Shibuya H, Harada H, Hatakeyama M, Seiki M, Fujita T, Inoue JI, Yoshida M, Taniguchi T (1987) Evidence for aberrant activation of the interleukin-2 autocrine loop by HTLV-1-encoded p40x and T3/Ti complex triggering. Cell 48:343–350

Matsumoto R, Wang D, Blonska M, Li H, Kobayashi M, Pappu B, Chen Y, Wang D, Lin X (2005) Phosphorylation of CARMA1 plays a critical role in T Cell receptor-mediated NF-kappaB activation. Immunity 23:575–585

Matsuoka M (2003) Human T-cell leukemia virus type I and adult T-cell leukemia. Oncogene 22:5131–5140

Matsuoka M, Green PL (2009) The HBZ gene, a key player in HTLV-1 pathogenesis. Retrovirology 6:71

Matsuoka M, Jeang KT (2007) Human T-cell leukaemia virus type 1 (HTLV-1) infectivity and cellular transformation. Nat Rev Cancer 7:270–280

Matta H, Chaudhary PM (2004) Activation of alternative NF-kappa B pathway by human herpes virus 8-encoded Fas-associated death domain-like IL-1 beta-converting enzyme inhibitory protein (vFLIP). Proc Natl Acad Sci USA 101:9399–9404

Matta H, Mazzacurati L, Schamus S, Yang T, Sun Q, Chaudhary PM (2007) Kaposi's sarcoma-associated herpesvirus (KSHV) oncoprotein K13 bypasses TRAFs and directly interacts with the IkappaB kinase complex to selectively activate NF-kappaB without JNK activation. J Biol Chem 282:24858–24865

Menke DM, Chadbum A, Cesarman E, Green E, Berenson J, Said J, Tiemann M, Parwaresch R, Thome SD (2002) Analysis of the human herpesvirus 8 (HHV-8) genome and HHV-8 vIL-6 expression in archival cases of Castleman disease at low risk for HIV infection. Am J Clin Pathol 117:268–275

Merchant M, Caldwell RG, Longnecker R (2000) The LMP2A ITAM is essential for providing B cells with development and survival signals in vivo. J Virol 74:9115–9124

Mesri EA, Cesarman E, Arvanitakis L, Rafii S, Moore MAS, Posnett DN, Knowles DM, Asch AS (1996) Human herpesvirus-8/Kaposi's sarcoma-associated herpesvirus is a new transmissible virus that infects B cells. J Exp Med 183:2385–2390

Miller CL, Lee JH, Kieff E, Longnecker R (1994) An integral membrane protein (LMP2) blocks reactivation of Epstein–Barr virus from latency following surface immunoglobulin cross-linking. Proc Natl Acad Sci USA 91:772–776

Miller G, Heston L, Grogan E, Gradoville L, Rigsby M, Sun R, Shedd D, Kushnaryov VM, Grossberg S, Chang Y (1997) Selective switch between latency and lytic replication of Kaposi's sarcoma herpesvirus and Epstein–Barr virus in dually infected body cavity lymphoma cells. J Virol 71:314–324

Moody CA, Scott RS, Amirghahari N, Nathan CA, Young LS, Dawson CW, Sixbey JW (2005) Modulation of the cell growth regulator mTOR by Epstein–Barr virus-encoded LMP2A. J Virol 79:5499–5506

Mori N, Sato H, Hayashibara T, Senba M, Hayashi T, Yamada Y, Kamihira S, Ikeda S, Yamasaki Y, Morikawa S, Tomonaga M, Geleziunas R, Yamamoto N (2002) Human T-cell leukemia virus type I Tax transactivates the matrix metalloproteinase-9 gene: potential role in mediating adult T-cell leukemia invasiveness. Blood 99:1341–1349

Morrison TE, Kenney SC (2004) BZLF1, an Epstein–Barr virus immediate-early protein, induces p65 nuclear translocation while inhibiting p65 transcriptional function. Virology 328:219–232

Morrison JA, Klingelhutz AJ, Raab-Traub N (2003) Epstein–Barr virus latent membrane protein 2A activates beta-catenin signaling in epithelial cells. J Virol 77:12276–12284

Moses AV, Fish KN, Ruhl R, Smith PP, Strussenberg JG, Zhu L, Chandran B, Nelson JA (1999) Long-term infection and transformation of dermal microvascular endothelial cells by human herpesvirus 8. J Virol 73:6892–6902

Nador RG, Cesarman E, Knowles DM, Said JW (1995) Herpes-like DNA sequences in a body-cavity-based lymphoma in an HIV-negative patient. N Engl J Med 333:943 (letter to the editor)

Nador RG, Cesarman E, Chadburn A, Dawson DB, Ansari MQ, Said J, Knowles DM (1996) Primary effusion lymphoma: a distinct clinicopathologic entity associated with the Kaposi's sarcoma-associated herpesvirus. Blood 88:645–656

Nakamura H, Lu M, Gwack Y, Souvlis J, Zeichner SL, Jung JU (2003) Global changes in Kaposi's sarcoma-associated virus gene expression patterns following expression of a tetracycline-inducible Rta transactivator. J Virol 77:4205–4220

Nasr R, Chiari E, El-Sabban M, Mahieux R, Kfoury Y, Abdulhay M, Yazbeck V, Hermine O, de The H, Pique C, Bazarbachi A (2006) Tax ubiquitylation and sumoylation control critical cytoplasmic and nuclear steps of NF-kappaB activation. Blood 107:4021–4029

Ng PW, Iha H, Iwanaga Y, Bittner M, Chen Y, Jiang Y, Gooden G, Trent JM, Meltzer P, Jeang KT, Zeichner SL (2001) Genome-wide expression changes induced by HTLV-1 Tax: evidence for MLK-3 mixed lineage kinase involvement in Tax-mediated NF-kappaB activation. Oncogene 20:4484–4496

Novack DV, Yin L, Hagen-Stapleton A, Schreiber RD, Goeddel DV, Ross FP, Teitelbaum SL (2003) The IkappaB function of NF-kappaB2 p100 controls stimulated osteoclastogenesis. J Exp Med 198:771–781

Ohsugi T, Kumasaka T, Okada S, Urano T (2007) The Tax protein of HTLV-1 promotes oncogenesis in not only immature T cells but also mature T cells. Nat Med 13:527–528

Okamoto K, Fujisawa J, Reth M, Yonehara S (2006) Human T-cell leukemia virus type-I oncoprotein Tax inhibits Fas-mediated apoptosis by inducing cellular FLIP through activation of NF-kappaB. Genes Cells 11:177–191

Panagopoulos D, Victoratos P, Alexiou M, Kollias G, Mosialos G (2004) Comparative analysis of signal transduction by CD40 and the Epstein–Barr virus oncoprotein LMP1 in vivo. J Virol 78:13253–13261

Parkin DM (2006) The global health burden of infection-associated cancers in the year 2002. Int J Cancer 118:3030–3044

Parravicini C, Corbellino M, Paulli M, Magrini U, Lazzarino M, Moore PS, Chang Y (1997) Expression of a virus-derived cytokine, KSHV vIL-6, in HIV-seronegative Castleman's disease. Am J Pathol 151:1517–1522

Parravicini C, Chandran B, Corbellino M, Berti E, Paulli M, Moore PS, Chang Y (2000) Differential viral protein expression in Kaposi's sarcoma-associated herpesvirus-infected diseases: Kaposi's sarcoma, primary effusion lymphoma, and multicentric Castleman's disease. Am J Pathol 156:743–749

Pathmanathan R, Prasad U, Chandrika G, Sadler R, Flynn K, Raab-Traub N (1995) Undifferentiated, nonkeratinizing, and squamous cell carcinoma of the nasopharynx. Variants of Epstein–Barr virus-infected neoplasia. Am J Pathol 146:1355–1367

Peloponese JM, Yeung ML, Jeang KT (2006) Modulation of nuclear factor-kappaB by human T cell leukemia virus type 1 Tax protein: implications for oncogenesis and inflammation. Immunol Res 34:1–12

Peloponese JJ, Yasunaga J, Kinjo T, Watashi K, Jeang KT (2009) Peptidylproline *cis-trans*-isomerase Pin1 interacts with human T-cell leukemia virus type 1 tax and modulates its activation of NF-kappaB. J Virol 83:3238–3248

Pfeffer S, Sewer A, Lagos-Quintana M, Sheridan R, Sander C, Grasser FA, van Dyk LF, Ho CK, Shuman S, Chien M, Russo JJ, Ju J, Randall G, Lindenbach BD, Rice CM, Simon V, Ho DD, Zavolan M, Tuschl T (2005) Identification of microRNAs of the herpesvirus family. Nat Methods 2:269–276

Pise-Masison CA, Brady JN (2005) Setting the stage for transformation: HTLV-1 Tax inhibition of p53 function. Front Biosci 10:919–930

Pise-Masison CA, Choi KS, Radonovich M, Dittmer J, Kim SJ, Brady JN (1998) Inhibition of p53 transactivation function by the human T-cell lymphotropic virus type 1 Tax protein. J Virol 72:1165–1170

Pise-Masison CA, Radonovich M, Mahieux R, Chatterjee P, Whiteford C, Duvall J, Guillerm C, Gessain A, Brady JN (2002) Transcription profile of cells infected with human T-cell leukemia virus type I compared with activated lymphocytes. Cancer Res 62:3562–3571

Poiesz BF, Ruscetti FW, Gazdar AF, Bunn PA, Minna JD, Gallo RC (1980) Detection and isolation of a type C retrovirus particles from fresh cultured lymphocytes of a patient with cutaneous T-cell lymphoma. Proc Natl Acad Sci USA 77:7415–7419

Pomerantz JL, Baltimore D (2002) Two pathways to NF-kappaB. Mol Cell 10:693–695

Portis T, Harding JC, Ratner L (2001) The contribution of NF-kappa B activity to spontaneous proliferation and resistance to apoptosis in human T-cell leukemia virus type 1 Tax-induced tumors. Blood 98:1200–1208

Pozzatti R, Vogel J, Jay G (1990) The human T-lymphotropic virus type I tax gene can cooperate with the ras oncogene to induce neoplastic transformation of cells. Mol Cell Biol 10:413–417

Prakash O, Tang ZY, Peng X, Coleman R, Gill J, Farr G, Samaniego F (2002) Tumorigenesis and aberrant signaling in transgenic mice expressing the human herpesvirus-8 K1 gene. J Natl Cancer Inst 94:926–935

Prince S, Keating S, Fielding C, Brennan P, Floettmann E, Rowe M (2003) Latent membrane protein 1 inhibits Epstein–Barr virus lytic cycle induction and progress via different mechanisms. J Virol 77:5000–5007

Rainbow L, Platt GM, Simpson GR, Sarid R, Gao SJ, Stoiber H, Herrington CS, Moore PS, Schulz TF (1997) The 222- to 234-kilodalton latent nuclear protein (LNA) of Kaposi's sarcoma-associated herpesvirus (human herpesvirus 8) is encoded by orf73 and is a component of the latency-associated nuclear antigen. J Virol 71:5915–5921

Raphaël M, Said J, Borisch B, Cesarman E, Harris NL (2008) Lymphomas associated with HIV infection. In: Swerdlow SH, Campo E, Harris NL, Jaffe ES, Pileri SA, Stein H, Thiele J (eds) WHO classification of tumours of haematopoietic and lymphoid tissues. IARC Press, Lyon, pp 340–342

Rappocciolo G, Hensler HR, Jais M, Reinhart TA, Pegu A, Jenkins FJ, Rinaldo CR (2008) Human herpesvirus 8 infects and replicates in primary cultures of activated B lymphocytes through DC-SIGN. J Virol 82:4793–4806

Rauch D, Gross S, Harding J, Niewiesk S, Lairmore M, Piwnica-Worms D, Ratner L (2009) Imaging spontaneous tumorigenesis: inflammation precedes development of peripheral NK tumors. Blood 113:1493–1500

Reed JA, Nador RG, Spaulding D, Tani Y, Cesarman E, Knowles DM (1998) Demonstration of Kaposi's sarcoma-associated herpesvirus cyclin D homolog in cutaneous Kaposi's sarcoma by colorimetric in situ hybridization using a catalyzed signal amplification system. Blood 91:3825–3832

Reid RL, Lindholm PF, Mireskandari A, Dittmer J, Brady JN (1993) Stabilization of wild-type p53 in human T-lymphocytes transformed by HTLV-I. Oncogene 8:3029–3036

Renne R, Zhong W, Herndier B, McGrath M, Abbey N, Kedes D, Ganem D (1996) Lytic growth of Kaposi's sarcoma-associated herpesvirus (human herpesvirus 8) in culture. Nat Med 2:342–346

Rezaie T, Child A, Hitchings R, Brice G, Miller L, Coca-Prados M, Héon E, Krupin T, Ritch R, Kreutzer D, Crick RP, Sarfarazi M (2002) Adult-onset primary open-angle glaucoma caused by mutations in optineurin. Science 295:1077–1079

Rickinson AB, Kieff E (1996) Epstein–Barr virus. In: Fields BN, Knipe DM, Howley PM (eds) Virology. Lippincott-Raven Publishers, Philadelphia, pp 2397–2446

Rivas C, Thlick AE, Parravicini C, Moore PS, Chang Y (2001) Kaposi's sarcoma-associated herpesvirus LANA2 is a B-cell-specific latent viral protein that inhibits p53 J Virol 75:429–438

Robek MD, Ratner L (1999) Immortalization of CD4(+) and CD8(+) T lymphocytes by human T-cell leukemia virus type 1 Tax mutants expressed in a functional molecular clone. J Virol 73:4856–4865

Rochford R, Miller CL, Cannon MJ, Izumi KM, Kieff E, Longnecker R (1997) In vivo growth of Epstein–Barr virus transformed B cells with mutations in latent membrane protein 2 (LMP2). Arch Virol 142:707–720

Sadagopan S, Sharma-Walia N, Veettil MV, Raghu H, Sivakumar R, Bottero V, Chandran B (2007) Kaposi's sarcoma-associated herpesvirus induces sustained NF-kappaB activation during de novo infection of primary human dermal microvascular endothelial cells that is essential for viral gene expression. J Virol 81:3949–3968

Sadler R, Wu L, Forghani B, Renne R, Zhong W, Herndier B, Ganem D (1999) A complex translational program generates multiple novel proteins from the latently expressed kaposin (K12) locus of Kaposi's sarcoma-associated herpesvirus. J Virol 73:5722–5730

Said JW, Tasaka T, Takeuchi S, Asou H, de Vos S, Cesarman E, Knowles DM, Koeffler HP (1996) Primary effusion lymphoma in women: report of two cases of Kaposi's sarcoma-herpes virus-associated effusion-based lymphoma in human immunodeficiency virus-negative women. Blood 88:3124–3128

Saitoh Y, Yamamoto N, Dewan MZ, Sugimoto H, Martinez Bruyn VJ, Iwasaki Y, Matsubara K, Qi X, Saitoh T, Imoto I, Inazawa J, Utsunomiya A, Watanabe T, Masuda T, Yamamoto N, Yamaoka S (2008) Overexpressed NF-kappaB-inducing kinase contributes to the tumorigenesis of adult T-cell leukemia and Hodgkin Reed–Sternberg cells. Blood 111:5118–5129

Samaniego F, Pati S, Karp JE, Prakash O, Bose D (2001) Human herpesvirus 8 K1-associated nuclear factor-kappa B-dependent promoter activity: role in Kaposi's sarcoma inflammation? J Natl Cancer Inst Monogr (28):15–23

Samols MA, Hu J, Skalsky RL, Renne R (2005) Cloning and identification of a microRNA cluster within the latency-associated region of Kaposi's sarcoma-associated herpesvirus. J Virol 79:9301–9305

Sanda T, Asamitsu K, Ogura H, Iida S, Utsunomiya A, Ueda R, Okamoto T (2006) Induction of cell death in adult T-cell leukemia cells by a novel IkappaB kinase inhibitor. Leukemia 20:590–598

Sarid R, Wiezorek JS, Moore PS, Chang Y (1999) Characterization and cell cycle regulation of the major Kaposi's sarcoma-associated herpesvirus (human herpesvirus 8) latent genes and their promoter. J Virol 73:1438–1446

Sasaki H, Nishikata I, Shiraga T, Akamatsu E, Fukami T, Hidaka T, Kubuki Y, Okayama A, Hamada K, Okabe H, Murakami Y, Tsubouchi H, Morishita K (2005) Overexpression of a cell adhesion molecule, TSLC1, as a possible molecular marker for acute-type adult T-cell leukemia. Blood 105:1204–1213

Satou Y, Yasunaga J, Yoshida M, Matsuoka M (2006) HTLV-I basic leucine zipper factor gene mRNA supports proliferation of adult T cell leukemia cells. Proc Natl Acad Sci USA 103:720–725

Senftleben U, Cao Y, Xiao G, Kraehn G, Greten F, Chen Y, Hu Y, Fong A, Sun S-C, Karin M (2001) Activation of IKKα of a second, evolutionary conserved, NF-κB signaling pathway. Science 293:1495–1499

Seo T, Park J, Lim C, Choe J (2004) Inhibition of nuclear factor kappaB activity by viral interferon regulatory factor 3 of Kaposi's sarcoma-associated herpesvirus. Oncogene 23:6146–6155

Sgarbanti M, Arguello M, ten Oever BR, Battistini A, Lin R, Hiscott J (2004) A requirement for NF-kappaB induction in the production of replication-competent HHV-8 virions. Oncogene 23:5770–5780

Shembade N, Harhaj NS, Liebl DJ, Harhaj EW (2007a) Essential role for TAX1BP1 in the termination of TNF-alpha-, IL-1- and LPS-mediated NF-kappaB and JNK signaling. EMBO J 26:3910–3922

Shembade N, Harhaj NS, Yamamoto M, Akira S, Harhaj EW (2007b) The human T-cell leukemia virus type 1 Tax oncoprotein requires the ubiquitin-conjugating enzyme Ubc13 for NF-kappaB activation. J Virol 81:13735–13742

Shembade N, Harhaj NS, Parvatiyar K, Copeland NG, Jenkins NA, Matesic LE, Harhaj EW (2008) The E3 ligase Itch negatively regulates inflammatory signaling pathways by controlling the function of the ubiquitin-editing enzyme A20. Nat Immunol 9:254–262

Siekevitz M, Feinberg MB, Holbrook N, Wong-Staal F, Greene WC (1987) Activation of interleukin 2 and interleukin 2 receptor (Tac) promoter expression by the transactivator (tat) gene product of human T-cell leukemia virus type 1. Proc Natl Acad Sci USA 84:5389–5393

Sinfield RL, Molyneux EM, Banda K, Borgstein E, Broadhead R, Hesseling P, Newton R, Casabonne D, Mkandawire N, Nkume H, Hodgson T, Liomba G (2007) Spectrum and presentation of pediatric malignancies in the HIV era: experience from Blantyre, Malawi, 1998–2003. Pediatr Blood Cancer 48:515–520

Sinha-Datta U, Horikawa I, Michishita E, Datta A, Sigler-Nicot JC, Brown M, Kazanji M, Barrett JC, Nicot C (2004) Transcriptional activation of hTERT through the NF-kappaB pathway in HTLV-I-transformed cells. Blood 104:2523–2531

Skaug B, Jiang X, Chen ZJ (2009) The role of ubiquitin in NF-kappaB regulatory pathways. Annu Rev Biochem 78:769–796

Sommer K, Guo B, Pomerantz JL, Bandaranayake AD, Moreno-Garcia ME, Ovechkina YL, Rawlings DJ (2005) Phosphorylation of the CARMA1 linker controls NF-kappaB activation. Immunity 23:561–567

Soulier J, Grollet L, Oksenhendler E, Cacoub P, Cazals-Hatem D, Babinet P, d'Agay M-F, Clauvel J-P, Raphael M, Degos L, Sigaux F (1995) Kaposi's sarcoma-associated herpesvirus-like DNA sequences in multicentric Castleman's disease. Blood 86:1275–1280

Speck P, Kline KA, Cheresh P, Longnecker R (1999) Epstein–Barr virus lacking latent membrane protein 2 immortalizes B cells with efficiency indistinguishable from that of wild-type virus. J Gen Virol 80(Pt 8):2193–2203

Staskus KA, Sun R, Miller G, Racz P, Jaslowski A, Metroka C, Brett-Smith H, Haase AT (1999) Cellular tropism and viral interleukin-6 expression distinguish human herpesvirus 8 involvement in Kaposi's sarcoma, primary effusion lymphoma, and multicentric Castleman's disease. J Virol 73:4181–4187

Stewart S, Dawson CW, Takada K, Curnow J, Moody CA, Sixbey JW, Young LS (2004) Epstein–Barr virus-encoded LMP2A regulates viral and cellular gene expression by modulation of the NF-kappaB transcription factor pathway. Proc Natl Acad Sci USA 101:15730–15735

Sturzl M, Hohenadl C, Zietz C, Castanos-Velez E, Wunderlich A, Ascherl G, Biberfeld P, Monini P, Browning PJ, Ensoli B (1999) Expression of K13/v-FLIP gene of human herpesvirus 8 and apoptosis in Kaposi's sarcoma spindle cells. J Natl Cancer Inst 91:1725–1733

Su TT, Guo B, Kawakami Y, Sommer K, Chae K, Humphries LA, Kato RM, Kang S, Patrone L, Wall R, Teitell M, Leitges M, Kawakami T, Rawlings DJ (2002) PKC-beta controls I kappa B kinase lipid raft recruitment and activation in response to BCR signaling. Nat Immunol 3:780–786

Suda T, Katano H, Delsol G, Kakiuchi C, Nakamura T, Shiota M, Sata T, Higashihara M, Mori S (2001) HHV-8 infection status of AIDS-unrelated and AIDS-associated multicentric Castleman's disease. Pathol Int 51:671–679

Sugano N, Chen W, Roberts ML, Cooper NR (1997) Epstein–Barr virus binding to CD21 activates the initial viral promoter via NF-kappaB induction. J Exp Med 186:731–737

Sun SC (2010) CYLD: a tumor suppressor deubiquitinase regulating NF-κB activation. Cell Death Differ 17(1):25–34

Sun SC, Ballard DW (1999) Persistent activation of NF-κB by the Tax transforming protein of HTLV-1: hijacking cellular IκB kinases. Oncogene 18:6948–6958

Sun SC, Ley SC (2008) New insights into NF-kappaB regulation and function. Trends Immunol 29:469–478

Sun CC, Thorley-Lawson DA (2007) Plasma cell-specific transcription factor XBP-1s binds to and transactivates the Epstein–Barr virus BZLF1 promoter. J Virol 81:13566–13577

Sun SC, Xiao G (2003) Deregulation of NF-kB and its upstream kinases in cancer. Cancer Metastasis Rev 22:405–422

Sun SC, Yamaoka S (2005) Activation of NF-κB by HTLV-I and implications for cell transformation. Oncogene 24:5952–5964

Sun L, Deng L, Ea C-K, Xia Z-P, Chen ZJ (2004) The TRAF6 ubiquitin ligase and TAK1 kinase mediate IKK activation by BCL10 and MALT1 in T lymphocytes. Mol Cell 14:289–301

Suzuki T, Fujisawa JI, Toita M, Yoshida M (1993) The trans-activator tax of human T-cell leukemia virus type I (HTLV-1) interacts with cAMP-responsive element (CRE) binding and CRE modulator proteins that bind to the 21-base-pair enhancer of HTLV-1. Proc Natl Acad Sci USA 90:610–614

Swanson-Mungerson MA, Caldwell RG, Bultema R, Longnecker R (2005) Epstein–Barr virus LMP2A alters in vivo and in vitro models of B-cell anergy, but not deletion, in response to autoantigen. J Virol 79:7355–7362

Swanson-Mungerson M, Bultema R, Longnecker R (2006) Epstein–Barr virus LMP2A enhances B-cell responses in vivo and in vitro. J Virol 80:6764–6770

Swart R, Ruf IK, Sample J, Longnecker R (2000) Latent membrane protein 2A-mediated effects on the phosphatidylinositol 3-Kinase/Akt pathway. J Virol 74:10838–10845

Takatsuki K (2005) Discovery of adult T-cell leukemia. Retrovirology 2:16

Takemoto S, Trovato R, Cereseto A, Nicot C, Kislyakova T, Casareto L, Waldmann T, Torelli G, Franchini G (2000) p53 stabilization and functional impairment in the absence of genetic mutation or the alteration of the p14(ARF)-MDM2 loop in ex vivo and cultured adult T-cell leukemia/lymphoma cells. Blood 95:3939–3944

Tanaka A, Takahashi C, Yamaoka S, Nosaka T, Maki M, Hatanaka M (1990) Oncogenic transformation by the tax gene of human T-cell leukemia virus type I in vitro. Proc Natl Acad Sci USA 87:1071–1075
Tao Q, Robertson KD, Manns A, Hildesheim A, Ambinder RF (1998) Epstein–Barr virus (EBV) in endemic Burkitt's lymphoma: molecular analysis of primary tumor tissue. Blood 91:1373–1381
Taylor GP, Matsuoka M (2005) Natural history of adult T-cell leukemia/lymphoma and approaches to therapy. Oncogene 24:6047–6057
Taylor JM, Nicot C (2008) HTLV-1 and apoptosis: role in cellular transformation and recent advances in therapeutic approaches. Apoptosis 13:733–747
Thorley-Lawson DA (2001) Epstein–Barr virus: exploiting the immune system. Nat Rev Immunol 1:75–82
Thorley-Lawson DA, Gross A (2004) Persistence of the Epstein–Barr virus and the origins of associated lymphomas. N Engl J Med 350:1328–1337
Tsuchiyama J, Yoshino T, Mori M, Kondoh E, Oka T, Akagi T, Hiraki A, Nakayama H, Shibuya A, Ma Y, Kawabata T, Okada S, Harada M (1998) Characterization of a novel human natural killer-cell line (NK-YS) established from natural killer cell lymphoma/leukemia associated with Epstein–Barr virus infection. Blood 92:1374–1383
Tsukahara T, Kannagi M, Ohashi T, Kato H, Arai M, Nunez G, Iwanaga Y, Yamamoto N, Ohtani K, Nakamura M, Fujii M (1999) Induction of Bcl-x(L) expression by human T-cell leukemia virus type 1 Tax through NF-kappaB in apoptosis-resistant T-cell transfectants with Tax. J Virol 73:7981–7987
Tsukasaki K, Tanosaki S, DeVos S, Hofmann WK, Wachsman W, Gombart AF, Krebs J, Jauch A, Bartram CR, Nagai K, Tomonaga M, Said JW, Koeffler HP (2004) Identifying progression-associated genes in adult T-cell leukemia/lymphoma by using oligonucleotide microarrays. Int J Cancer 109:875–881
Uhlik M, Good L, Xiao G, Harhaj EW, Zandi E, Karin M, Sun S-C (1998) NF-kappaB-inducing kinase and IkappaB kinase participate in human T-cell leukemia virus I Tax-mediated NF-kappaB activation. J Biol Chem 273:21132–21136
Valentine R, Dawson CW, Hu C, Shah KM, Owen TJ, Date KL, Maia SP, Shao J, Arrand JR, Young LS, O'Neil JD (2010) Epstein–Barr virus-encoded EBNA1 inhibits the canonical NF-kappa-B pathway in carcinoma cells by inhibiting IKK phosphorylation. Mol Cancer 9:1
Vallabhapurapu S, Karin M (2009) Regulation and function of NF-kappaB transcription factors in the immune system. Annu Rev Immunol 27:693–733
Verdonck K, González E, Van Dooren S, Vandamme AM, Vanham G, Gotuzzo E (2007) Human T-lymphotropic virus 1: recent knowledge about an ancient infection. Lancet Infect Dis 7:266–281
Wada K, Niida M, Tanaka M, Kamitani T (2009) Ro52-mediated monoubiquitination of IKK{beta} downregulates NF-{kappa}B signaling. J Biochem 146:821–832
Wäldele K, Silbermann K, Schneider G, Ruckes T, Cullen BR, Grassmann R (2006) Requirement of the human T-cell leukemia virus (HTLV-1) tax-stimulated HIAP-1 gene for the survival of transformed lymphocytes. Blood 107:4491–4499
Wang D, Liebowitz D, Kieff E (1985) An EBV membrane protein expressed in immortalized lymphocytes transforms established rodent cells. Cell 43:831–840
Wang H, Nicholas MW, Conway KL, Sen P, Diz R, Tisch RM, Clarke SH (2006) EBV latent membrane protein 2A induces autoreactive B cell activation and TLR hypersensitivity. J Immunol 177:2793–2802
Wu X, Sun SC (2007) Retroviral oncoprotein Tax deregulates NF-kB by activating Tak1 and mediating Tak1-IKK physical association. EMBO Rep 8:510–515
Wu CJ, Conze DB, Li T, Srinivasula SM, Ashwell JD (2006) Sensing of Lys 63-linked polyubiquitination by NEMO is a key event in NF-kappaB activation. Nat Cell Biol 8: 398–406
Xiao G, Sun SC (2000) Activation of IKKalpha and IKKbeta through their fusion with HTLV-I tax protein. Oncogene 19:5198–5203

Xiao G, Harhaj EW, Sun S-C (2000) Domain-specific interaction with IKKγ is an essential step in Tax-mediated activation of IKK. J Biol Chem 275:34060–34067

Xiao G, Cvijic ME, Fong A, Harhaj EW, Uhlik MT, Waterfield M, Sun SC (2001a) Retroviral oncoprotein Tax induces processing of NF-kappaB2/p100 in T cells: evidence for the involvement of IKKalpha. EMBO J 20:6805–6815

Xiao G, Harhaj EW, Sun SC (2001b) NF-kappaB-inducing kinase regulates the processing of NF-kappaB2 p100. Mol Cell 7:401–409

Xiao G, Fong A, Sun SC (2004) Induction of p100 processing by NF-kappaB-inducing kinase involves docking IkappaB kinase alpha (IKKalpha) to p100 and IKKalpha-mediated phosphorylation. J Biol Chem 279:30099–30105

Xie P, Hostager BS, Bishop GA (2004) Requirement for TRAF3 in signaling by LMP1 but not CD40 in B lymphocytes. J Exp Med 199:661–671

Yasunaga J, Matsuoka M (2007) Human T-cell leukemia virus type I induces adult T-cell leukemia: from clinical aspects to molecular mechanisms. Cancer Control 14:133–140

Yin M-J, Christerson LB, Yamamoto Y, Kwak Y-T, Xu S, Mercurio F, Barbose M, Cobb MH, Gaynor RB (1998) HTLV-I Tax protein binds to MEKK1 to stimulate IκB kinase activity and NF-κB activation. Cell 93:875–884

Yoshida M (2001) Multiple viral strategies of HTLV-1 for dysregulation of cell growth control. Annu Rev Immunol 19:475–496

Yoshida M, Miyoshi I, Hinuma Y (1982) Isolation and characterization of retrovirus from cell lines of human adult T-cell leukemia and its implication in the disease. Proc Natl Acad Sci USA 79:2031–2035

Yoshimi R, Chang TH, Wang H, Atsumi T, Morse HC 3rd, Ozato K (2009) Gene disruption study reveals a nonredundant role for TRIM21/Ro52 in NF-kappaB-dependent cytokine expression in fibroblasts. J Immunol 182:7527–7538

Yu MC, Yuan JM (2002) Epidemiology of nasopharyngeal carcinoma. Semin Cancer Biol 12:421–429

Yu Q, Minoda Y, Yoshida R, Yoshida H, Iha H, Kobayashi T, Yoshimura A, Takaesu G (2008) HTLV-1 Tax-mediated TAK1 activation involves TAB 2 adapter protein. Biochem Biophys Res Commun 365:189–194

Zhao LJ, Giam CZ (1991) Interaction of T-cell lymphotropic virus type I (HTLV-1) transcriptional activator Tax with cellular factors that bind specifically to the 21-base-pair repeats in the HTLV-1 enhancer. Proc Natl Acad Sci USA 88:11445–11449

Zhao LJ, Giam CZ (1992) Human T-cell lymphotropic virus type I (HTLV-1) transcriptional activator, Tax, enhances CREB binding to HTLV-1 21-base-pair repeats by protein-protein interaction. Proc Natl Acad Sci USA 89:7070–7474

Zhao T, Yasunaga J, Satou Y, Nakao M, Takahashi M, Fujii M, Matsuoka M (2009) Human T-cell leukemia virus type 1 bZIP factor selectively suppresses the classical pathway of NF-kappaB. Blood 113:2755–2764

Zhou H, Wertz I, O'Rourke K, Ultsch M, Seshagiri S, Eby M, Xiao W, Dixit VM (2004) Bcl10 activates the NF-kappaB pathway through ubiquitination of NEMO. Nature 427:167–171

Inhibition of NF-κB Signaling as a Strategy in Disease Therapy

Thomas D. Gilmore and Michael R. Garbati

Abstract As described extensively in this issue, NF-κB transcription factors regulate a number of important physiological processes, including inflammation and immune responses, cell growth and survival, and the expression of certain viral genes. Moreover, NF-κB activity is elevated in and contributes to the pathology of several human diseases, including many cancers and chronic inflammatory diseases. Therefore, there has been great interest in the characterization and development of methods to limit NF-κB signaling for pharmacological intervention. This article describes some of the approaches that have been employed to inhibit NF-κB using in vitro and in vivo experimental models. Moreover, some examples of the clinical use of NF-κB inhibitors are discussed, primarily for the treatment of two B-cell malignancies, multiple myeloma and diffuse large B-cell lymphoma. Finally, the rationale and strategies for inhibiting specific NF-κB subunit activity for disease therapy are discussed.

Contents

T. D. Gilmore (✉) and M. R. Garbati
Biology Department, Boston University, 5 Cummington Street, Boston, MA 02215, USA
e-mail: gilmore@bu.edu

Current Topics Microbiology (2011) 349: 245-263
DOI: 10.1007/82_2010_105

Published Online: 27 November 2010

1 Introduction to NF-κB Transcription Factors

NF-κB transcription factors regulate the expression of several hundred cellular genes involved in many key cellular and physiological processes, including immune and inflammatory responses, cell adhesion, differentiation, oxidative stress responses, and apoptosis (see www.nf-kb.org, under Target Genes). Moreover, NF-κB activity is mis-regulated in a variety of human diseases, especially ones that involve immunity, inflammation, and cell survival (Tables 1, 2). In addition, several viruses have co-opted the NF-κB pathway, either by encoding viral proteins that activate or repress NF-κB signaling as part of their pathogenic process or by containing NF-κB binding sites in their enhancer regions such that certain viral genes are controlled by NF-κB (Hiscott et al. 2006; Sun and Cesarman 2010). Therefore, the search for agents that modify the NF-κB signaling pathway has been a subject of intense interest.

The mammalian NF-κB signaling pathway is a multi-component, often complex, pathway that ultimately results in the activation of a set of dimeric transcription factors that are collectively referred to as the NF-κB transcription factors (Hayden and Ghosh 2008). In mammals, the NF-κB transcription factors include two subfamilies: the "NF-κB" proteins p50 and p52, and the "Rel" proteins RelA (aka p65), c-Rel and RelB. These five proteins are related through an approximately 300-amino acid N-terminal dimerization/DNA-binding domain known as the Rel Homology domain (RHD). Individual NF-κB and Rel subfamily proteins

Table 1 Human cancers with constitutive activation of NF-κB

Hematopoietic/lymphoid cancers
Acute lymphoblastic leukemia; acute myelogenous leukemia; acute T-cell leukemia; acute non-lymphocytic leukemia; chronic lymphocytic leukemia; Burkitt's lymphoma; diffuse large B-cell lymphoma; Hodgkin's lymphoma; mantle cell lymphoma; multiple myeloma; MALT lymphoma; myelodysplastic syndrome; Waldenström macroglobulinemia
Carcinomas
Breast; cervix; ovary;vulva; endometrial (uteris); prostate; kidney; bladder; lung; mesothelioma; liver; pancreas; esophageal/gastric; laryngeal; stomach; colon; thyroid; parathyroid; melanoma; squamous cell carcinoma; head and neck; cylindromatosis; Brooke-Spiegler syndrome; hilar cholangiocarcinoma; oral carcinoma
Neural cancers
Astrocytoma; neuroblastoma; glioblastoma

For references related to NF-κB and cancers, see www.nf-kb.org, under Diseases

Table 2 Human diseases and disorders with activated NF-κB

Chronic inflammatory diseases
Allergies; asthma; atherosclerosis; arthritis and other rheumatic diseases; Crohn's disease; chronic obstructive pulmonary disease (COPD); acid-induced lung injury; inflammatory bowel disease; inflammatory lung disease; peritoneal endometriosis; Behçet's disease; psoriasis; nasal sinusitis; tuberculosis; periodonitis; endometriosis; silicosis; lupus erythrematosis; lupus nephritis; autoimmunity; antiphospholipid syndrome; leptospirosis renal disease; chronic fatigue syndrome; familial Mediterranean fever; hereditary periodic fever syndrome
Metabolic/endocrine disorders
Obesity; diabetes mellitus (types 1 and 2); hypercholesterolemia
Acute disorders
Sepsis; stroke; cerebral aneurysm; angina pectoris; ischemia/reperfusion; appendicitis; pancreatitis
Neuropathological diseases and disorders
Familial amyloidotic polyneuropathy; inflammatory neuropathy; traumatic brain injury; spinal cord injury; Parkinson disease; multiple sclerosis; Alzheimer disease; amyotropic lateral sclerosis; Huntington's disease; retinal neurotoxicity; cataracts; glaucoma
Other
Complex regional pain syndrome; migraine; muscular dystrophy (type 2A); muscle wasting; cardiac hypertrophy; chronic heart failure; catabolic disorders; fetal growth retardation; pulmonary diseases, including pulmonary hypertension, cystic fibrosis and hyaline membrane disease; nephrotic syndrome; alcoholic liver disease; Paget's disease; hearing loss; sleep apnea; psychosocial stress diseases

For references related to NF-κB and diseases/disorders, see www.nf-kb.org, under Diseases

are more similar to each other than they are to members of the other subfamily (e.g., the RHDs of p50 and p52 are more similar than are the RHDs of p50 and c-Rel). The p50 and p52 proteins, which are essentially comprised of the RHD, are processed by proteolysis from larger precursors (p105 and p100, respectively) and usually do not activate transcription by themselves. In contrast, RelA, c-Rel, and RelB are not proteolytically processed and contain C-terminal transactivation domains. Almost all combinations of heterodimers and homodimers of these five proteins have been detected in mammalian cells, and these dimers can have different affinities for target DNA-binding sites on genes and have different protein–protein interactions on DNA. These differences can result in distinct transcriptional responses to different stimuli or in different cell types.

2 Regulation of NF-κB Signaling

In most cell types and under most resting conditions, NF-κB complexes are either inactive or have low basal nuclear activity. That is, NF-κB complexes are located in the cytoplasm due to their interaction with any of several inhibitor IκB proteins (IκBα, IκBβ, IκBε, NF-κB p105, NF-κB p100) (Hayden and Ghosh 2008). Activation of NF-κB complexes occurs through signal-induced degradation of IκB.

A relevant upstream signal, often the binding of a ligand (such as tumor necrosis factor [TNF] or a bacterial pathogen) to its cognate receptor (TNFR or Toll-like receptor [TLR]), leads to proteasome-mediated degradation of IκB and thus, nuclear translocation of NF-κB.

Degradation of IκB is nearly always controlled by the IκB kinase (IKK) complex. When activated, IKK phosphorylates IκB, which promotes IκB ubiquitination and subsequent degradation by the 20S proteasome. The IKK complex consists of catalytic (IKKα/β) and non-catalytic (e.g., NEMO) subunits. There are two generally accepted NF-κB activaton pathways that can be distinguished by which IKK complex is activated and sometimes by the upstream inducer. In the "classical" pathway, an IKKα/IKKβ heterodimer or an IKKβ homodimer (both in a complex with a NEMO dimer) phosphorylates IκBα, leading to the activation of NF-κB dimers such as p50-RelA or p50-c-Rel. In a second pathway, the "alternative" (or non-canoncial) pathway, NF-κB-inducing kinase (NIK)-induced phosphorylation of an IKKα homodimer (in the apparent absence of NEMO) leads to the induction of p52-RelB complexes by virtue of IKKα-mediated phosphorylation and limited proteolysis of p100 in p100-RelB dimers.

3 Introduction to Inhibition of NF-κB Signaling

Over 800 inhibitors of NF-κB signaling have been reported. The reader is referred to Gilmore and Herscovitch (2006) and our website (www.nb-kb.org) for extensive lists of these inhibitors. Rather than catalog these individual inhibitors again, we discuss here the general strategies for inhibition of NF-κB, and provide a few examples of the use of NF-κB inhibitors for the treatment of disease.

There are three general types of inhibitors that have been used to target NF-κB: biomolecular inhibitors, natural products (and their derivatives), and synthetic chemicals. Biomolecular (and peptide) inhibitors include decoy oligonucleotides (containing the κB site), ribozymes, siRNAs, the IκB super-repressor, dominant-negative molecules, and interfering peptides. Natural products include a variety of (primarily) plant-, marine-, and microbe-derived compounds that target various steps in the NF-κB pathway (Folmer et al. 2008; Khanna et al. 2007; Ríos et al. 2009). These natural products fall into three broad categories: antioxidants, IKK inhibitors, and thiol-reactive compounds that can target several NF-κB signaling steps. Finally, there are synthetic molecules. In most cases, these have been designed against components of the IKK complex (Edwards et al. 2009; Karin et al. 2004; Lee and Hung 2008), in large part because of the key role that the IKK complex plays in regulating downstream NF-κB signaling and because of previous success in developing synthetic inhibitors of protein kinases with therapeutic value.

Inhibitors of NF-κB signaling have been discovered in a variety of ways. In many cases, natural products that have been ascribed anti-inflammatory or anti-cancer therapy (e.g., green tea, curcumin, gold, etc.) have been tested for their abilities of block activation of NF-κB following stimulation with lipopolysaccharide (LPS) or TNF. In other cases, in vitro assays (e.g., for proteasome or IKK activity) or cell-based assays (e.g., for stabilization of IκBα; Davis et al. 2007), activation of an integrated κB site reporter locus (Lai et al. 2006), or nuclear translocation of NF-κB (Xie et al. 2009) have been screened with chemical compound libraries. Given that the NF-κB pathway is a multi-component pathway, there are several methods and steps to inhibit NF-κB activation (Fig. 1). In the following sections, strategies that have been used to block the step-wise activation of NF-κB are described.

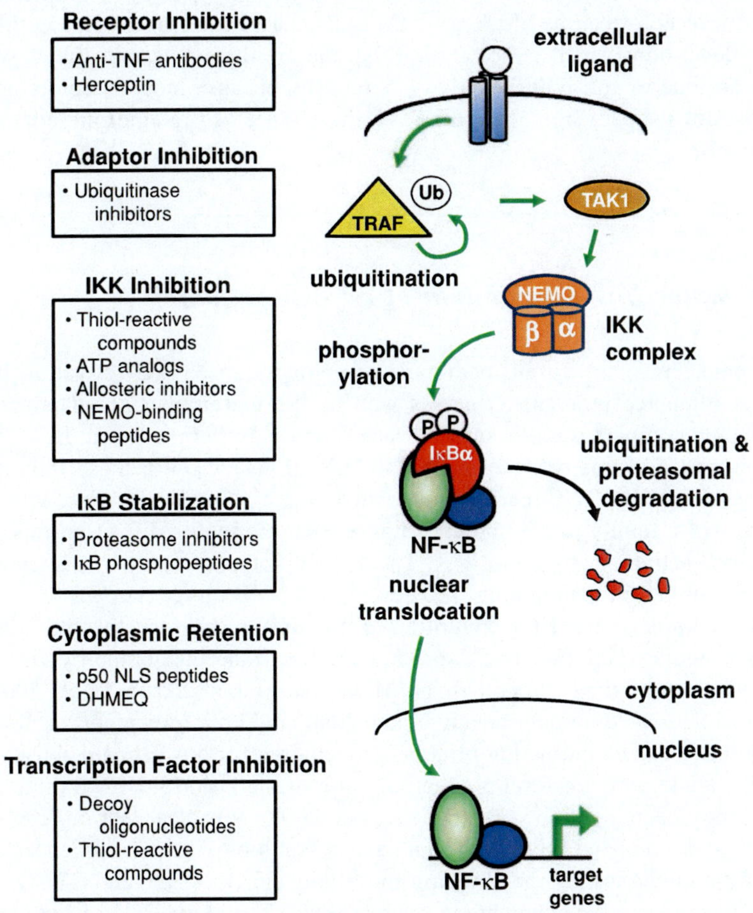

Fig. 1 Strategies for inhibition of NF-κB signaling. Shown at the right is a general diagram of NF-κB signaling, which follows from binding of an extracellular ligand to its cell-surface receptor and ultimately results in activation of NF-κB-specific target genes. The *boxes* shown at the left contain some types of molecules that can inhibit the corresponding steps in NF-κB activation. See text for more details

3.1 Receptor-Based Inhibition of NF-κB

Because the binding of a number of ligands to their cell-surface receptors initiates NF-κB signaling, one way to inhibit this pathway is to block receptor engagement. Perhaps the most common application of this strategy has been through the use of anti-TNF antibodies such as etanercept, infliximab, and adalimumab, which block binding of TNF to the TNFR. Anti-TNF antibodies have been used clinically to counteract the effects of TNF in a number of chronic inflammatory diseases (Taylor and Feldman 2009). Of note, activation of the heregulin receptor, which can act as a breast cancer oncoprotein, has been reported to activate NF-κB (Bhat-Nakshatri et al. 2002; Pianetti et al. 2001). Signal transduction initiated by the heregulin receptor can be blocked by the anti-breast cancer agent Herceptin (Guo et al. 2004); however, it is not certain that the anti-breast cancer effects of Herceptin are due to anti-NF-κB activity. Similarly, because most receptors activate multiple downstream signaling pathways, these types of strategies are not specific for NF-κB.

3.2 Adaptor-Based Inhibition of NF-κB Signaling

Upon engagement of a transmembrane receptor by an NF-κB-activating ligand, there is often receptor clustering, as well as the recruitment of adaptor/signal-transducing complexes to the internal face of the plasma membrane. In several of the common receptor pathways (TNFR, TLR, IL-1R, CD40), these intracellular complexes include TNF-receptor-associated factor (TRAF) proteins, which are members of a family of E3 ubiquitin ligases that are required for transmission of the NF-κB activating signal to IKK. The TRAF proteins frequently also associate with E2 ubiquitin-conjugating proteins UBC13/UEV1A. The TRAF-UBC13/UEV1A complex then K63 ubiquitinates proteins in the receptosome complex, which promotes recruitment of the IKK complex to the membrane by virtue of a K63 ubiquitin-binding domain in NEMO (reviewed in Skaug et al. 2009). In several situations, dominant-negative, knockout, and knockdown approaches have shown that these ubiqutinating proteins are required for downstream activation of NF-κB. In addition, a natural product inhibitor of the UBC13–UEV1A interaction has recently been identified (Tsukamoto et al. 2008). It is clear that mis-regulation of these steps in NF-κB activation can have potent biological consequences in that inactivating mutations in the ubiquitin-modifying enzymes A20 and CYLD, which act on receptosome components to decrease NF-κB activity, have been found in human cancers (Courtois and Gilmore 2006). Based on the redundancy of TRAFs and UBCs and their roles in multiple signaling pathways, these steps have not generally been considered to be a fruitful means for specifically blocking activation of NF-κB.

3.3 Inhibition of IKK

IKK has been a major focus for the development and characterization of NF-κB inhibitors because of its central role in signaling to NF-κB and because of the success in developing kinase inhibitors for therapy (e.g., Gleevec against BCR-ABL). To date, over 200 compounds have been shown to inhibit activation of NF-κB through inhibition of IKK activity (Gilmore and Herscovitch 2006). In many cases, IKK inhibitors have been characterized based on their abilities to inhibit a constitutively active form of IKKβ (S177,181E), in which two serine residues in the activation loop of IKKβ have been replaced by phosphomimetic glutamate residues.

Chemical inhibitors of IKK are of three general types: (1) ATP analogs that show specificity for interaction with IKK as compared to other kinases; (2) compounds with allosteric effects on IKK structure; and (3) compounds that interact with Cys-179 in the activation loop of IKKβ and block its ability to be activated. ATP analogs include natural products such as β-carboline and its derivatives, and several synthetic compounds developed by pharmaceutical companies, including SC-839 which has an approximately 200-fold preference for IKKβ as compared to IKKα (reviewed in Karin et al. 2004; Lee and Hung 2008). On the other hand, the synthetic IKKβ inhibitor BMS-345541 binds to an allosteric site on the kinase (Burke et al. 2003). Several thiol-reactive compounds, such as parthenolide, certain epoxyquinoids, and arsenite, have been shown to block IKKβ activity through Cys-179 (Kapahi et al. 2000; Kwok et al. 2001; Liang et al. 2003; Liang et al. 2006), probably through direct conjugation to the thiol group of this cysteine. Although not formally proven, it is likely that interaction of such compounds with Cys-179 interferes with phosphorylation-induced activation of IKKβ, in that Cys-179 is located between Ser-177 and Ser-181 which are part of the kinase activation loop and must be phosphorylated for IKKβ to be activated in response to many upstream signals, such as LPS and TNF (Perkins 2006; Scheidereit 2006). However, several such thiol-reactive compounds (Kwok et al. 2001; Liang et al. 2003) can also block the kinase activity of the constitutively active S171,181E IKKβ mutant, which does not require activation; therefore, the mechanism of action of these Cys-179-reactive compounds may be more complicated than simple steric hindrance of the accessibility of Ser-177,181 to induced phosphorylation.

IκB kinase (IKK) activation can also be blocked by dominant-negative forms of IKKα and β, which are capable of blocking activation of NF-κB; such dominant-negative mutants can be created either by mutations in the ATP-binding site, deletion of the kinase domain or mutations in the kinase activation loop (Scheidereit 2006). Because of their distinct roles in the classical (IKKβ-dependent) and alternative (IKKα-dependent) pathways, dominant-negative IKK mutants can show stimulus-dependent inhibitory activity. Similarly, dominant-negative versions of NIK can block activation of the alternative NF-κB pathway.

NEMO can also serve as a target for IKK complex inhibition. In particular, introduction of a cell-permeable peptide corresponding to the NEMO-binding domain (NBD) of IKKβ can block both the binding of NEMO to IKK and induction of the classical NF-κB pathway by TNF (reviewed in Strickland and Ghosh 2006). Moreover, the NBD peptide has shown efficacy in mouse models of inflammation by both topical and systemic administration. Similarly, peptides corresponding to the region of NEMO required for oligomerization can also block NF-κB activation (Agou et al. 2004). Chemical inhibitors of NEMO have not yet been identified or developed.

The IKK-related kinases, TBK1 and IKKε, also contribute to NF-κB activation in certain settings and to anti-viral inflammatory responses through non-NF-κB pathways (reviewed in Clément et al. 2008; Hiscott et al. 2006). Recent studies have suggested that the ability of IKKε and TBK1 to activate c-Rel plays an essential role in the growth and survival of breast and lung cancers, respectively (Barbie et al. 2009; Boehm et al. 2007; Eddy et al. 2005). Synthetic and natural product inhibitors of TBK1/IKKε, which have anti-inflammatory effects, have been described (Clark et al. 2009; Godl et al. 2005; Park et al. 2009), but such molecules have not been tested for anti-cancer effects.

3.4 Inhibition of IκB Degradation

Degradation of IκB is a second common step required for the activation of NF-κB. Although there are several IκB proteins, the major IκB in most cells, especially inflammatory cells and many cancer cell types, is IκBα. There are three strategies to block proteasome-mediated degradation of IκBα: (1) by promoting the increased synthesis of IκBα; (2) by blocking IκBα ubiquitination; and (3) by inhibiting the proteasome.

A few natural peptides/proteins appear to inhibit NF-κB by up-regulating expression of IκBα. For example, treatment of rat cortical cultures with β-amyloid peptide, which is deposited in the brain plaques of Alzheimer's disease patients, leads to increased IκBα mRNA and protein, as well as a decrease in activated NF-κB (Bales et al. 1998). Similarly, the cytokines IL-10, IL-11, and IL-13, which have potent anti-inflammatory activities, can increase IκBα mRNA levels and suppress nuclear localization of NF-κB (Ehrlich et al. 1998; Lentsch et al. 1997; Trepicchio and Dorner 1998).

In the classical NF-κB activation pathway, following stimulus-provoked IKKβ-mediated phosphorylation of IκBα at Ser-32,36, phospho-IκBα is K48-ubiquintated at Lys-21,22 by the SCF-βTrCP E3 ubiquitin ligase complex, which leads to rapid degradation of IκBα (Skaug et al. 2009). Similarly, in the alternative NF-κB pathway, the SCF-βTrCP E3 ligase complex mediates ubiquitination of C-terminal residues of p100 following its phosphorylation by IKKα (Skaug et al. 2009).

Among natural blockers of IκB ubiquitination, the YopJ protein of the bacterial pathogen *Yersinia* prevents NF-κB nuclear translocation by acting as a dequbiquitinase for IκBα (Zhou et al. 2005). The small molecule Ro106-9920 can block IκBα ubiquitination, and can act as an inhibitor of oral inflammation in two mouse models, although the target of this compound is not known (Swinney et al. 2002). Inhibition of IκBα ubiquitination can also be effected by microinjection of phosphopeptides corresponding to Ser-32,36 of IκBα (Yaron et al. 1997), by treatment with RNAi to βTrCP or by over-expression of a dominant-negative βTrCP mutant (Tang et al. 2005).

Many inhibitors of the proteasome have been reported to block NF-κB activation in cell-based systems (Gilmore and Herscovitch 2006). These compounds inhibit NF-κB activation by blocking proteasome-mediated degradation of IκB (but do not inhibit IκB phosphorylation). There are three general classes of proteasome inhibitors. One class consists of peptide aldehydes, which can inhibit the chymotrypsin-like activity of the proteasome complex; these include MG101, MG132, and MG115 (Grisham et al. 1999; Jobin et al. 1998; Palombella et al. 1994). A second class includes microbial products lactacystin and its precursor β-lactone, which block proteasome activity by acylating an active site threonine residue in the β subunits of the 20S proteasome (Fenteany and Schreiber 1998; Hayes et al. 2006). A third class is comprised of peptide boronic acids (or dipeptidyl boronates), such as PS-262, PS-273, PS-341, and PS-402. These molecules block the chymotrypsin-like activity in the 20S subunit core (Adams 2004). Most prominent among these is PS-341 (now generally called bortezomib), which has significant efficacy against multiple myeloma (MM), as well as several other hematologic and solid tumors (Jagannath et al. 2010).

3.5 Inhibition of NF-κB Nuclear Translocation

After IκB is degraded, NF-κB accumulates in the nucleus. As with many other nuclear proteins, the nuclear entry of NF-κB subunits appears to be mediated via specific importin α subunits (Fagerlund et al. 2008). One approach to block nuclear accumulation of NF-κB is to use cell-permeable peptides containing the nuclear localizing sequence of p50. These peptides act by saturating the nuclear import machinery responsible for the uptake of NF-κB dimers containing p50 (Letoha et al. 2005; Lin et al. 1995; Torgerson et al. 1998). However, some of these peptides (e.g., SN-50) also block the nuclear translocation of several non-NF-κB transcription factors (Torgerson et al. 1998). The fungal compound dehydroxymethylepoxyquinomicin (DHMEQ), which has anti-inflammatory and antitumor activity in several mouse models, has been reported to inhibit nuclear translocation of RelA and c-Rel, but not p50 (Umezawa and Chaicharoenpong 2002). Interestingly, residues adjacent to a highly conserved cysteine residue in a DNA-binding loop appear to mediate the specificity of DHMEQ for RelA versus p50 (Watanabe et al. 2008).

3.6 *Inhibition of NF-κB-Dependent DNA Binding and Transactivation*

The final step required for activation of an NF-κB response is DNA binding and transcriptional activation of relevant target genes. DNA binding, and hence transcriptional activation, can be blocked either by chemical inhibition of NF-κB or the application of κB-site decoy oligonucleotides. It is now becoming clear that many of the compounds that target Cys-179 of IKKβ also interact with a conserved cysteine residue in the DNA-binding loop of NF-κB/Rel proteins to block their DNA-binding ability (Pande et al. 2009); for example, parthenolide, epoxyquinone A monomer, and 15-deoxy-$\Delta^{12,14}$-prostaglandin J_2 all show both activities (García-Piñeres et al. 2004; Kwok et al. 2001; Liang et al. 2006; Straus et al. 2000). Thus, such compounds are likely to block activation of NF-κB at both the IKKβ activation and DNA-binding steps. However, such compounds no doubt also block the activity of many cellular protein targets that have reactive or redox-regulated cysteine residues required for their activity.

κB-site decoy oligonucleotides and more stable oligo-peptide analogs can block activation of NF-κB-dependent pathways by competing for the binding of activated NF-κB dimers to their chromosomal targets (Edwards et al. 2009). Such decoy oligonucleotides have been effective in several animal models of inflammation, and some have entered clinical trials for dermatitis and psoriasis (Table 3).

Table 3 Some NF-κB inhibitors in clinical trials

Compound	Target	Disease(s)	Company/organization	Phase	Clinical trial identifier or reference
NF-κB ODN[1]	NF-κB	Atopic dermatitis	Anesiva, Inc.	II	NCT0012533 (US)
NF-κB ODN	NF-κB	Psoriasis, periodontal disease, atopic dermatitis	AnGes MG; Meyer Pharmaceuticals	II	(Japan)
NF-κB ODN	NF-κB	Eczema, psoriasis	Corgentech, Inc. ACTRN12605000403639 (Australia)	I/II	
CDDO-Me[2]/ RTA 402	IKK	Solid tumors, lymphoid malignancies	Reata Pharmaceuticals; MD Anderson Cancer Center	I	NCT00508807 (US); Tran et al. (2008); Shishodia et al. (2006)
Curcumin	IKK	Pancreatic	MD Anderson Cancer Center	II	NCT00094445

[1] ODN, decoy oligonucleotide

[2] CDDO-Me, C-28 methyl ester of 2-cyano-3,12-dioxoolean-1,9-dien-28-oic acid

4 Inhibition of NF-κB as Anticancer Therapy: Multiple Myeloma and Diffuse Large B-cell Lymphoma as Models

The NF-κB pathway is constitutively active in many different types of human cancer (Table 1) (reviewed in Arkan and Greten 2010; Bassères and Baldwin 2006). This continuous activation of NF-κB contributes to tumor growth and survival by inappropriately activating genes involved in cell cycle regulation, adhesion, and anti-apoptosis. There are four general mechanisms by which continuous activation of NF-κB has been shown to occur in cancer cells: (1) by secretion of autocrine factors by tumor cells; (2) by the action of oncogenic viral genes; (3) by secretion of factors from adjacent stromal cells; and (4) by mutation of upstream or core NF-κB pathway genes (reviewed in Courtois and Gilmore 2006). That activation of NF-κB is key to tumorigenesis has been demonstrated by many experiments, which have shown that inhibition of NF-κB signaling can either slow tumor cell growth, induce apoptosis, or sensitize tumor cells to inducers of apoptosis (such as by chemotherapeutic drugs) (reviewed in Fan et al. 2008). Multiple myeloma (MM) and diffuse large B-cell lymphoma (DLBCL) are two relatively common B-cell malignancies for which activation of NF-κB has been characterized in some molecular detail. In each case, chronic activation of NF-κB can occur due to a variety of mutations, either activating mutations in genes encoding positive regulators of NF-κB or inactivating mutations in negative regulators of NF-κB (Compagno et al. 2009; Davis et al. 2010; Gilmore 2007; Lenz et al. 2008).

Multiple myeloma is a malignancy of mature plasma B cells and is heavily dependent on growth factors secreted by its stromal cell environment. Many primary MMs and MM cell lines have mutations in genes encoding components of both classical (p105, TRAF2/3, CYLD) and alternative (p100, NIK, CD40, LTβR) NF-κB signaling pathways (Gilmore 2007). MM cell growth is extremely sensitive to proteasome inhibitors (e.g., bortezomib), which are highly effective against MM in the clinic (Jagannath et al. 2010; Laubach et al. 2009). Bortezomib is an efficient blocker of NF-κB in MM cells in vitro (Cusack et al. 2001; Hideshima et al. 2002), but it is not clear that its anti-MM effects are mediated entirely through inhibition of NF-κB. Namely, bortezomib has non-NF-κB effects on cancer cell growth and additional cancer-related protein targets are affected by its proteasome inhibitory activity (Adams 2004; Hideshima et al. 2002; Takigawa et al. 2006; Zheng et al. 2004). Moreover, one recent study failed to detect profound effects of bortezomib on NF-κB DNA-binding activity in human blood samples (Su et al. 2010). Thus, whether the therapeutic effect of bortezomib in the treatment of MM (and other cancers) is due to its effect on NF-κB is not clear.

The argument for anti-NF-κB therapy against specific subtypes of DLBCL is stronger. DLBCL describes a heterogenous group of B-cell malignancies with variable response to cheomotherapy (Wiestner and Staudt 2003). By gene expression profiling, DLBCLs can be divided into two main classes, which may reflect their cell of origin: those DLBCLs with gene expression profiles similar to germinal center B cells (the GCB subtype) and those with gene expression profiles similar to activated B cells (the ABC subtype). Patients with the ABC profile generally have a poorer prognosis after standard chemotherapy that those with the GCB profile. Moreover, ABC-like DLBCLs have higher basal NF-κB activity than GCB DLBCLs. In some cases, the constitutive NF-κB activity in DLBCLs is known to be due to upstream activating mutations in the B-cell receptor protein CD79 or the adaptor CARD11, or to inactivating mutations in the ubiquitin-modifying protein A20 (Compagno et al. 2009; Davis et al. 2010; Lenz et al. 2008).

The growth and survival of ABC-like DLBCL cell lines with activated NF-κB can be preferentially affected by NF-κB inhibitors in vitro; that is, the growth of ABC-type DLBCL cell lines (with activated NF-κB) is selectively inhibited by the IκB super-repressor or IKKβ small-molecule inhibitors as compared to GCB-type DLBCL cell lines (which have less constitutive NF-κB activity) (Davis et al. 2001; Lam et al. 2005). The usefulness of adjunct inhibition of NF-κB for ABC-type DLBCL has recently been demonstrated in a clinical trial in which it was found that ABC-type DLBCL patients show increased response and survival as compared to GCB-type patients after combined treatment with the proteasome inhibitor bortezomib (anti-NF-κB) and doxorubicin (Dunleavy et al. 2009). However, either agent alone did not differentiate between GCB and ABC patients (Dunleavy et al. 2009). It is not yet clear whether selective inhibition of IKKβ will be effective against ABC-like DLBCLs, in part because up-regulation of IKKα can compensate for inhibition of IKKβ in some ABC-type DLBCL cells (Lam et al. 2008). Casein kinase 1α has also been identified as required for constitutive NF-κB activation in ABC-type DLBCL (Bidère et al. 2009) and thus, this kinase may serve as a specific therapeutic target for DLBCL.

5 Inhibition of Specific NF-κB Subunits as a Therapeutic Strategy: c-Rel as a Target

Almost all NF-κB inhibitors described to date are general inhibitors of NF-κB signaling. General inhibitors of NF-κB are likely to be problematic because of the prevalent role of NF-κB in normal cell and tissue physiology. Indeed, inhibition of total NF-κB activity in certain cell types locally promotes severe inflammatory responses (Pasparakis 2009). For example, mice with conditional knockout of NEMO or IKKβ in the liver develop hepatocarinogenesis, due to the extensive inflammation and cell disorganization caused by increased liver cell apoptosis (Sakurai et al. 2006; Luedde et al. 2007; Pasparakis 2009). Therefore, a more effective, though perhaps difficult to achieve, strategy may be to target specific NF-κB subunits. Among the NF-κB proteins, there are two reasons to believe that c-Rel would be the most appropriate first target: (1) c-Rel expression is primarily restricted to immune cells, and (2) c-Rel knockout mice are fully viable (reviewed in Gilmore et al. 2004).

Inhibition of c-Rel may be relevant to certain human cancers and inflammatory diseases. For example, c-Rel is the only frankly oncogenic NF-κB protein in lymphoid cell in vitro transformation assays and the *REL* (human c-*rel*) gene is amplified in many B-cell lymphomas (Courtois and Gilmore 2006). Indeed, Tian and Liou (2009) have shown that siRNA-mediated inhibition of c-Rel can block the growth of certain mouse B-lymphoma cells, and c-Rel has been identified as a target for lung cancer in an shRNA-based screen (Barbie et al., 2009). Alterations at the *REL* locus have also been associated with rheumatoid arthritis (Eyre et al. 2010; Gregersen et al. 2009). Of note, c-Rel knockout mice show increased resistance to experimentally induced arthritis (Campbell et al. 2000).

There are three ways that we can imagine effecting specific inhibition of c-Rel: (1) by down-regulation of c-Rel expression (e.g., by siRNA, ribozymes, etc.); (2) by inhibition of a protein that is specifically required for c-Rel activity; or (3) by inhibiting the unique c-Rel transactivation domain, which is required for c-Rel's oncogenic and immune cell functions (Gilmore et al. 2004). STA-5326, a drug with anti-inflammatory activity in clinical trials, has been reported to be a selective inhibitor of c-Rel nuclear translocation but its mechanism of action is not known (Keino et al. 2008). Also, the widely used immunosuppressent FK506 can specifically block c-Rel nuclear translocation in some cell systems (Sen et al. 1995; Venkataraman et al. 1995).

Generally speaking, however, transcription factors have not been regarded as achievable therapeutic targets. Nevertheless, it is clear that nature has achieved small molecule-based regulation of transcription factors, such as the steroid hormone receptors, and regulation of estrogen and androgen receptors by hormone-based modulators has had abundant clinical success. Of note, the estrogen and glucocorticoid receptors can inhibit NF-κB signaling, by acting at a variety of levels (De Bosscher et al. 2006; Edwards et al. 2009; Kalaitzidis and Gilmore 2005).

6 Summary and Perspectives

Because of the key role that enhanced NF-κB activity plays in cancer and chronic inflammatory diseases, it is almost certain that there will be continued interest in the identification and characterization of compounds that can reduce NF-κB activity. The recent court ruling (Garber 2009) invalidating a broad patent covering NF-κB inhibitors may further stimulate discovery among pharmaceutical companies. Although a large number of NF-κB inhibitors have been characterized, several broad challenges remain, both at the level of basic research and clinical application. For example, it is still not clear how antioxidants inhibit NF-κB signaling or whether the ability of many natural products to inhibit NF-κB in tissue culture studies has relevance to their effects on human physiology. Furthermore, it is not clear whether clinical efficacy will be achieved more safely through the use of inhibitors of NF-κB signaling that are extremely specific (e.g., against single NF-κB subunits) or by inhibitors with broader activity (e.g., against multiple steps in NF-κB signaling or with combined activity against NF-κB and other pathways).

Given the prominent role that NF-κB plays in liver, heart, immune cell and perhaps even brain physiology, we believe that the most promising near-term uses for NF-κB inhibitors are likely to be for conditions where such inhibitors can be applied topically (e.g., skin tumors or inflammatory skin diseases), locally (e.g., airway inflammation), or in a highly directed fashion (e.g., to a specific cell or tumor type).

Acknowledgments We thank Dr. Eric Widmaier (Boston University) for comments on the manuscript. Research in our laboratory is supported by NIH grants CA047763 and CA047763-21S3 (to TDG). For a comprehensive list of NF-κB inhibitors and their targets, see our lab website at www.nf-kb.org (click on Inhibitors).

References

Adams J (2004) The development of proteasome inhibitors as anticancer drugs. Cancer Cell 5:417–421

Agou F, Courtois G, Chiaravalli J, Baleux F, Coïc YM, Traincard F, Israël A, Véron M (2004) Inhibition of NF-κB activation by peptides targeting NF-κB essential modulator (NEMO) oligomerization. J Biol Chem 279:54248–54257

Arkan MC, Greten FR (2010) IKK and NF-κB mediated functions in carcinogenesis. Current topics in microbiology and immunology. Springer, Berlin (this issue)

Bales KR, Du Y, Dodel RC, Yan GM, Hamilton-Byrd E, Paul SM (1998) The NF-κB/Rel family of proteins mediates Aβ-induced neurotoxicity and glial activation. Brain Res Mol Brain Res 57:63–72

Barbie DA, Tamayo P, Boehm JS, Kim SY, Moody SE, Dunn IF, Schinzel AC, Sandy P, Meylan E, Scholl C, Fröhling S, Chan EM, Sos ML, Michel K, Mermel C, Silver SJ, Weir BA, Reiling JH, Sheng Q, Gupta PB, Wadlow RC, Le H, Hoersch S, Wittner BS, Ramaswamy S, Livingston DM, Sabatini DM, Meyerson M, Thomas RK, Lander ES, Mesirov JP, Root DE, Gilliland DG, Jacks T, Hahn WC (2009) Systematic RNA interference reveals that oncogenic KRAS-driven cancers require TBK1. Nature 462:108–112

Bassères D, Baldwin AS (2006) Nuclear factor-κB and inhibitor of κB kinase pathways in oncogenic initiation and progression. Oncogene 25:6817–6830

Bhat-Nakshatri P, Sweeney CJ, Nakshatri H (2002) Identification of signal transduction pathways involved in constitutive activation in breast cancer cells. Oncogene 21:2066–2078

Bidère N, Ngo VN, Lee J, Collins C, Zheng L, Wan F, Davis RE, Lenz G, Anderson DE, Arnoult D, Vazquez A, Sakai K, Zhang J, Meng Z, Veenstra TD, Staudt LM, Lenardo MJ (2009) Casein kinase 1α governs antigen-receptor-induced NF-κB activation and human lymphoma cell survival. Nature 458:92–96

Boehm JS, Zhao JJ, Yao J, Kim SY, Firestein R, Dunn IF, Sjostrom SK, Garraway LA, Weremowicz S, Richardson AL, Greulich H, Stewart CJ, Mulvey LA, Shen RR, Ambrogio L, Hirozane-Kishikawa T, Hill DE, Vidal M, Meyerson M, Grenier JK, Hinkle G, Root DE, Roberts TM, Lander ES, Polyak K, Hahn WC (2007) Integrative genomic approaches identify *IKBKE* as a breast cancer oncogene. Cell 129:1065–1079

Burke JR, Pattoli MA, Gregor KR, Brassil PJ, MacMaster JF, McIntyre KW, Yang X, Iotzova VS, Clarke W, Strnad J, Qiu Y, Zusi FC (2003) BMS-345541 is a highly selective inhibitor of IκB kinase that binds at an allosteric site of the enzyme and blocks NF-κB-dependent transcription in mice. J Biol Chem 278:1450–1456

Campbell IK, Gerondakis S, O'Donnell K, Wicks IP (2000) Distinct roles for the NF-κB1 (p50) and c-Rel transcription factors in inflammatory arthritis. J Clin Invest 105:1799–1806

Clark K, Plater L, Peggie M, Cohen P (2009) Use of the pharmacological inhibitor BX795 to study the regulation and physiological roles of TBK1 and IκB kinase ε: a distinct kinase mediates Ser-172 phosphorylation and activation. J Biol Chem 284:14136–14146

Clément JF, Meloche S, Servant MJ (2008) The IKK-related kinase: from innate immunity to oncogenesis. Cell Res 18:889–899

Compagno M, Lim WK, Grunn A, Nandula SV, Brahmachary M, Shen Q, Bertoni F, Ponzoni M, Scandurra M, Califano A, Bhagat G, Chadburn A, Dalla-Favera R, Pasqualucci L (2009) Mutations of multiple genes cause deregulation of NF-κB in diffuse large B-cell lymphoma. Nature 459:717–721

Courtois G, Gilmore TD (2006) Mutations in the NF-κB signaling pathway: implications for human disease. Oncogene 25:6831–6843

Cusack JC Jr, Liu R, Houston M, Abendroth K, Elliott PJ, Adams J, Baldwin AS Jr (2001) Enhanced chemosensitivity to CPT-11 with proteasome inhibitor PS-341: implications for systemic nuclear factor-κB inhibition. Cancer Res 61:3535–3540

Davis RE, Brown KD, Siebenlist U, Staudt LM (2001) Constitutive nuclear factor κB activity is required for survival of activated B cell-like diffuse large B cell lymphoma cells. J Exp Med 194:1861–1874

Davis RE, Zhang YQ, Southall N, Staudt LM, Austin CP, Inglese J, Auld DS (2007) A cell-based assay for IκBα stabilization using a two-color dual luciferase-based sensor. Assay Drug Dev Technol 5:85–103

Davis RE, Ngo VN, Lenz G, Tolar P, Young RM, Romesser PB, Kohlhammer H, Lamy L, Zhao H, Yang Y, Xu W, Shaffer AL, Wright G, Xiao W, Powell J, Jiang JK, Thomas CJ, Rosenwald A, Ott G, Muller-Hermelink HK, Gascoyne RD, Connors JM, Johnson NA, Rimsza LM, Campo E, Jaffe ES, Wilson WH, Delabie J, Smeland EB, Fisher RI, Braziel RM, Tubbs RR, Cook JR, Weisenburger DD, Chan WC, Pierce SK, Staudt LM (2010) Chronic active B-cell-receptor signaling in diffuse large B-cell lymphoma. Nature 463:88–92

De Bosscher K, Vanden Berge W, Haegeman G (2006) Cross-talk between nuclear receptors and nuclear factor κB. Oncogene 25:6868–6886

Dunleavy K, Pittaluga S, Czuczman MS, Dave SS, Wright G, Grant N, Shovlin M, Jaffe ES, Janik JE, Staudt LM, Wilson WH (2009) Differential efficacy of bortezomib plus chemotherapy within molecular subtypes of diffuse large B-cell lymphoma. Blood 113:6069–6076

Eddy SF, Guo S, Demicco EG, Romieu-Mourez R, Landesman-Bollag E, Seldin DC, Sonenshein GE (2005) Inducible IκB kinase/IκB kinase ε expression is induced by CK2 and promotes aberrant nuclear factor-κB activation in breast cancer cells. Cancer Res 65:11375–11383

Edwards MR, Bartlett NW, Clarke D, Birrell M, Belvisi M, Johnston SL (2009) Targeting the NF-κB pathway in asthma and chronic obstructive pulmonary disease. Pharmacol Ther 121:1–13

Ehrlich LC, Hu S, Peterson PK, Chao CC (1998) IL-10 down-regulates human microglial IL-8 by inhibition of NF-κB activation. Neuroreport 9:1723–1726

Eyre S, Hinks A, Flynn E, Martin P, Wilson AG, Maxwell JR, Morgan AW, Emery P, Steer S, Hocking LJ, Reid DM, Harrison P, Wordsworth P, Thomson W, Worthington J, Barton A (2010) Confirmation of association of the *REL* locus with rheumatoid arthritis susceptibility in the UK population. Ann Rheum Dis 69:1407–1408

Fagerlund R, Melén K, Cao X, Julkunen I (2008) NF-kB p52, RelB and c-Rel are transported into the nucleus via a subset of importin alpha molecules. Cell Signal 20:1442–1451

Fan Y, Dutta J, Gupta N, Fan G, Gélinas C (2008) Regulation of programmed cell death by NF-κB and its role in tumorigenesis and therapy. Adv Exp Med Biol 615:223–250

Fenteany G, Schreiber SL (1998) Lactacystin, proteasome function, and cell fate. J Biol Chem 273:8545–8548

Folmer F, Jaspars DM, Diederich M (2008) Marine natural products as targeted modulators of the transcription factor NF-κB. Biochem Pharmacol 75:603–617

Garber K (2009) Ariad's NFκB patent claims shot down on appeal. Nat Biotechnol 27:494–495

García-Piñeres AJ, Lindenmeyer MT, Merfort I (2004) Role of cysteine residues of p65/NF-κB on the inhibition by the sesquiterpene lactone parthenolide and N-ethyl maleimide, and on its transactivating potential. Life Sci 75:841–856

Gilmore TD (2007) Multiple myeloma: lusting for NF-κB. Cancer Cell 12:95–97

Gilmore TD, Herscovitch M (2006) Inhibitors of NF-κB signaling: 785 and counting. Oncogene 25:6887–6899

Gilmore TD, Kalaitzidis D, Liang M-C, Starczynowski DT (2004) The c-Rel transcription factor and B-cell proliferation: a deal with the devel. Oncogene 23:2275–2286

Godl K, Gruss OJ, Eickhoff J, Wissing J, Blencke S, Weber M, Degen H, Brehmer D, Õrfi L, Horváth Z, Kéri G, Müller S, Cotton M, Ullrich A, Daub H (2005) Proteomic characterization of the angiogenesis inhibitor SU6668 reveals multiple impacts on cellular kinase signaling. Cancer Res 65:6919–6926

Gregersen PK, Amos CI, Lee AT, Lu Y, Remmers EF, Kastner DL, Seldin MF, Criswell LA, Plenge RM, Holers VM, Mikuls TR, Sokka T, Moreland LW, Bridges Jr SL, Xie G, Begovich AB, Siminovitch KA (2009) *REL*, encoding a member of the NF-κB family of transcription factors, is a newly defined risk locus for rheumatoid arthritis. Nat Genet 41:820–823

Grisham MB, Palombella VJ, Elliott PJ, Conner EM, Brand S, Wong HL, Pien C, Mazzola LM, Destree A, Parent L, Adams J (1999) Inhibition of NF-κB activation in vitro and in vivo: role of 26S proteasome. Methods Enzymol 300:345–363

Guo G, Wang T, Gao Q, Tamae D, Wong P, Chen T, Chen WC, Shively JE, Wong JY, Li JJ (2004) Expression of ErbB2 enhances radiation-induced NF-κB activation. Oncogene 23:535–545

Hayden MS, Ghosh S (2008) Shared principles in NF-κB signaling. Cell 132:344–362

Hayes CJ, Sherlock AE, Selby MD (2006) Enantioselective total syntheses of (-)-*clasto*-lactacystin β-lactone and 7-*epi*-(-)-*clasto*-lactacystin β-lactone. Org Biomol Chem 4:193–195

Hideshima T, Chauhan D, Richardson P, Mitsiades C, Mitsiades N, Hayashi T, Munshi N, Dang L, Castro A, Palombella V, Adams J, Anderson KC (2002) NF-κB as a therapeutic target in multiple myeloma. J Biol Chem 277:16639–16647

Hiscott J, Nguyen T-LA, Arguello M, Nakhaei P, Paz S (2006) Manipulation of the nuclear factor-κB pathway and the innate immune response by viruses. Oncogene 25:6844–6867

Jagannath S, Kyle RA, Palumbo A, Siegel DS, Cunningham S, Berenson J (2010) The current status and future of multiple myeloma in the clinic. Clin Lymphoma Myeloma 10:E1–E16

Jobin C, Hellerbrand C, Licato LL, Brenner DA, Sartor RB (1998) Mediation by NF-κB of cytokine induced expression of intercellular adhesion molecule 1 (ICAM-1) in an intestinal epithelial cell line, a process blocked by proteasome inhibitors. Gut 42:779–787

Kalaitzidis D, Gilmore TD (2005) Transcription factor cross-talk: the estrogen receptor and NF-κB. Trends Endocrinol Metab 16:46–52

Kapahi P, Takahashi T, Natoli G, Adams SR, Chen Y, Tsien RY, Karin M (2000) Inhibition of NF-κB activation by arsenite through reaction with a critical cysteine in the activation loop of IκB kinase. J Biol Chem 275:36062–36066

Karin M, Yamamoto Y, Wang QM (2004) The IKK NF-κB system: a treasure trove for drug development. Nat Rev Drug Discov 3:17–26

Keino H, Watanabe T, Sato Y, Niikura M, Wada Y, Okada A (2008) Therapeutic effect of the potent IL-12/IL-23 inhibitor STA-5326 on experimental autoimmune uveoretinitis. Arthritis Res Ther 10:R122

Khanna D, Sethi G, Ahn KS, Pandey MK, Kunnumakkara AB, Sung B, Aggarwal A, Aggarwal BB (2007) Natural products as a gold mine for arthritis treatment. Curr Opin Pharmacol 7:344–351

Kwok BH, Koh B, Ndubuisi MI, Elofsson M, Crews CM (2001) The anti-inflammatory natural product parthenolide from the medicinal herb Feverfew directly binds to and inhibits IκB kinase. Chem Biol 8:759–766

Lai C, Jiang X, Li X (2006) Development of luciferase reporter-based cell assays. Assay Drug Dev Technol 4:307–315

Lam LT, Davis RE, Pierce J, Hepperle M, Xu Y, Hottelet M, Nong Y, Wen D, Adams J, Dang L, Staudt LM (2005) Small molecule inhibitors of IκB kinase are selectively toxic for subgroups of diffuse large B-cell lymphoma defined by gene expression profiling. Clin Cancer Res 11:28–40

Lam LT, Davis RE, Ngo VN, Lenz G, Wright G, Xu W, Zhao H, Yu X, Dang L, Staudt LM (2008) Compensatory IKKα activation of classical NF-κB signaling during IKKβ inhibition identified by an RNA interference sensitization screen. Proc Natl Acad Sci USA 105:20798–20803

Laubach JP, Mitsiades CS, Mahindra A, Schlossman RL, Hideshima T, Chauhan D, Carreau NA, Ghobrial IM, Raje N, Munshi NC, Anderson KC, Richardson PG (2009) Novel therapies in the treatment of multiple myeloma. Nat Rev Clin Oncol 6:596–603

Lee DF, Hung MC (2008) Advances in targeting IKK and IKK-related kinases for cancer therapy. Clin Cancer Res 14:5656–5662

Lentsch AB, Shanley TP, Sarma V, Ward PA (1997) In vivo suppression of NF-κB and preservation of IκBα by interleukin-10 and interleukin-13. J Clin Invest 100:2443–2448

Lenz G, Davis RE, Ngo VN, Lam L, George TC, Wright GW, Dave SS, Zhao H, Xu W, Rosenwald, A, Ott G, Müller-Hermelink H-K, Gascoyne RD, Connors JM, Rimsza LM, Campo E, Jaffe ES, Delabie J, Smelan EB, Fisher RI, Chan WC, Staudt LM (2008) Oncogenic CARD11 mutations in human diffuse large B cell lymphoma. Science 319:1676–1679

Letoha T, Somlai C, Takacs T, Szabolcs A, Jarmay K, Rakonczay Z Jr, Hegyi P, Varga I, Kaszaki J, Krizbai I, Boros I, Duda E, Kusz E, Penke B (2005) A nuclear import inhibitory peptide ameliorates the severity of cholecystokinin-induced acute pancreatitis. World J Gasteroenterol 11:990–999

Liang M-C, Bardhan S, Li C, Pace EA, Porco JA Jr, Gilmore TD (2003) Jesterone dimer, a synthetic derivative of the fungal metabolite jesterone, blocks activation of transcription factor nuclear factor κB by inhibiting the inhibitor of κB kinase. Mol Pharmacol 64:123–131

Liang M-C, Bardhan S, Pace EA, Rosman D, Beutler JA, Porco JA Jr, Gilmore TD (2006) Inhibition of transcription factor NF-κB signaling proteins IKKβ and p65 through specific cysteine residues by epoxyquinone A monomer: correlation with its anti-cancer cell growth activity. Biochem Pharmacol 71:634–645

Lin YZ, Yao SY, Veach RA, Torgerson TR, Hawiger J (1995) Inhibition of nuclear translocation of transcription factor NF-κB by a synthetic peptide containing a cell membrane-permeable motif and nuclear localization sequence. J Biol Chem 270:14255–14258

Luedde T, Bereza N, Kotsikoris V, van Loo G, Nenci A, De Vos R, Roskams T, Trautwein C, Pasparakis M (2007) Deletion of NEMO/IKKγ in liver parenchymal cells causes steatohep-tatis and hepatocellular carincoma. Cancer Cell 11:119–132

Palombella VJ, Rando OJ, Goldberg AL, Maniatis T (1994) The ubiquitin-proteasome pathway is required for processing the NF-κB1 precursor protein and the activation of NF-κB. Cell 78:773–785

Pande V, Sousa SF, Ramos MJ (2009) Direct covalent modification as a strategy to inhibit nuclear factor-κB. Curr Med Chem 16:4261–4273

Park SJ, Lee MY, Bon BS, Youn HS (2009) TBK1-targeted suppression of TRIF-dependent signaling pathway of Toll-like receptors by 6-shogaol, an active component of ginger. Biosci Biotechnol Biochem 73:1474–1478

Pasparakis M (2009) Regulation of tissue homeostasis by NF-κB signaling: implications for inflammatory diseases. Nat Rev Immunol 9:778–788

Perkins ND (2006) Post-translational modifications regulating the activity and function of the nuclear factor κB pathway. Oncogene 25:6717–6730

Pianetti S, Arsura M, Romieu-Mourez R, Coffey RJ, Sonenshein GE (2001) Her-1/Neu overexpression induces NF-κB via a PI3-kinase/Akt pathway involving calpain-mediated degradation of IκB-α that can be inhibited by the tumor suppressor PTEN. Oncogene 20: 1287–1299

Ríos JL, Recio MC, Escandell JM, Andújar I (2009) Inhibition of transcription factors by plant-derived compounds and their implications in inflammation and cancer. Curr Pharm Des 15:1212–1237

Sakurai T, Maeda S, Chang L, Karin M (2006) Loss of hepatic NF-κB activity enhances chemical carcionogenesis through sustained c-Jun N-terminal kinase 1 activation. Proc Natl Acad Sci USA 103:10544–10551

Scheidereit C (2006) IκB kinase complexes: gateways to NF-κB activation and transcription. Oncogene 25:6685–6705

Sen J, Venkataraman L, Shinkai Y, Pierce JW, Alt FW, Burakoff SJ, Sen R (1995) Expression and induction of nuclear factor-κB-related proteins in thymocytes. J Immunol 154:3213–3221

Shishodia S, Sethi G, Konopleva M, Andreeff M, Aggarwal BB (2006) A synthetic triterpenoid, CDDO-Me, inhibits IκBα kinase and enhances apoptosis induced by TNF and chemotherapeutic agents through down-regulation of expression of nuclear factor κB-regulated gene products in human leukemic cells. Clin Cancer Res 12:1828–1838

Skaug B, Jiang X, Chen ZJ (2009) The role of ubiquitin in NF-κB regulatory pathways. Annu Rev Biochem 78:769–796

Straus DS, Pascual G, Li M, Welch JS, Ricote M, Hsiang C-H, Sengchanthalangsy LL, Ghosh G, Glass CK (2000) 15-deoxy-$\Delta^{12,14}$-prostaglandin J_2 inhibits multiple steps in the NF-κB signaling pathway. Proc Natl Acad Sci USA 97:4844–4849

Strickland I, Ghosh S (2006) Use of cell permeable NBD peptides for suppression of inflammation. Ann Rheum Dis 65(Suppl 3):iii75–iii82

Su Y, Amiri KI, Horton LW, Yu Y, Ayers GD, Koehler E, Kelley MC, Puzanov I, Richmond A, Sosman JA (2010) A phase I trial of bortezomib with temozolomide in patients with advanced melanoma: toxicities, antitumor effects, and modulation of therapeutic targets. Clin Cancer Res 16:348–357

Sun S-C, Cesarman E (2010) NF-κB as a target for oncogenic viruses. In: Current topics in microbiology and immunology. Springer, Berlin (this issue)

Swinney DC, Xu Y-Z, Scarafia LE, Lee I, Mak AY, Gan Q-F, Ramesha CS, Mulkins MA, Dunn J, So O-Y, Biegel T, Dinh M, Volkel P, Barnett J, Dalrymple SA, Lee S, Huber M (2002) A small molecule ubiquitination inhibitor blocks NF-κB-dependent cytokine expression in cells and rats. J Biol Chem 277:23573–23581

Takigawa N, Vaziri SA, Grabowski DR, Chikamori K, Rybicki LR, Bukowski RM, Ganapathi MK, Ganapathi R, Mekhail T (2006) Proteasome inhibition with bortezomib enhances activity of topoisomerase I-targeting drugs by NF-κB-independent mechanisms. Anticancer Res 26:1869–1876

Tang W, Li Y, Yu D, Thomas-Tikhonenko A, Spiegelman VS, Fuchs SY (2005) Targeting β-transducin repeat-containing protein E3 ubiquitin ligase augments the effects of antitumor drugs on breast cancer cells. Cancer Res 65:1904–1908

Taylor PC, Feldmann (2009) Anti-TNF biologic agents still the therapy of choice for rheumatoid arthritis. Nat Rev Rheumatol 5:578–582

Tian W, Liou H-C (2009) RNAi-mediated c-Rel silencing leads to apoptosis of B cell tumor cells and suppresses antigenic immune response in vivo. PLoS ONE 4:e5028

Torgerson TR, Colosia AD, Donahue JP, Lin Y-Z, Hawiger J (1998) Regulation of NF-κB, AP-1, NFAT, and STAT1 nuclear import in T lymphocytes by noninvasive delivery of peptide carrying the nuclear localization sequence of NF-κB p50. J Immunol 161:6084–6092

Tran TA, McCoy MK, Sporn MB, Tansey MG (2008) The synthetic triterpenoid CDDO-methyl ester modulates microglial activities, inhibits TNF production, and provides dopaminergic neuroprotection. J Neuroinflammation 5:14

Trepicchio WL, Dorner AJ (1998) The therapeutic utility of Interleukin-11 in the treatment of inflammatory disease. Expert Opin Investig Drugs 7:1501–1504

Tsukamoto S, Takeuchi T, Rotinsulu H, Mangindaan RE, van Soest RW, Ukai K, Kobayashi H, Namikoshi M, Ohta T, Yokosawa H (2008) Leucettamol A: a new inhibitor of Ubc13-Uev1A interaction isolatd from a marine sponge, *Leucetta* aff. *microrhaphis*. Bioorg Med Chem Lett 18: 6319–6320

Umezawa K, Chaicharoenpong C (2002) Molecular design and biological activities of NF-κB inhibitors. Mol Cells 14:163–167

Venkataraman L, Burakoff SJ, Sen R (1995) FK506 inhibits antigen receptor-mediated induction of c-rel in B and T lymphoid cells. J Exp Med 181:1091–1099

Watanabe M, Nakashima M, Togano T, Higashihara M, Watanabe T, Umezawa K, Horie R (2008) Identification of the RelA domain responsible for action of a new NF-κB inhibitor DHMEQ. Biochem Biophys Res Commun 376:310–314

Wiestner A, Staudt LM (2003) Towards molecular diagnosis and targeted therapy of lymphoid malignancies. Semin Hematol 40:296–307

Xie Y, Rinderspacher A, Liu Y, Gong G, Smith DH, Wyler M, Brandén L, Deng SX (2009) Small-molecule modulators of the NF-κB pathway newly identified by a translocation-based cellular assay. Curr Top Med Chem 9:1172–1180

Yaron A, Gonen H, Alkalay I, Hatzubai A, Jung S, Beyth S, Mercurio F, Manning AM, Ciechanover A, Ben-Neriah Y (1997) Inhibition of NF-κB cellular function via specific targeting of the IκB-ubiquitin ligase. EMBO J 16:6486–6494

Zheng B, Georgakis GV, Li Y, Bharti A, McConkey D, Aggarwal BB, Younes A (2004) Induction of cell cycle arrest and apoptosis by the proteasome inhibitor PS-341 in Hodgkin disease cell lines is independent of inhibitor of nuclear factor-κB mutations or activation of the CD30, CD40, and RANK receptors. Clin Cancer Res 10:3207–3215

Zhou H, Monack DM, Kayagaki N, Wertz I, Yin J, Wolf B, Dixit VM (2005) *Yersinia* virulence factor YopJ acts as a deubiquitinase to inhibit NF-κB activation. J Exp Med 202:1327–1332

Index